D1598174

Highly Coherent
Semiconductor Lasers

Highly Coherent Semiconductor Lasers

Motoichi Ohtsu

Artech House
Boston • London

Library of Congress Cataloging-in-Publication Data

Ohtsu, Motoichi.
   Highly coherent semiconductor lasers / Motoichi Ohtsu.
     p. cm.
   Includes bibliographical references and index.
   ISBN 0-89006-462-8
   1. Semiconductor lasers.   I.   Title.
   TA1700.038   1991   91-31852
   621.36'6–dc20   CIP

© 1992   ARTECH HOUSE, INC.
685 Canton Street
Norwood, MA 02062

International Standard Book Number: 0-89006-462-8
Library of Congress Catalog Card Number: 91-31852

10 9   8   7   6   5   4   3   2   1

To
Chiyako
Tamaki
Itsumi

CONTENTS

PREFACE

Among the variety of lasers, the semiconductor laser maintains its unique status because of its outstanding advantages. For example, the laser device fabrication process is compatible with the mass production of semiconductor integrated circuits, a variety of laser devices are available, lasing frequency can be widely tuned, lasing power and frequency can be modulated with wide bandwidth and high efficiency, and so on. Because of these advantages, semiconductor lasers have been popularly used for a variety of applications, ranging from basic physics (for example, elementary particle physics and quantum optics) to industrial photonic systems (such as optical communication systems and optical disk players). It can be expected that the number of application systems will continue to increase rapidly.

However, scientists and engineers who are interested in using semiconductor lasers still face some problems. These obstacles include complicated laser device structures that obscure the principle of laser oscillation and high levels of noise. The main purpose of this book is to provide the reader with useful information that can be used to solve these problems. To achieve this purpose, this book reviews the principle of laser oscillation, device structures, noise characteristics, possible application systems, and the outlook for the future. Specific, detailed descriptions on noise characteristics and methods of noise reduction are given to enable the production of highly coherent semiconductor lasers.

This book, to my knowledge, is the first single-author publication to cover this wide a range of semiconductor laser topics. I hope that this book will enable undergraduate and graduate students, junior scientists, and engineers to systematically study the semiconductor laser; to fabricate novel, light-emitting devices; and to develop advanced application systems.

I would like to express my thanks to C.-H. Shin for his critical comments and review of the manuscript. Intensive discussions with K. Nakagawa, H. Furuta, S. Jiang, M. Kourogi, and W. Wang were quite valuable in preparing the manuscript. For the preparation of figures and list of references, I am indebted to my students, Y. Awaji, Y. Toda, Y. Shimizu, M. Kawai, K. Yamada, S. Sayama, and T. Yamashita.

M. Ohtsu
June, 1991

Chapter 1
INTRODUCTION

1.1 REQUIREMENTS OF HIGHLY COHERENT SEMICONDUCTOR LASERS

It has long been known that the transmission capacity of a microwave communication system is proportional to the frequency of the microwave oscillator. After the development of microwave communication technologies in the 1950s, several trials were carried out using lightwave as a high-frequency oscillator to increase transmission capacity. Based on these trials, a laser was invented in 1960 [1]; immediately afterwards, optical communication systems were proposed and basic experiments using lasers were presented [2]. However, because laser frequency stability was not sufficient and its modulation techniques had not been developed, practical use of the optical communication systems lagged behind the experiments.

After glass fiber with transmission loss as low as 20 dB/km and a room-temperature, *continuous wave* (CW) semiconductor lasers were developed in 1970, research and development of optical communication systems made rapid progress. Because the semiconductor laser is small and inexpensive, and exhibits low power consumption, it can be used as a practical light source not only for communication systems but for other optical measurement system as well. However, as the Q-value of the cavity of the semiconductor laser is low, the magnitudes of its FM and IM noises sometimes are too large for these application systems. Thus, the semiconductor laser has been used only as a light source for an *intensity modulation–direct detection* (IM-DD) optical communication system. This means that the system has yet to take advantage of the high optical frequency of the laser. However, based on the successful experiments on frequency stabilization of the semiconductor laser [3], research in coherent optical communication began and has shown remarkable progress [for example, 4]. Furthermore, feasibility studies of using the semiconductor lasers in several optical measurement systems have been carried out as well. For example, a laser linewidth narrower than 4 MHz is essential to reduce the bit error rate as low as 10^{-9} in the PSK heterodyne optical communication system with the bit rate of 1 Gb/s [5]. And in the case of the ring resonator-type optical fiber gyroscope [6], a laser linewidth of 100 kHz is required to achieve the sensitivity exhibited by an ideally coherent light source. Under these situations, it can be noted that a highly coherent semiconductor laser, along with techniques such as optical phase locking between these highly stable semiconductor lasers, are indispensable for advanced optical systems. Furthermore, it should also be noted that an optical frequency counter is required to utilize fully the high-quality lightwaves generated from these lasers.

1.2 FIVE REQUIREMENTS TO BE MET

Techniques of frequency control and phase locking for high-quality microwave oscillators (e.g., quartz crystal oscillators, cesium (Cs) atomic clocks, rubidium (Rb) atomic clocks, and hydrogen (H) masers) have been well developed for applications in communication, in primary standards of time and so forth [7, 8]. Several techniques also have been developed for gas lasers to achieve a frequency stability of 8 $\times$ 10^{-17} [9], and subhertz linewidth has been realized for a dye laser [10]. It could be effective to investigate applying these established techniques to semiconductor lasers.

It can be deduced that at least the following five requirements should be met simultaneously to realize a highly coherent semiconductor laser:

1. stabilization of the center frequency of the field spectrum, to obtain a light source with low frequency drift;
2. improvement of accuracy and reproducibility of the stabilized frequency, to obtain a light source with a well-calibrated frequency;
3. linewidth reduction of the field spectrum, to obtain a light source with a low frequency or phase jitter;
4. frequency or phase tracking to a highly coherent master laser, to make a synchronized frequency chain by transferring the high coherence of a master laser to several slave lasers, which is required for applications to coherent-heterodyne or coherent-homodyne optical communication, heterodyne or homodyne optical measurements, and so forth; and
5. stable and widegband frequency sweep, to realize a wideband, tunable, coherent light source for multiplexing in coherent optical communication, high-resolution laser spectroscopy, precise optical measurements, and the like.

Because the frequency can be changed by varying the current injected into the semiconductor laser, these requirements could be met simultaneously by the negative electrical feedback through controlling the injection current. Figure 1.1 shows a schematic diagram of an experimental setup by which the five requirements can be met simultaneously [11, 12]. Each block ((1) through (5) in this figure) represents a feedback loop for treating requirements mentioned previously. The designs of blocks (1), (2), (3), and (5) in this figure were based on the techniques used for gas and dye

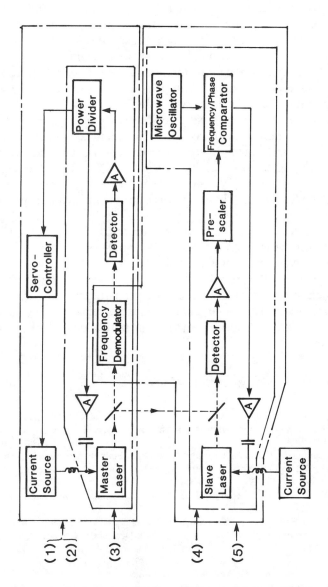

Figure 1.1 A synthesized negative electrical feedback system by which the five requirements can be met simultaneously. Each block, (1) through (5), represents a feedback loop for treating requirements (1) through (5).

lasers [13, 14]; the designs of blocks (1), (2), and (4) were based on the techniques for microwave oscillators [7, 8, and for example 15]. (For more information on (5), see the detailed description of a wideband frequency sweep system with a frequency tunable range of about 1 Peta Hertz in Section 7.2.2.) This system would be bulky if constructed for gas or dye lasers; for semiconductor lasers, however, it can be very compact. Size can be reduced by integrating several electronic or optical components with the laser devices in one chip, and an ultrahigh coherence miniature light source can be realized in the future. Although the method of negative electrical feedback is highly accurate and stable, several other techniques are applicable to semiconductor lasers. These techniques will also be described in this book.

In Chapter 2, the lasing principle, basic device structure, lasing characteristics, and noise properties of semiconductor lasers will be described. Chapter 3 presents techniques of noise detection and modulation to control the laser frequency. Chapter 4 describes the techniques to meet requirements (1), (2), and (3). Section 5.1 is devoted to the requirement (4). Techniques for meeting requirement (5) will be reviewed in Sections 5.2 and 7.2. Chapter 6 describes the application systems that can be realized by using these highly coherent semiconductor lasers. Chapter 7 describes several advanced laser devices developed especially for achieving a low FM noise operation, a lightwave frequency counting system, the generation of nonclassical photon, and manipulation of atoms and photons. Chapter 8 contains concluding remarks. In the Appendixes, the procedure for the quantization of the light field will be given; several measures for evaluating the noise properties will be defined; accurate systems of FM noise measurements will be presented; relaxation oscillation frequency will be defined; and theoretical analysis of the optical phase-locked loop will be presented.

REFERENCES

[1] Bromberg, J.L., "The Birth of the Laser," *Physics Today,* Vol. 41, October 1988, pp. 26–33.
[2] Gordon, J.P., "Quantum Effects in Communication Systems," *Proc. IRE,* Vol. 50, No. 9, September 1982, pp. 1898–1908.
[3] Tsuchida, H., S. Sanpei, M. Ohtsu, and T. Tako, "Frequency Stability Measurement of Feedback Stabilized AlGaAs DH Laser," *Japanese J. Applied Physics,* Vol. 19, No. 2, December 1980, pp. L721–L724.
[4] Okoshi, T, and K. Kikuchi, *Coherent Opical Fiber Communications,* KTK Scientific Publishers, Tokyo, 1988.
[5] Ohtsu, M., and S. Kotajima, "Linewidth Reduction of a Semiconductor Laser by Electrical Feedback," *IEEE J. Quantum Electronics,* Vol. QE-21, No. 12, December 1985, pp. 1905–1912.
[6] Ohtsu, M., and S. Araki, "Using a 1.5-μm DFB InGaAsP Laser in a Passive Ring Cavity-Type Fiber Gyroscope," *Applied Optics,* Vol. 26, No. 3, February 1987, pp. 464–470.
[7] Kartashoff, P., *Frequency and Time,* Academic Press, London, 1978.
[8] Vanier, J., and C. Audoin, *The Quantum Physics of Atomic Frequency Standards,* Adam Hilger, Bristol, U.K., 1989.

[9]   Hils, D., and J.L. Hall, "Ultra-Stable Cavity-Stabilized Lasers with Subhertz Linewidth," *Frequency Standards and Metrology* (Proceedings of 4th Symp., Ancona, Italy, September 5–9, 1988), Ed. A. De Marchi, Springer Verlag, Berlin, 1989, pp. 162–173.

[10] Hall, J.L., M. Zhu, F. Shimizu, and K. Shimizu, "External Frequency Stabilization of a Commercial Dye Laser at the Subhertz Level," Proc. the 16th Int. Quantum Electronics Conf. (IQEC'88), Tokyo, July 18–21, 1988 (*IEE Japan,* Tokyo, 1988), paper number TuP21.

[11] Ohtsu, M., "Realization of Ultrahigh Coherence in Semiconductor Laser by Negative Electrical Feedback," *IEEE J. Lightwave Technology,* Vol. 6, No. 2, February 1988, pp. 245–256.

[12] Ohtsu, M., and T. Tako, "Coherence in Semiconductor Lasers," *Progress in Optics,* Vol. 25, ed. E. Wolf, Elsevier Science Publishers, Amsterdam, 1988, pp. 193–278.

[13] Brillet, A., and P. Cerez., "Laser Frequency Stabilization by Saturated Absorption," *J. Physique,* Vol. 42, January 1981, pp. 73–82.

[14] Hall, J.L., D. Hils, C. Salomon, and M. Rayman, "Stable Lasers: Progress and Applications," *Tech. Dig. Conf. Lasers and Electro-optics* (Baltimore, MD), May 21–24, 1985, paper number FM3.

[15] *Proc. IEEE* (Special Issue on Frequency Stability), Vol. 54, No. 2, February 1966.

Chapter 2
STRUCTURE AND OSCILLATION
MECHANISMS

2.1 COHERENCE OF LIGHT

The word *coherence* has two popular meanings. To explain these, the electric field vector is expressed as

$$E(r, t) = E_0 \cdot \cos(k \cdot r - 2\pi\omega t) \tag{2.1}$$

where E_0 is the amplitude, k is the wave vector, r is the spatial coordinate vector, t is the time, and ω is the frequency.

The first is "spatial coherence," which is related to the term **kr** in this equation. This means, as shown by Figure 2.1(a), that the interference can take place and generate clear interference fringes on the screen when the two lights (from two light sources or the same light source but spatially separated) are superposed. Spatial coherence implies that the spatial distributions of the wavefronts of the two lights are similar, especially when the lights emit from one source, which means that the spatial fluctuation of the wavefront is small.

The second meaning is "temporal coherence," which is related to the term $2\pi\omega t$ in (2.1). This means, as shown by Figure 2.1(b), that the photodetector can generate a clear, sinusoidally oscillating beat signal between the two lights. Temporal coherence implies that the temporal behavior of the two lights are similar. If these two lights are obtained from a common source, the magnitudes of the frequency fluctuations from this source are very low.

Based on these simple descriptions, we can easily see that it is possible to generate a spatially incoherent but temporally coherent light. For example, spatial coherence can be disturbed if the light transmits through a piece of thin ground-glass plate, even though the temporal coherence can be still maintained.

From the explanations, the coherent light can be interpreted as a smooth, sinusoidally oscillating lightwave. The discussions in this book will concentrate on tem-

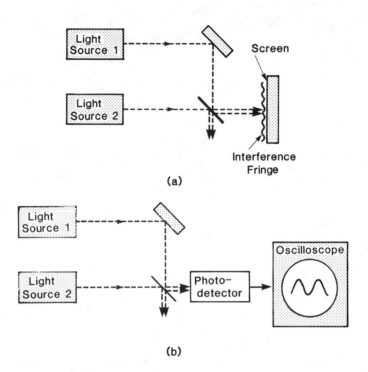

Figure 2.1 Schematic explanation of the concept of coherence: (a) spatial coherence; (b) temporal coherence.

porally coherent light, such as that generated by a laser, with which a wide variety of applications can be realized, as shown by Figure 2.2. They range from technological applications such as communication and sensing to scientific applications such as quantum optics and atomic physics. Details of these application systems will be described in Chapter 6.

Although the explanation of the coherent light did not give the strict definition. Furthermore, the light emitted from a conventional laser is not always the strictly defined coherent light. The coherent state of light can be defined through the quantization of light. For this quantization, see Appendix I. One of the states given by eq. (AI.47) is called the coherent state $|\alpha\rangle$, if the expansion coefficients c_{Np} have the form

$$c_{Np} = \frac{\alpha_{Np}}{\sqrt{Np!}} \cdot \exp(-|\alpha|^2/2) \tag{2.2}$$

where α is a complex number. The quantity $|c_{Np}|^2$ is the probability of finding that the light is in the state $|N_p\rangle$, which is expressed as

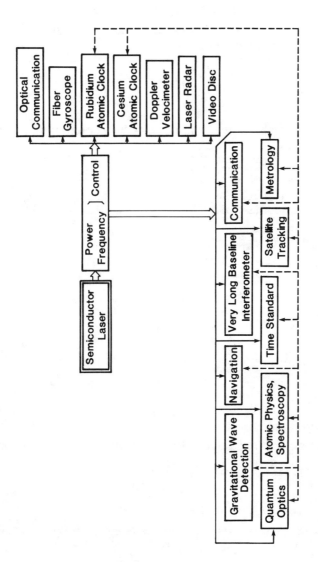

Figure 2.2 Applications of highly coherent semiconductor lasers.

$$|c_{Np}|^2 = \frac{|\alpha|^{2Np}}{Np!} \cdot \exp(-|\alpha|^2) \tag{2.3}$$

This expression has been well known in probability theory because it is identical to the Poisson distribution. By substituting eqs. (AI.37) and (2.2) into (AI.47), the coherent state is defined by the expression

$$|\alpha\rangle = \exp(-|\alpha|^2/2) \sum_{Np=0}^{\infty} \frac{\alpha^{Np}}{\sqrt{Np!}} (a^+)^{Np} |0\rangle \tag{2.4}$$

We can easily find that the expectation value of the photon number $\langle N_p \rangle$ for this state is

$$\langle N_p \rangle = \langle \alpha | a^+ a | \alpha \rangle = |\alpha|^2 \tag{2.5}$$

For the discussions described later, note that the following relation holds:

$$[a, \exp(\alpha a^+)] = \alpha \cdot \exp(\alpha a^+) \tag{2.6}$$

where $\exp(\alpha a^+)$ is a polynomial composed of the operators, which is defined by

$$\exp(\alpha a^+) \equiv \sum_{m=0}^{\infty} \frac{1}{m!} (\alpha a^+)^m \tag{2.7}$$

Validity of (2.6) can be confirmed easily, by using (AI.16). After transforming (2.6) into

$$a \cdot \exp(\alpha a^+) = \alpha \cdot \exp(\alpha a^+) + \exp(\alpha a^+) \cdot a \tag{2.8}$$

applying both sides of this relation on $|0\rangle$, and finally, using (AI.27), we can derive a relation

$$a|\alpha\rangle = \alpha|\alpha\rangle \tag{2.9}$$

This relation means that the coherent state is an eigenstate of operator a and its eigenvalue is α. Furthermore, the following relations hold for the coherent state:

$$\begin{aligned} \langle \alpha | a^+ &= \alpha^* \langle \alpha | \\ \langle \alpha | a | \alpha \rangle &= \alpha \\ \langle \alpha | a^+ a | \alpha \rangle &= |\alpha|^2 \end{aligned} \tag{2.10}$$

where * represents the complex conjugate, as was the case of c.c.. Calculations similar to eqs. (AI.43) and (AI.44) can easily yield

$$
\begin{aligned}
\langle E_x \rangle &= \langle \alpha | E_x | \alpha \rangle \\
&= E_{x0}(\alpha + \alpha^*) \cdot \sin kz \\
\langle E_x^2 \rangle &= \langle \alpha | E_x^2 | \alpha \rangle \\
&= E_{x0}^2 [(\alpha + \alpha^*)^2 + 1] \cdot \sin^2 kz
\end{aligned}
\tag{2.11}
$$

These relations mean that the quantum mechanical expectation value of E_x takes a nonzero value; that is, the wave properties of the light can be observed by measurement. However, its standard deviation takes a nonzero value of $\Delta E_x = E_{x0} \cdot \sin kz$, which is due to the spontaneous emission fluctuations.

We can show easily that a cross-correlation coefficient

$$
\gamma \equiv \frac{\langle \psi | a | \psi \rangle \, \langle \psi | a^+ | \psi \rangle}{\langle \psi | a^+ a | \psi \rangle}
\tag{2.12}
$$

is no larger than unity for a general state vector $|\psi\rangle$. However, $\gamma = 1$ for the coherent state $|\alpha\rangle$. This means that, as was discussed in Appendix I by using eqs. (AI.22) and (AI.23), the two running waves propagating in the $+z$ and $-z$ directions are strongly correlated with each other. In other words, an interference fringe or a beat signal between the two waves can be observed, as discussed in the simple definitions in the beginning of this section.

Further properties of the coherent state can be derived. If an observable physical quantity with the operator X is measured when the light is in the state $|\psi\rangle$, the standard deviation is a measure for the uncertainty in the measurement (see eq. (AI.45)), which is expressed as

$$
\Delta X \equiv \sqrt{\langle X^2 \rangle - \langle X \rangle^2}
\tag{2.13}
$$

where

$$
\begin{aligned}
\langle X^2 \rangle &\equiv \langle \psi | X^2 | \psi \rangle \\
\langle X \rangle &\equiv \langle \psi | X | \psi \rangle
\end{aligned}
$$

Hermitian operators X_1 and X_2, which do not commute, cannot be measured simultaneously with absolute exactness; and an uncertainty always is left. A relation between the uncertainties ΔX_1 and ΔX_2 can be derived as

$$
\Delta X_1 \cdot \Delta X_2 \geq \frac{1}{2} |[X_1, X_2]| \equiv \frac{1}{2} |\langle \psi | [X_1, X_2] | \psi \rangle|
\tag{2.14}
$$

This is the well-known Heisenberg uncertainty relation. For example, substitution of eq. (AI.12) into this equation yields

$$\Delta p \cdot \Delta q \geqslant \hbar/2 \qquad (2.15)$$

for the position and momentum operators q and p.

An expression of the magnetic field vector can be derived by using (AI.8), (AI.13), and (AI.14), which is expressed as

$$H_y(z,t) = 2i \sqrt{\frac{\epsilon_0}{\mu_0}} \cdot E_{x0}(a - a^+) \cdot \cos kz \qquad (2.16)$$

This magnetic field and the electric field given by eq. (AI.18) are Hermitian operators because the operators $(a + a^+)$ and $(a - a^+)$ are Hermitians. Furthermore, by noting the relation derived by eq. (AI.16),

$$[(a + a^+), (a - a^+)] = -2 \qquad (2.17)$$

eq. (2.14) yields

$$\Delta(a + a^+) \cdot \Delta(a - a^+) \geqslant 1 \qquad (2.18)$$

especially for the coherent state, $\Delta(a + a^+) \cdot \Delta(a + a^+) = 1$, which means that the coherent state is the minimum uncertainty state satisfying eq. (2.18). It also means that a relation between the uncertainties of the electric and magnetic fields, derived from eqs. (AI.18), (2.16), and (2.18),

$$\Delta E_x \cdot \Delta H_y \geqslant \frac{1}{2} \hbar \left(\frac{8\pi\omega^2}{kV} \right) \qquad (2.19)$$

takes the minimum. Because the classical status of E_x and H_y are the waves with the $\pi/2$ phase difference, the minimum uncertainty of (2.19) corresponds to the classical status of the wave with the minimum fluctuations.

When the photon number is large enough, that is, $\langle N_p \rangle \gg 1$, a commutation relation holds between the photon number N_p and phase operator ϕ, from which the uncertainty relation can be derived as

$$\Delta N_p \cdot \Delta\phi \geqslant \frac{1}{2} \qquad (2.20)$$

For this relation, the coherent state also takes the minimum uncertainty; especially, as the coherent state yields

$$\Delta N_p \equiv \sqrt{\langle (a^+a)^2 \rangle - \langle a^+a \rangle^2}$$
$$= |\alpha| = 1/\sqrt{\langle N_p \rangle} \tag{2.21}$$

it leads to

$$\Delta N_p/\langle N_p \rangle = 1/\sqrt{\langle N_p \rangle} \tag{2.22}$$

and from eq. (2.20)

$$\Delta\phi = \frac{1}{2}\sqrt{\langle N_p \rangle} \tag{2.23}$$

This relation means that precise and simultaneous measurements of the amplitude (or power) and phase of the light are possible for the coherent state within the limit of $\langle N_p \rangle \gg 1$.

On the other hand, because the physical meaning of eq. (2.20) is lost for $\langle N_p \rangle \leqslant 1$, a more general uncertainty relation, also valid for $\langle N_p \rangle \leqslant 1$, has been derived [1] by using alternative operators, S and C, which are defined by

$$S \equiv \frac{1}{2i\sqrt{a^+a + 1}}(a^+ - a) \tag{2.24}$$

$$C \equiv \frac{1}{2 \cdot \sqrt{a^+a + 1}}(a^+ + a) \tag{2.25}$$

Because the operators S and C are Hermitian and related to phase ϕ of a classical lightwave such that

$$S = \sin\phi$$
$$C = \cos\phi \tag{2.26}$$

in the limit $\langle N_p \rangle \gg 1$, they can be interpreted as operators representing a phase of the optical field. Uncertainty relation between S, C, and the photon number, is given by

$$(\Delta N_p)^2 \frac{(\Delta S)^2 + (\Delta C)^2}{\langle S \rangle^2 + \langle C \rangle^2} \geqslant \frac{1}{4} \tag{2.27}$$

which is more accurate than that of eq. (2.20). Furthermore, the following uncertainty relation holds for ΔS and ΔC:

$$\Delta S \cdot \Delta C \geqslant (\tfrac{1}{4}) \cdot \exp(-\langle N_p \rangle) \tag{2.28}$$

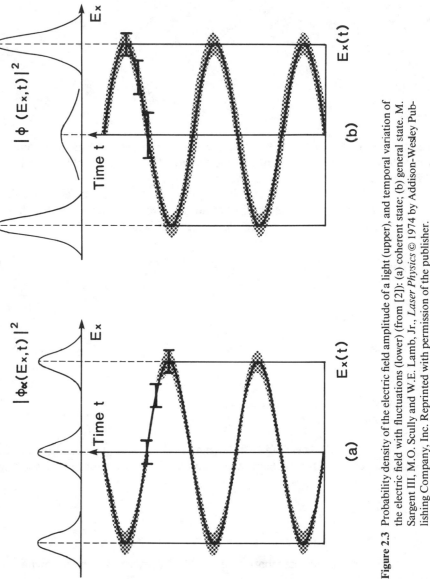

Figure 2.3 Probability density of the electric field amplitude of a light (upper), and temporal variation of the electric field with fluctuations (lower) (from [2]): (a) coherent state; (b) general state. M. Sargent III, M.O. Scully and W.E. Lamb, Jr., *Laser Physics* © 1974 by Addison-Wesley Publishing Company, Inc. Reprinted with permission of the publisher.

The solution of a time-independent Schrödinger equation can be derived if the coherent state of eq. (2.4) is expressed by the coordinate representation, as was the procedure given by eq. (AI.38). The solution of a time-dependent Schrödinger equation also can be derived by replacing $|\alpha\rangle$ by $|\alpha\rangle \exp(-i2\pi\omega t)$ in the solution of the time-independent Schrödinger equation. This time-dependent is given by [2]

$$
\phi_\alpha(E_x,t) = \frac{1}{\sqrt{\sqrt{2\pi}E_{x0}}} \cdot \exp\left\{ \frac{1}{2}[\alpha \cdot \exp(-i2\pi\omega t)]^2 \right.
$$
$$
\left. - \frac{1}{2}|\alpha|^2 \right\} \cdot \exp\left\{ -\frac{1}{2}\left[\frac{1}{\sqrt{2}E_{x0}} E_x - \sqrt{2}\alpha \exp(-i2\pi\omega t) \right]^2 \right\} \quad (2.29)
$$

where q has been replaced by E_X, using (AI.7). Therefore, the probability density of finding that the value of the electric field amplitude is E_x at time t is

$$
|\phi_\alpha(E_x,t)|^2 = \frac{1}{\sqrt{2\pi}E_{x0}} \exp\left\{ -\left[\frac{1}{\sqrt{2}E_{x0}} E_x - \sqrt{2}\alpha \cdot \cos(2\pi\omega t + \theta) \right]^2 \right\}
$$

$$(2.30)$$

where

$$
\alpha \equiv |\alpha| \exp(-i\theta) \quad (2.31)
$$

Equation (2.30) represents a Gaussian wave packet with a center of $2E_{x0}|\alpha| \cos(2\pi\omega t + \theta)$ and a half-width at the half-maximum of $\sqrt{2} \cdot E_{x0}$. That is, as is shown by Figure 2.3(a), the packet bounces back and forth sinusoidally without changing its width [2]. In other words, the coherent state maintains uncertainty at a minimum, and its packet of probability density "coheres." Therefore, the coherent state resembles the classical field as closely as quantum mechanics permits. For reference, the general state of the light varies in time, as shown by Figure 2.3(b).

2.2 DEVICE STRUCTURES

Although a semiconductor laser can be considered a kind of common solid-state laser, it has unique characteristics because of the small cavity size, large cavity loss, and large and fast variation of the active electron density in the conduction band. It has been widely used for a variety of industrial applications due to its small size, low power consumption, and low price. Figure 2.4 shows the energy levels of the electrons in a semiconductor crystal, which has a band structure. The energy band, representing the state of electrons trapped in the crystalline lattice, is called a *valence band*. The energy band for the state of the electrons free of this trap is called a *conduction band*. These bands are separated from each other, and the space between them is called the *energy gap*. Vacancy is generated after an electron in the valence band is excited by the conduction band; and this corresponds to the appearance of a particle with a positive electric charge, which is called a *positive hole*. The electrons in the conduction band and positive holes in the valence band are called *carriers*.

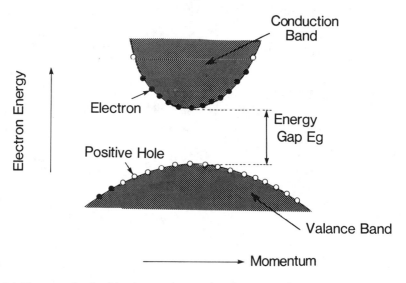

Figure 2.4 The energy levels of the electrons in a semiconductor crystal.

A direct transition-type semiconductor is used as the laser material. In such a semiconductor, the electron in the conduction band descends to the valence band, recombines with a positive hole, and conserves its momentum without colliding with impurities or phonons in the crystal. Spontaneous or stimulated emission occurs by this transition. The central frequency of the gain spectral profile for laser oscillation depends on the value of the energy gap, which corresponds to the right-hand side of eq. (AI.46). Direct transition-type semiconductors are found among composite semiconductors, which are composed of more than two elements. Because the value of the energy gap can be varied by changing the mole fraction of each element in the trinary or quarternary composite semiconductors, the lasing wavelength covering from infrared to visible light can be realized, as shown by Figure 2.5. A trinary composite semiconductor obtained by doping Al, In, or Sb in GaAs has been popularly used in, for example, a compact disc player. It can be expressed as $Al_xGa_{1-x}As$, where x represents the mole fraction ($0 \leq x \leq 1$). A quarternary composite semiconductor $In_xGa_{1-x}As_yP_{1-y}$ has been used for optical fiber communication systems. Development of a visible AlGaInP laser of 0.67 μm wavelength also shows its rapid pace. Figures 2.6(a) and (b) show that the value of the energy gap depends on the mole fractions x and y, and the refractive index decreases with the increase in the energy gap. Furthermore, these characteristics are utilized to confine the electrons and light effectively in the semiconductor laser cavity, which is shown in Figure 2.7.

Material			Emission Wavelength [μm]			
Active Layer	Clad Layer	Substrate	0.5	1.0	5	10
III–V						
AlGaAs	AlGaAs	GaAs				
GaInAsP	GaInP	GaAs				
GaInAsP	GaInP	GaAs				
GaInAsP	AlGaInP	GaAs				
AlGaInP	AlGaInP	GaAs				
GaInAsP	AlGaAs	AsAs				
GaInAsP	InP	InP				
AlGaAsSb	AlGaAsSb	GaSb				
InAsSbP	InAsSbP	InAs				
IV–VI						
PbSnSeTe	PbSnSeTe	PbTe				
II–VI						
ZnSSe		GaAs				

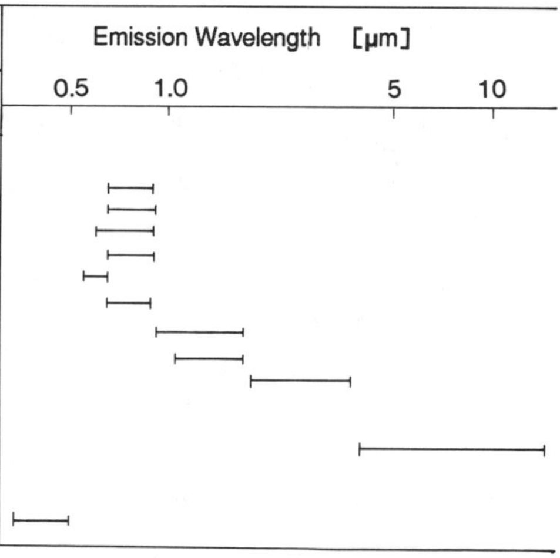

Figure 2.5 Possible lasing wavelengths by III-V, IV-VI, and II-VI compound semiconductors.

Figures 2.7(a) and (b) show a semiconductor laser and its cross section on the y-z plane. The light is emitted by the carrier recombination in the GaAs layer of the p-type, called an *active layer*. The p-type Al$_x$Ga$_{1-x}$As and the n-type Al$_y$Ga$_{1-y}$As layers next to the active layer are called *clad layers*. This structure is called *double hetero structure* because it is composed of two hetero junctions. After electrons are injected from the current source to the active layer via the n-type clad layer, they are confined in the active layer because of the energy barrier between the active and p-type clad layers, which is called the *hetero barrier* (see Fig. 2.7(c)). The spatial distribution of the electrons along the y-axis is effectively concentrated in the active layer by the double hetero structure, and the electrons recombine with the positive holes by emitting the light. Because the diffusion length of the electron injected into the active layer is about 1–2 μm, the thickness d of the active layer usually is designed to be thinner than this value. Furthermore, because the lowest transverse mode oscillation usually is required for the application system, the value of d is fixed to as low as about 0.1 μm.

The width of the active layer w along the x-axis is reduced to confine electrons effectively. As in the case of a dielectric waveguide such as the optical fiber, this reduction also means that only the lowest transverse mode can oscillate. Although

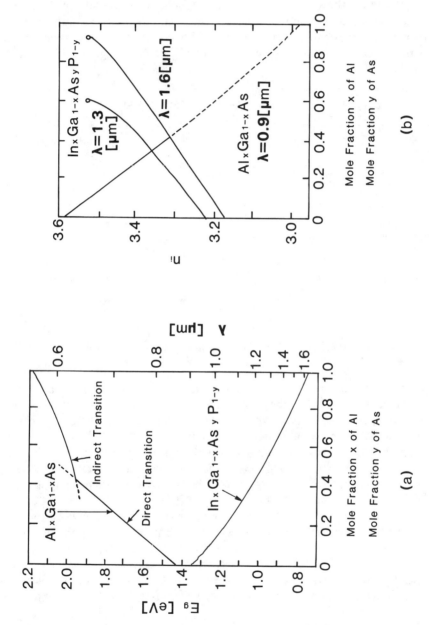

Figure 2.6 Dependences of the energy gap E_g and (a) corresponding wavelength λ and (b) refractive index n_i on the mole fractions x and y of $Al_xGa_{1-x}As$ and $In_xGa_{1-x}As_yP_{1-y}$

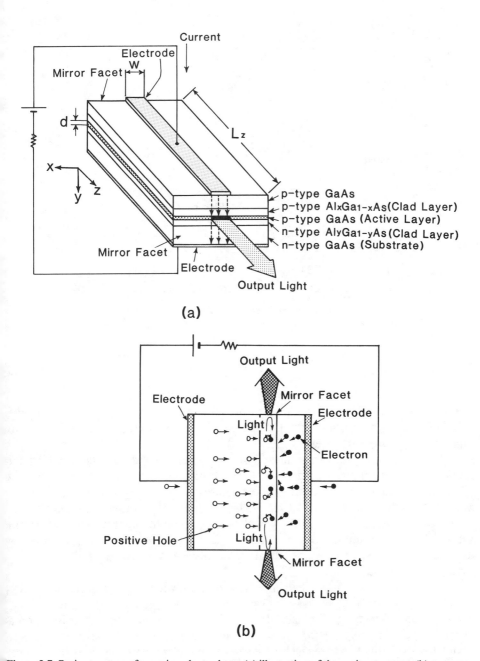

Figure 2.7 Basic structure of a semiconductor laser: (a) illustration of the cavity structure; (b) cross-sectional view in y-z plane; (c) energy bands; (d) spatial distributions of refractive index and electric field of laser light.

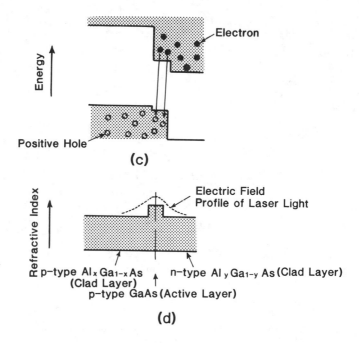

Figure 2.7 continued

the oscillation condition of the lowest transverse mode is met by $w < 0.5$ μm, the value of w usually is fixed to larger than about 2 μm due to technical limitations in fabricating a narrow-stripe electrode.

The electrons, thus, are confined in a waveguide cavity having a rectangular cross section with the size of $d \times w$. The light is confined in the active layer and propagates along the z-axis in the double hetero-structure waveguide in Figure 2.7, because the refractive index of the active layer is larger than those of the clad layers, as was shown by Figure 2.6(d). A typical ratio between the light power confined in the active layer and the total power (this ratio is called a *confinement factor*) is as low as about 0.2; however, its confinement is sufficiently large to realize a CW and room-temperature oscillation.

The cavity length along the z-axis is fixed, usually to about 300 μm. The Fabry-Perot cavity is formed by making flat mirrors on the waveguide facets through cleaving or chemical etching. The laser having the structure just described is called a *stripe-type double hetero-structure laser*. The value of internal loss α_l is typically about 10 cm^{-1}, due to scattering by the crystal lattice and absorption by impurities. The reflectivity of the cleaved facet is determined by the refractive index of the material n_i with respect to the ith mode of laser oscillation, which is given by

$$R_1 = R_2 = [(n_i - 1)/(n_i + 1)]^2 \qquad (2.32)$$

The reflectivity of a GaAs is 0.3 because $n_i = 3.5$. (Dielectric thin films are sometimes coated on the facets to increase or decrease the reflectivity, thus satisfying the requirements from practical application systems.) As a result, the value of the cavity loss α_{tl} given by

$$\alpha_{tl} = \alpha_l + (1/2L) \ln(1/R_1R_2) \qquad (2.33)$$

is about 50 cm^{-1}. It corresponds to the cavity Q factor of 6×10^3, which means the cavity loss is very large compared with those of other kinds of lasers. By increasing the injection current I over its threshold value I_{th}, the laser power increases as the current increases. An example of the relation between the injection current and the laser power, called the *I-L curve,* is given by Figure 2.8.

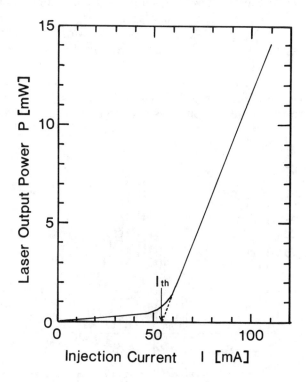

Figure 2.8 Relation between the laser output power and injection current (*I-L* curve), where I_{th} represents the threshold value of the dc injection current.

Equation (2.34) shows that the separation between the adjacent longitudinal modes is $\Delta\lambda_i$ = 0.34 nm or $\Delta\nu_i$ = 140 GHz for n_i = 3.5, λ_i = 0.85 μm, and L = 300 μm:

$$\Delta\lambda_i = \lambda_i^2/2n_iL \qquad\qquad (2.34)$$
$$\Delta\nu_i = c/2n_iL$$

The width of the gain spectral profile is about 100 times larger than this separation, which means that a large number of longitudinal modes can oscillate simultaneously. An example of the spectral profile of this multilongitudinal mode oscillation is shown in Figure 2.9. Each longitudinal mode also is accompanied by several transverse modes. To realize the lowest transverse mode oscillation, a technique of transverse mode control is employed in the device's fabrication, in which the dimension of the active layer along the x-axis in Figure 2.6(a) is limited to reduce the size of the cross-section of the active layer, as already was done in fabricating a single-mode optical fiber. It can be realized by employing the "index-guided" structure; that is, the difference of the refractive index is formed along the x-axis to increase the confinement factor to the optical field along this axis. Most commercially available semiconductor lasers have such a structure. Figure 2.10 shows examples of lasers with these structures. [3].

On the other hand, a laser having a stripe electrode several μm wide is called a *gain-guided laser*. Here, the gain is within a limited region of the waveguide along the x-axis. The transverse mode control is not effective in this case, and as has been

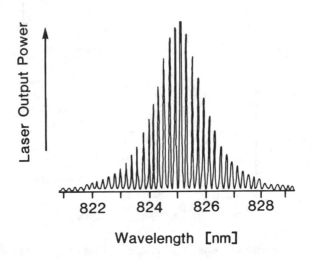

Figure 2.9 Field spectral profile of a multilongitudinal mode laser.

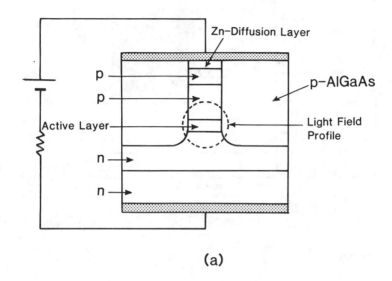

(a)

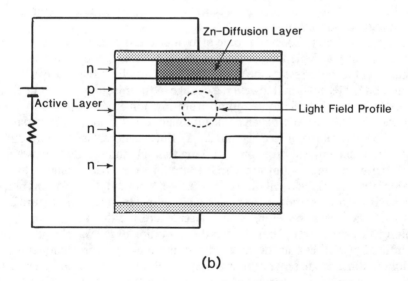

(b)

Figure 2.10 Cross-sectional view of the index-guided laser (from [3]): (a) buried hetero structure (BH) type; (b) channeled substrate planar (CSP) type; (c) transverse junction stripe (TJS) type.

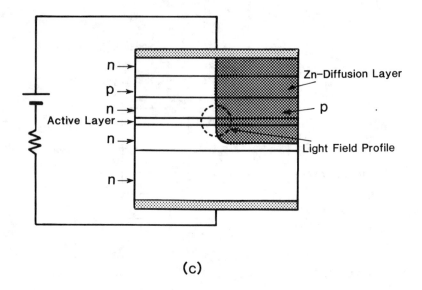

(c)

Figure 2.10 continued

shown by Figure 2.9, the multilongitudinal mode oscillates as well. One possible reason for this multilongitudinal mode oscillation of the gain-guided laser is a hole burned along the x-axis.

Figure 2.11 shows a spectral profile of an index-guided laser, whose oscillation is limited to nearly a single longitudinal mode. As in this figure, it has been found empirically that a transverse-mode controlled laser usually has a nearly single longitudinal mode of oscillation. However, a change in the injection current or temperature can cause laser oscillation to jump from one longitudinal mode to another because the gain difference between adjacent longitudinal modes is very small. This jump is called *mode hopping* (see Section 2.5.1). Furthermore, fast, high modulation of the injection current can bring on multilongitudinal mode oscillation as well.

A longitudinal mode control technique modifies the cavity structure to realize a single longitudinal mode oscillation even during fast modulation. For this purpose, a cavity having a low loss only for a specific longitudinal mode is used. Figure 2.12(a) and (b) show the typical structure of such lasers; here, a diffraction grating is fabricated along the active layer [3]. Although the resolution of the wavelength selection of the diffraction grating is as low as 0.1 nm, it is enough for semiconductor lasers, whose longitudinal mode separation is as large as about 0.3–0.5 nm. Figure 2.12(a) represents the laser with a *distributed feedback* (DFB) cavity, in which a diffraction grating is fabricated on or below the active layer. The wavelength corresponding to the maximum reflectivity of the DFB cavity is

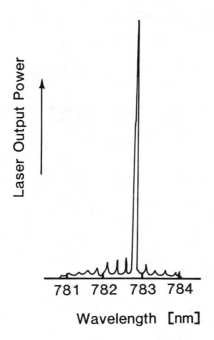

Figure 2.11 Field spectral profile of an index-guided laser.

$$\lambda = \lambda_B \pm \delta\lambda_l \qquad\qquad (2.35)$$

where λ_B ($= 2n_i\Lambda/m$) is the Bragg wavelength, Λ is the grating period, and m is an integer representing the order of diffraction. The term $\delta\lambda_l$ is a quantity whose value depends on the refractive index and the groove depth of the grating, and cavity length L. Although the highest reflectivity is realized at two wavelengths located in the symmetrical positions around the Bragg wavelength, a single longitudinal mode oscillation at one of the two wavelengths can be realized by breaking this symmetry by introducing a quarter-wavelength shift of the grating (see Section 7.1.1).

Figure 2.12(b) represents a laser with a *distributed Bragg reflector* (DBR), in which the diffraction grating is butt-jointed on one or both sides of the active layer. For a low absorption loss, a diffraction grating is made of material with band-gap energy larger than that of the active layer material. Although highly accurate crystal growing is required to realize the low-loss butt joint, the single longitudinal mode oscillation is always realized due to lack of symmetry, which is different from Figure 2.12(a). However, the output power is lower than that in Figure 2.12(a) in its shorter active layer.

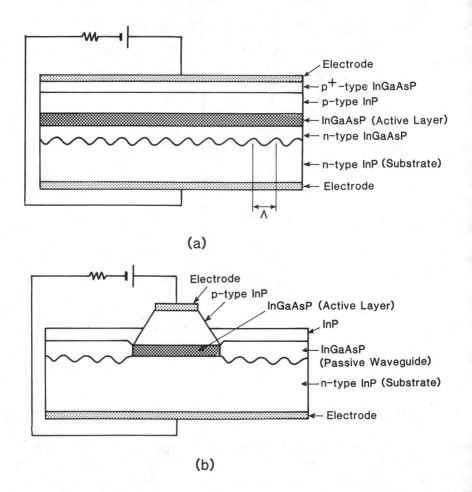

Figure 2.12 Structures of longitudinal mode controlled lasers (from [3]): (a) a distributed feedback (DFB) laser; (b) a distributed Bragg reflector (DBR) laser.

Even in these lasers, the laser power of the other modes become larger at a high bias level due to the spatial hole burning effect along the z-axis. Figure 2.13(a) shows a novel device structure developed to reduce this phenomenon by adjusting the value of the current injected into each segmented electrode [4]. Furthermore, Figure 2.13(b) shows a laser with a tuning range of over 6.2 nm, realized by dividing the electrodes on the active layer and using a grating to control the laser power and the wavelength [5]. A phase modulator is also fabricated between the two sections to stabilize the laser oscillation.

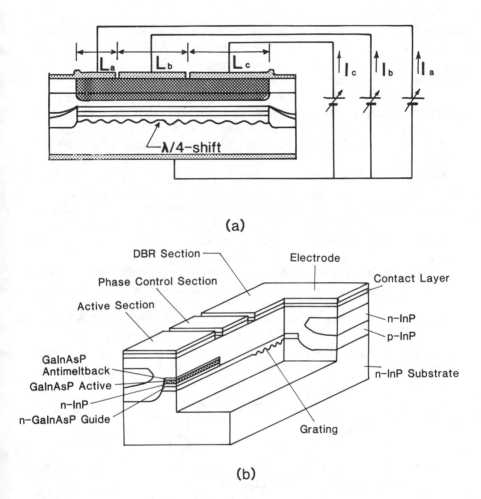

(a)

(b)

Figure 2.13 Structures of semiconductor lasers with segmented electrodes: (a) to reduce burning of holes (from [4]); (b) for wide-range wavelength tuning (from [5]).

It has been possible to control the lasing characteristics, such as a gain spectral profile, by changing the energy band structure with the help of the ultrathin-film epitaxial growing technique, which is developing rapidly in present years. As shown by Figure 2.14(a), if the thickness, width, and length of the active layer is reduced to about 20 nm—comparable with the broadening of the electronic wave function—the motion of electrons along the direction perpendicular to the film plane is quantized. The resultant discrete energy levels are illustrated in Figure 2.14(b), which

28

shows that the quantum-size effect appears in the gain and loss properties of the material. The laser employing this effect is called *quantum well* (QW) *laser.* As shown in Figure 2.15, because the gain spectral linewidth of such a laser is narrower than those of the conventional lasers for quantized energy, low threshold current density and high device efficiency are realized. Furthermore, the dynamic properties and noise characteristics are also improved. The thin film exhibiting the quantum-size effect already has been developed, and the novel lasers with two- and three-dimensional quantum-size effects are under development, too; these are called the *quantum wire laser* and *quantum box laser,* respectively. Although the gain is increased and the gain spectral linewidth is decreased by the enhanced confinement of carriers, these lasers still show multilongitudinal mode oscillation, as the gain spectral linewidth still is larger than the separation of the longitudinal mode. Longitudinal mode control still is required for these lasers. These quantum well structure lasers have been fabricated, and wavelength tunability as wide as 100 nm has been achieved by using an external cavity structure [6] (see Sections 5.2.2 and 7.1.3).

The threshold current depends on the cavity loss and the width of the active layer, typically from 1 mA to several 10 mA at room temperature. The quantum well lasers demonstrate a very low threshold, about 0.55 mA [7]. Practical output power ranges from several mW to several tens of mW at room temperature; however, power as high as several hundreds of mW have been realized by a gain-guided and multilongitudinal mode laser. For example, 300 mW of output power has been obtained

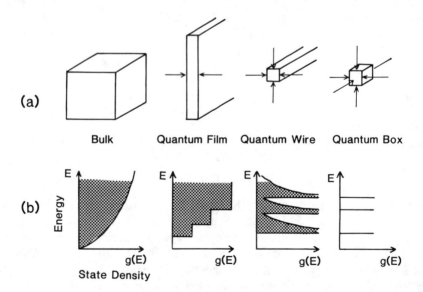

Figure 2.14 Semiconductor laser structures with (a) a micro-sized active region and (b) the profiles of their energy bands.

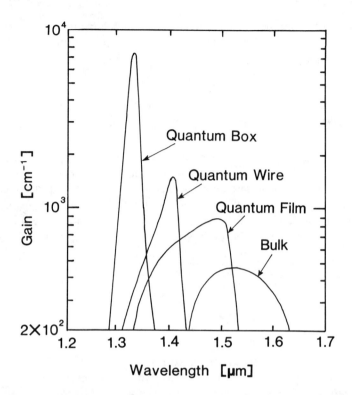

Figure 2.15 Gain spectral profiles of semiconductor lasers with a micro-sized active region.

by introducing a broad stripe structure into a 0.67 μm wavelength visible AlGaInP laser [8]. Total output power as high as 76 W also has been realized in an AlGaAs laser array, composed of 20 active waveguides fabricated close together in parallel on a common substrate [9].

Device efficiency, defined as a ratio between the light output power and the electrical power supplied from the current source, is about 10 %, which is comparable to that of a CO_2 laser. However, the differential quantum efficiency, defined as the increase of the photon number per unit increase of the electron injected from the current source, is as high as 40–60%. This efficiency corresponds to the value of the slope of the *I-L* curve of Figure 2.8. Due to so much differential quantum efficiency, the semiconductor laser is regarded as highly efficient.

The divergence angle of the laser beam emitted from the cavity is very large due to a large diffraction effect under the condition of $d < \lambda < w$, where d, w, and λ represent the thickness, width of the active layer, and wavelength, respectively. And the divergence angle along the direction of the active layer surface θ_w is smaller than the angle θ_d along the direction perpendicular to it, due to the relation given earlier. Their typical values are about 15° and 30°, respectively. This divergence angle is much larger than those of other lasers, and the output laser beam does not have a circular cross-section. A microscope objective lens is required to collimate the output laser beam.

2.3   FORMULATION OF LASER OSCILLATION

Current injected into a *p-n* junction can provide electrons and positive holes in the conduction and valence bands, respectively, which work as carriers. Laser oscillations are generated by stimulated emission from these carriers and optical positive feedback from a waveguide-type cavity. Rate equations for the photon density N_{pi} of the *i*th longitudinal mode and carrier density N_c have been proposed [10, 11]. For single longitudinal mode oscillation in simple form, equations are expressed as

$$\frac{dN_{pi}}{dt} = g(N_c - N_G)N_{pi} + \frac{CN_c}{\tau_r} - \frac{N_{pi}}{\tau_p} \qquad (2.36)$$

$$\frac{dN_c}{dt} = \frac{I}{eVa} - g(N_c - N_G)N_{pi} - \frac{N_c}{\tau_s} \qquad (2.37)$$

Here, g is a constant proportional to the stimulated emission rate, and N_G is the minimum carrier density required to keep a positive gain for oscillation. The term C is the spontaneous emission coefficient, representing the portion of the spontaneous emission energy that works as a trigger for the laser oscillation of the *i*th mode. The value of C has been estimated as 1×10^{-6} to 1×10^{-4} [11]. The term τ_r is the lifetime of the carriers, which is dependent on radiative recombination; τ_s is the total lifetime of the carriers, which is dependent on radiative and nonradiative recombination. The term τ_p is the photon lifetime in the laser cavity, which is equal to $n_i/c\alpha_{tl}$; I is the injection current; e is the electron charge, and V_a is the volume of the active layer.

Using these rate equations can lead to quantitative descriptions of the characteristics of laser power and several transient phenomena. By including spatial profiles of carrier density distribution and optical fields in these equations, relations between the structures of laser waveguides and several oscillation characteristics have been discussed. The results of these discussions are commonly applied in designing reliable laser structures.

For more quantitative estimations of oscillation gain, the density-matrix approach with third-order approximation developed for gas lasers [12] can be used. This approach has been applied to semiconductor lasers [13], and resultant rate equations of the square of the field amplitude E_i of the *i*th mode and the carrier density N_c are

$$\frac{d|E_i|^2}{dt} = \frac{c}{n_i}[\tilde{\alpha}_i^{(1)} - \alpha_{th} - \tilde{\alpha}_i^{(3)}|E_i|^2 - \tilde{\alpha}_{i(j)}^{(3)}|E_j|^2] \cdot |E_i|^2 + \frac{Ch\nu_{li}N_c}{2n_i\epsilon_0\tau_r} \tag{2.38}$$

$$(i, j = 1,2,3,\ldots: i \neq j) \tag{2.39}$$

$$\frac{dN_c}{dt} = n_i \sqrt{\frac{\epsilon_0}{\mu_0}} \sum_i \frac{2}{h\nu_{li}} \tilde{\alpha}_i^{(1)}|E_i|^2 - \frac{N_c}{\tau_s} + \frac{I}{eV_a}$$

In (2.38), c is the speed of light in vacuum, n_i is the relative index of the active layer, $\tilde{\alpha}_i^{(1)}$ is the linear gain, α_{th} is the cavity loss, which is c/n_i times the α_{tl} (see eq. (2.33)).

In (2.39), ϵ_0 is the permittivity constant of the vacuum, μ_0 is the permeability constant of the vacuum, and ν_{li} is the oscillation frequency of the ith mode.

In discussing phenomena such as mode hopping and mode partition, these rate equations can be applied because (2.38) contains the self-saturation coefficient $\tilde{\alpha}_i^{(3)}$ as well as the cross-saturation coefficient $\tilde{\alpha}_{i(j)}^{(3)}$ for representing the gain saturation. The temporal variation of N_c given by (2.39) is fast because the carrier lifetime τ_s is as short as 3 ns. This means that the adiabatic approximation cannot be applied for N_c, which also means that the coefficient $\tilde{\alpha}_i^{(1)}$, $\tilde{\alpha}_i^{(3)}$, and $\tilde{\alpha}_{i(j)}^{(3)}$ in (2.38) are not constant but depend on N_c. The formulation for describing the dynamics of a semiconductor laser is different from that for conventional lasers because of the dependence on N_c.

These rate equations also can be obtained by fully applying quantum-mechanical treatments. They have been derived by combining the quantum-mechanical theory for gas and solid-state lasers with the theory for interband transition of carriers in semiconductors [14]. In this treatment, first we derive equations for the photon creation and anhilation operators (a^+ and a in Appendix I) and for the operator for the dipole moment induced by interband transitions, then we apply the adiabatic approximation for the dipole moment; this leads to the quantum-mechanical rate equations for photon number density $N_p(= a^+a)$ and carrier density N_c. They can be expressed as

$$\frac{dNp}{dt} = -\frac{N_p}{\tau_p} + E_{sp} + GN_p + F_p(t) \tag{2.40}$$

$$\frac{dNc}{dt} = P - R_{sp} - GN_p - E_{sp} + F_c(t) \tag{2.41}$$

In (2.40), E_{sp} is the rate of spontaneous emission proportional to C of (2.36), G is a coefficient representing the rate of stimulated emission, and $F_p(t)$ is the Langevin force for photon density fluctuations. In (2.41), P is the pumping rate, R_{sp} is the total rate of spontaneous emission, and $F_c(t)$ is the Langevin force for carrier density fluctuations. Equations (2.40) and (2.41) contain quantum-mechanical fluctuation terms; that is, they correspond to the quantum-mechanical descriptions of (2.36) and (2.37).

Rate equations (2.40) and (2.41) describe only the power of the laser, and cannot be used to describe the topics, that is, the temporal coherence characteristics of the laser, reviewed in the following chapters. In general, rate equations cannot be used to describe topics such as oscillation frequency, quantum frequency noise, spectral linewidth, and phase locking phenomena. For these descriptions, we must use equations for the phase of lightwave, as derived by [15]. The equations for the photon creation operator a^+ is derived by adiabatic approximation of the dipole moment, as in (2.40) and (2.41); this leads to the following equation for amplitude $A^+(t)$ of the lightwave:

$$\frac{dA^+}{dt} = \beta(d - A^+A)A^+ + \tilde{F}\exp(-i2\pi\Omega t) \tag{2.42}$$

where

$$A(t) = a^+(t) \cdot \exp(-i2\pi\Omega t) \tag{2.43}$$

In (2.42), Ω is the frequency of laser oscillation. The d in the first term on the right-hand side of this equation is a complex linear gain, the second term represents the gain saturation, and the third term is the Langevin force representing quantum noise. Removing the Langevin force from this equation, reduces it to the well-known Van der Pol's equation.

The equation for carrier density fluctuations δN_c can be derived from (2.41), and the equations for amplitude fluctuations δA and phase fluctuations $\delta\phi$ of the lightwave can be derived from (2.42). These equations are expressed as [16]

$$\frac{d(\delta N_c)}{dt} = -\left(\frac{1}{\tau_s} + \frac{\nu_s}{\mu^2}\frac{d\chi_r}{dN_c}A_0^2\right) \cdot \delta N_c - 2\frac{\nu_s}{\mu^2}\chi_r A_0 \cdot \delta A + F_c(t) \tag{2.44}$$

$$\frac{d(\delta A)}{dt} = \frac{1}{2}\frac{\nu_s}{\mu^2}\frac{d\chi_r}{dN_c}A_0 \cdot \delta N_c + F_A(t) \tag{2.45}$$

$$\frac{d(\delta\phi)}{dt} = -\frac{1}{2}\frac{\nu_c}{\mu^2}\frac{d\chi_i}{dN_c} \cdot \delta N_c + F_\phi(t) \tag{2.46}$$

In these equations, χ_r and χ_i are the real and imaginary parts of the nonlinear complex susceptibility, respectively; and A_0 is the stationary value of the field amplitude of the lightwave; F_c, F_A, and F_ϕ are Langevin forces. The characteristics of frequency noise, spectral linewidth, and temporal coherence can be described by these equations.

2.4 NOISE CHARACTERISTICS

Properties of the *intensity modulated* (IM) noise and *frequency modulated* (FM) noise in semiconductor lasers are discussed in this section. Fundamental noise is the intrinsic quantum noise due to the fundamental mechanism of laser operation. In addition, external noises come from power sources, environmental fluctuations, and so forth. The magnitude of the external noise could be larger than the intrinsic noise. Definitions of the measures representing the noise magnitude are given in Appendix II.

2.4.1 Intensity Noise

The following discussion concentrates on the characteristics of the noises in a single longitudinal mode laser, more strictly, a nearly single longitudinal mode laser, assuming that the additional noises presented in Section 2.5 have been removed.

The fundamental IM noise is induced by the spontaneous emission fluctuations. The power spectral density of this quantum noise is derived from (2.45) and expressed as [17]

$$S_{\delta I/I}(f) = \frac{\epsilon_0 h \nu_l n_{sp} c \left(\ln \dfrac{1}{R} \right)}{8\pi^2 \tau_p n_i P_0} \frac{1}{f^2 + [(I/I_{th} - 1)/2\pi\tau_p]^2} \tag{2.47}$$

where ν_l is the nominal laser frequency, P_0 is the output laser power, and the laser facet reflectivities were assumed to be equal with each other ($R_1 = R_2 \equiv R$). The n_{sp} in this equation is the spontaneous emission factor proportional to the spontaneous emission coefficient C of (2.36) and given by

$$n_{sp} = \frac{1}{1 - \exp[(h\nu_l + E_{Fv} - E_{Fc})/k_B T]} \tag{2.48}$$

where E_{Fv} and E_{Fc} are the quasi-Fermi levels of the valence and conduction band, respectively; k_B is Boltzmann's constant; T is the temperature, and the value of n_{sp} falls between 1 and 2. Equation (2.47) demonstrates that the profile of this power spectral density is Lorentzian, and its dc value is

$$S_{\delta I/I}(f) = \frac{\epsilon_0 h \nu_l n_{sp} c \left(\ln \dfrac{1}{R} \right) \tau_p}{2 n_i P_0} \frac{1}{(I/I_{th} - 1)^2} \tag{2.49}$$

Therefore, the dc value is inversely proportional to the square of the normalized bias level ($I/I_{th} - 1$). The *half-width at a half maximum* (HWHM) of the spectral profile of (2.47) Δf_h is given by

$$\Delta f_h = (I/I_{th} - 1)/2\pi\tau_p \tag{2.50}$$

which is proportional to the normalized bias level. For example, the value of Δf_h for the 0.8 μm wavelength AlGaAs laser is 1.6×10^{11} Hz, found by substituting $\nu_l = 3.75 \times 10^{14}$ Hz, $n_{sp} = 2$, $\tau_p = 1$ ps, and $I/I_{th} = 2$. Integrating (2.47) for $0 \leqslant f \leqslant \infty$, we easily find that the total IM noise power is inversely proportional to the normalized bias level, which means that the semiconductor laser operating at a higher bias level shows a lower IM noise power even though the noise bandwidth is wider.

In addition to the quantum noise (2.47), the IM noise could be induced by the carrier density fluctuations due to the optical pumping by the spontaneously emitted light. Therefore, this carrier-induced IM noise also can be regarded as the quantum noise. This carrier-induced IM noise is derived from eqs. (2.40) and (2.41) and expressed as

$$S_{\delta I/I}(f) = \frac{A_s^2 + B_s^2 f^2}{(a_s^2 - f^2)^2 - b_s^2 f^2} \tag{2.51}$$

Here, A_s, B_s, and b_s are the constants that depend on the values of the second-order moments of the Langevin forces in (2.40) and (2.41). As is well known, the values of these moments can be compared with each coefficient of (2.40) and (2.41) by using the fluctuation-dissipation theorem [2].

The profile of the power spectral density represented in (2.51) exhibits a resonant peak at the Fourier frequency of about a_s. A detailed expression for the resonant frequency has been obtained [18]:

$$f_r = \frac{1}{2\pi} \sqrt{\frac{I/I_{th} - 1}{\tau_s \tau_p}} \tag{2.52}$$

This is called the *relaxation oscillation frequency,* which depends on the carrier lifetime τ_s, photon lifetime τ_p, and the normalized injection current I/I_{th}. As is described in Appendix IV, this resonance phenomenon occurs because the dynamic behavior of the photon in the cavity is governed by the second-order lag system. That is, the carriers injected into the active layer exhibit a time lag, τ_s, until they emit photons by carrier recombination, and the emitted photons also exhibit a time lag, τ_p, until they disappear from the cavity. Such a second-order lag system generally exhibits resonance, called *relaxation oscillation.* The value of this oscillation frequency, shown in (2.52), ranges from 1 GHz to several tens of GHz because τ_s and τ_p are approximately 3 ns and 1 ps, respectively. Because the magnitude of the carrier-induced IM noise (eq. (2.51) is larger than that given by (2.49), the measured power spectral density is governed mainly by (2.51), as is shown in Figure 2.16. The solid curve in this figure is the calculated result, based on (2.49) and (2.51), on which the effect of carrier density fluctuation produces a resonant peak at the relaxation oscillation frequency [3, 16]. And this relaxation oscillation frequency corresponds to the high-frequency cutoff.

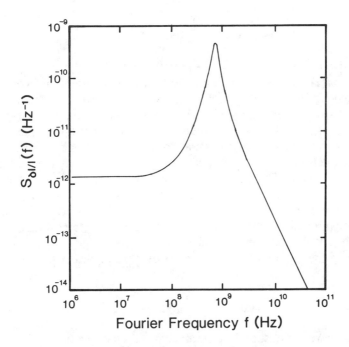

Figure 2.16 Power spectral density of the IM noise of a single longitudinal mode laser.

Furthermore, the carrier density fluctuations could activate current fluctuations, which also activate temperature fluctuations due to the self-heating of the laser device. This, too, can be regarded as the quantum noise. In addition to these is IM noise from the current fluctuations of the current source, and fluctuations of the threshold current or quantum efficiency activated by ambient temperature fluctuations. Although the noise characteristics of the Fourier frequency lower than 1 MHz are not shown in this figure, we know empirically that the noise caused by temperature variation and flicker noise ($1/f$ noise) usually is observed in this range. It has been proposed that one possible origin of the $1/f$ noise is the carrier mobility fluctuations [19].

2.4.2 Frequency Noise

FM noise from several sources can be derived from eq. (2.46). Figure 2.17 illustrates the power spectral density of FM noise. The first fundamental noise source (curve A in Figure 2.17) is the fluctuations resulting from spontaneous emission, the second term of eq. (2.46), which induces white FM noise. The power spectral density of FM noise from this source can be expressed as [20]

$$S_y(f) = \frac{h}{8\pi^2 \nu_l P_0} \left(\frac{c}{n_i L}\right)^2 \left(\alpha_l L + \ln \frac{1}{R}\right) \left(\ln \frac{1}{R}\right) n_{sp} \qquad (2.53)$$

In this equation, the quantity y represents the normalized frequency fluctuations $\delta\nu(t)/\nu_l$, with $\delta\nu(t)$ the frequency fluctuations, and ν_l the nominal frequency of the laser. The second intrinsic noise source is the carrier density fluctuations (the first term of eq. (2.46) and curve B of Figure 2.17) induced by fluctuations of spontaneous emission. That is, in addition to the quantum noise given by (2.53), the frequency of the ith longitudinal mode could fluctuate due to the fluctuations of the refractive index by the fluctuations of the carrier density, which are optically pumped by the spontaneous emission. The ratio between the power spectral density due to the carrier-induced fluctuations and that of (2.53) is represented by α^2, where α has been called α-parameter or linewidth enhancement factor [21]. We can understand, from the preceding discussions, that IM and FM noises are correlated with each other via the carrier density fluctuations. That is, the α-parameter is given by the ratio between the changes in the real and imaginary parts of the complex susceptibility $\Delta\chi'$ and $\Delta\chi''$:

$$\alpha = \Delta\chi'/\Delta\chi'' \qquad (2.54)$$

where $\Delta\chi'$ and $\Delta\chi''$ correspond, respectively, to the change of refractive index and the gain of the active medium. It has been reported that the α-parameter took a value in the range 2–9 [22]. The center frequencies of the spectral profiles of χ' and χ'' are different from each other because the gain spectrum has a complicated profile due to the intrinsic band structure of the semiconductor energy level. Therefore, the value of α depends on the material of the active medium, the waveguide structure, and so on. Curve B of Figure 2.17 shows that the contribution of the carrier density fluctuations brings to a resonant peak at the relaxation oscillation frequency to the total magnitude of the FM noise, which corresponds to the high frequency cutoff. Below this frequency, the ratio between the values due to carrier density fluctuations and spontaneous emission correspond to α^2. In addition to these contributions, we see slowly fluctuating components due to the drift of the longitudinal mode frequency. This is due to self-heating by the current fluctuations induced by the carrier density fluctuations (curve C). These contributions should be regarded as quantum noise, too.

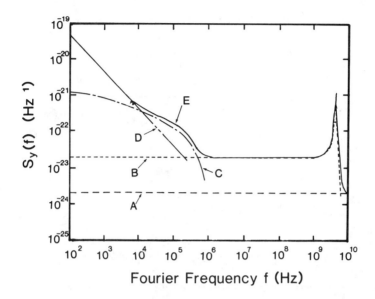

Figure 2.17 Power spectral density of the quantum FM noise of a single longitudinal mode laser: A is the fluctuation of spontaneous emission; B is the fluctuation of carrier density; C is the fluctuation of temperature; D is the $1/f$ fluctuation; E is the total magnitude of the FM noise.

Additional noise, flicker noise ($1/f$ noise), can be seen in the low Fourier frequency range (curve D of Figure 2.17). The origin of this noise can be the same as that of the $1/f$ noise of the IM noise. Furthermore, as an external noise source, current fluctuations from the current source and ambient temperature fluctuations could activate the FM noise, which is expressed as

$$\delta\nu = -\nu_l \left\{ \left(\frac{A_c}{n_i} \right) \cdot \delta N_c(I) + (\alpha_T + \beta_T) \cdot [\delta T_1(I) + \delta T_2] \right\} \tag{2.55}$$

The first-term of the right-hand side represents the change in refractive index n_i due to the carrier density change $dN_c(I)$ induced by the change of the injection current. The quantity A_c is a proportional constant, which will be given by eq. (3.41). The second and third terms represent the thermal effect of the carrier length L (its thermal expansion coefficient is given by $\alpha_T = \partial L/\partial T$) and the change in refractive index n_i (its thermal coefficient is given by $\beta_T = \partial n_i/\partial T$), respectively. Both effects result from the temperature change $\delta T_1(I)$ due to the self-heating of the semiconductor materials caused by a change of the injection current and from the ambient temperature change δT_2. Typical values of the parameters in this equation are given by Table 2.1 [23]. Table 2.2 summarizes the rates of the frequency drift due to slow changes in current and ambient temperature [23]. Figure 2.18 shows the estimated values of the square root of the Allan variance $\sigma_y^2(\tau)$ for the magnitude of each fluctuation described [20], where the definition of the Allan variance is as given in Appendix II. Curve A in this figure corresponds to the curve A of Figure 2.17, which is expressed from eq. (2.53) as

$$\sigma_y(\tau) = \sqrt{\frac{h}{16\pi^2 v_i P_0}\left(\frac{c}{n_i L}\right)^2 \left(\alpha_i L + \ln\frac{1}{R}\right)\left(\ln\frac{1}{R}\right) n_{sp}\tau^{-1}} \qquad (2.56)$$

Table 2.1
Values of Coefficients in (2.55) (from [23])

	AlGaAs Laser (0.8 μm)	InGaAsP Laser (1.5 μm)
A_c	-4.0×10^{-27} m^3	-7.0×10^{-27} m^3
n_i	3.5	3.5
α_T	5×10^{-6} K^{-1}	5.4×10^{-6} K^{-1}
β_T	1×10^{-4} K^{-1}	1.0×10^{-4} K^{-1}

Table 2.2
Variations of Lasing Wavelength λ and Frequency v with a Change in dc Current and Ambient Temperature (from [23])

Variation of Wavelength and Frequency	AlGaAsLaser(0.8μm)	InGaAsLaser(1.5μm)
$\dfrac{d\lambda}{dI}$	+0.006nm/mA	+0.008nm/mA
$\dfrac{dv}{dI}$	−2.8GHz/mA	−1.1GHz/mA
$\dfrac{d\lambda}{dT'}$	+0.06nm/K	+0.08nm/K
$\dfrac{dv}{dT'}$	−28GHz/K	−11GHz/K

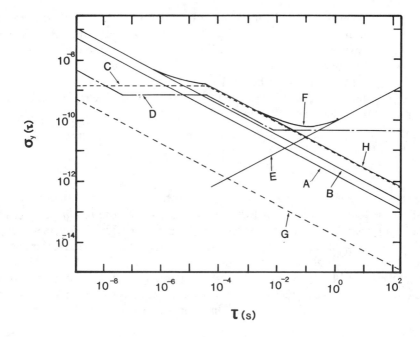

Figure 2.18 The square root of the Allan variance of the FM noise of a single longitudinal mode laser (from [20]): A is the fluctuation of spontaneous emission; B is the fluctuation of carrier density; C is the fluctuation of temperature (here, curves A, B, and C correspond to curves A, B, and C in Figure 2.17, respectively); D is the fluctuation of injection current from a current source; E is the fluctuation of ambient temperature; F is the FM noise under free-running conditions (summation of the values of the curves A–D); G is the shot noise limit in the case of frequency control; H is the total quantum FM noise (summation of the values of the curves A, B, and C).

In summary, the instantaneous frequency fluctuation at the time t is given by

$$\delta\nu(t) = \frac{1}{2\tau_p}(1 + \alpha^2) \cdot \Gamma_s(t) + \Gamma_{ex}(t) \tag{2.57}$$

which was derived from eq. (2.46) to provide a more concrete expression. The first term on the right-hand side of this equation gives the quantum noise, in which the photon lifetime τ_p, being inversely proportional to the cavity loss α_{tl} of eq. (2.33), appears because (2.53) has shown that the magnitude of the quantum noise is proportional to the cavity loss. The term $\Gamma_s(t)$ is the instantaneous value of the spontaneous emission fluctuations; α is the α-parameter for the semiconductor laser. The second term, $\Gamma_{ex}(t)$, is the magnitude of external noise. The noise presented here is the total FM noise of the semicondcutor laser.

If the contributions from only the spontaneous emission fluctuations and carrier density fluctuations are considered, the FM noise is approximated as the white noise in the Fourier frequency range below the relaxation oscillation frequency. Under this white noise approximation, the *full-width at a half maximum* (FWHM) of the field spectral profile (i.e., the linewidth of the field spectral profile) can be an accurate measure of the FM noise magnitude (see Appendix II). By substituting (2.53) into (AII.9), the linewidth can be expressed as

$$\Delta\nu = \frac{h\nu_l}{8\pi P_0}\left(\frac{c}{n_i L}\right)^2\left(\alpha_l L + \ln\frac{1}{R}\right)\left(\ln\frac{1}{R}\right)n_{sp}(1 + \alpha^2) \tag{2.58}$$

where the parameter α^2 has been added to take into account the contribution of the carrier density fluctuations. This formula has been called the *modified Schawlow-Townes's formula* [24]. This equation shows that the linewidth is inversely proportional to the lasing power. The typical value of the linewidth reported so far has been 1–100 MHz. The actual values of the linewidth often vary, depending on the device and operating conditions. By carefully reducing the spatial hole burning, cavity loss, and the value of the α-parameter by using a segmented electrode, long cavity, and a multiquantum-well DFB laser device, linewidths as narrow as 85 kHz have been realized recently [25].

Equation (2.58) shows that the linewidth should approach zero with increasing the laser power. However, sometimes, the linewidth takes a nonzero value at $P_0^{-1=0}$; this has been called a *power-independent linewidth.* The values of this linewidth have been reported as between 0.6 and 0.9 MHz [26, 27]. The origins of the linewidth have been attributed to the power-independent carrier density fluctuations [26], fast thermal fluctuations of electronic state occupancy [28], flicker noise (curve *D* of Figure 2.17) induced by carrier mobility fluctuations [19], and other factors.

2.5   COHERENCE DETERIORATION INDUCED IN SEMICONDUCTOR LASERS BY SPECIFIC NOISE

Often, several specific kinds of noise can be generated in semiconductor lasers because of their low cavity Q and the wideband response characteristics of carrier density fluctuations. Because these kinds of noise impede attempts to improve coherence, their origins should be investigated and a technique found for suppressing them. Reflected lightwave noise, mode-hopping noise, and mode-partition noise typically are troublesome; their characteristics are reviewed in this section.

2.5.1   Oscillation Instabilities Induced by Reflected Lightwaves

It has been observed that laser oscillation became highly unstable when the emitted light was injected into the laser cavity after it had been reflected from a mirror surface, fiber edge, optical disk surface, or other reflective item (see Figure 2.19). Changes in oscillation characteristics have been observed, such as changes in the threshold current, wavelength shifting [29], linewidth broadening [30], increases in IM noise [31], changes in relaxation oscillation characteristics [32], and coherence collapse [33]. These instabilities frequently are induced, as the reflected wave can be easily injected into the cavity because of its low facet reflectivity. This deterministic instability occurred when the phase-delayed signal was injected into the self-sustained oscillator; finally, it leads to chaos [34]. Chaotic behavior of semiconductor lasers has been experimentally confirmed by injection of the reflected wave [35].

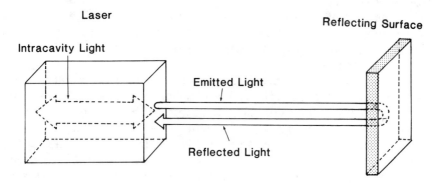

Figure 2.19 Schematic explanation for noise generation mechanism induced by injection of the reflected light.

Computer simulations have been made by employing a three-mirror model. However, the accuracy of this model can be reduced if the round-trip time is too long compared with the rise time of laser oscillations. The longest time limit for the round trip of this model is about 0.1 ns, which corresponds to a separation between the laser facet and the external mirror of about 1.5 cm. If the separation is larger than 1.5 cm, a more accurate model should be employed, for which a Van der Pol's equation is used by adding a term representing the electric field of the reflected wave with a phase delay [36,37]. In single-mode oscillation, the electric field of the lightwave is expressed as

$$\tilde{E}_i(t) = E_i(t) \cdot \exp(-i2\pi \nu_{li} t) \tag{2.59}$$

The Van der Pol's equation for $\tilde{E}_i(t)$ can be derived from (2.38), given by

$$\frac{d^2 \tilde{E}_i}{dt^2} = \frac{c}{2n_i} \frac{d}{dt} \left[(\tilde{\alpha}_i^{(1)} - \alpha_{th}) \tilde{E}_i - \frac{4}{3} \tilde{\alpha}_i^{(3)} \tilde{E}_i^3 \right]$$
$$- \Omega^2(N_c) \cdot \tilde{E}_i^2 + \kappa \frac{d}{dt} \tilde{E}_i(t - T) \tag{2.60}$$

where $\Omega(N_c)$ is the resonance angular frequency of the cavity mode, κ is the coupling coefficient of the reflected wave into the laser cavity, and T is the round-trip time between the laser facet and the external mirror (i.e., the delay time). The angular frequency Ω depends on the carrier density N_c and is expressed as

$$\Omega^2(N_c) = \Omega_0^2\left[1 - \frac{2A_c}{n_i}(N_c - N_{c,th})\right] \tag{2.61}$$

where A_c is the coefficient in eq. (2.55) representing the proportionality between the changes in the refractive index and the carrier density. The terms Ω_0 and $N_{c,th}$ are the resonant angular frequency of the cavity mode and the carrier density at the threshold. Computer simulations can analyze the temporal variation in $\tilde{E}_i(t)$ by using eqs. (2.39), (2.60), and (2.61).

Equation (2.60) is a nonlinear difference-differential equation that depends on the carrier density variations of (2.39). It shows that the electric field exhibits irregular behavior because it suffers the effect of feedback with delay time T. Figure 2.20 shows variations of laser output power P_0 simulated by using eqs. (2.39), (2.60), and (2.61) [37]. We can see that the magnitude of fluctuation increases with increasing κ, or increasing injected power. Instability can be noticed, in this figure, when the injection rate is as low as 0.003%; and finally, at 5%, a pulsive oscillation takes place. This means that an accurate optical isolator should be used. It has been shown empirically that the optical isolation of about 60 dB is required to reduce the effect of the reflected lightwave for practical application.

However, their high cost precludes industrial applications of optical isolators made of ferromagnetic Faraday rotators. To overcome this difficulty, several trials have been made using lasers insensitive to the effects of a reflected wave, such as a laser with low temporal coherence. Reproducible low temporal coherence has been realized by utilizing a multilongitudinal oscillation of refractive index-guided lasers. Although the magnitude of the IM noise of multimode lasers is larger than that of single-mode lasers, due to mode hopping and mode partition, multimode lasers are insensitive to the effects of the reflected wave because of the low temporal coherence in the superposed lightwaves, which can suppress the increase of IM noise under injection of the reflected light.

Multimode oscillation can be realized, for example, by superposing an rF injection current of several hundred MHz to the dc current [38] or by inducing sustained oscillation by increasing the difference in refractive index between the active and cladding layers [39]. Lasers prepared by these techniques oscillate with about 10 longitudinal modes, which reduce temporal coherence in the superposed lightwave. Therefore, they are sensitive to the effects of a reflected wave and IM noise is not increased even if a reflected wave is injected. This insensitivity has been confirmed experimentally [40].

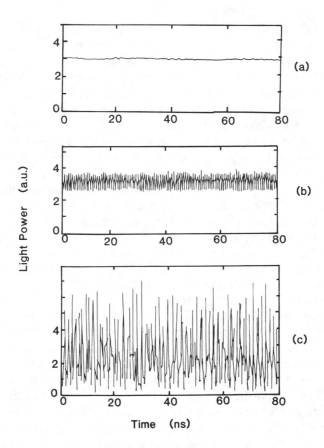

Figure 2.20 Calculated results of the temporal laser power variations caused by the injection of a reflected light (from [37]). The distance between the output facet of the laser cavity and the external reflection surface is 5 cm. The ratio between the emitted power and the injected power after reflection is (a) 0%, (b) 0.003%, and (c) 5%, respectively.

The artificially prepared low-coherence lasers just described can be replaced in the future by improved single-mode lasers free from the effect of reflected waves. Development of such a high-performance single-mode laser and more practical optical isolator is essential if the temporal coherence of the semiconductor lasers is ultimately to be improved.

2.5.2 Mode-Hopping and Mode-Partition Noise

Because the gain spectral width of semiconductor lasers is more than 100 times larger than the longitudinal mode separation, there are always unwanted vestigial side modes, even in a longitudinal mode-controlled semiconductor laser; the concepts of a single longitudinal-mode semiconductor laser can only be approximated. The present discussion is limited to the two longitudinal modes to simplify the analysis by using eqs. (2.38) and (2.39). The gain saturation is caused by the intraband relaxation of carriers in the conduction band, whose relaxation time constant τ_{in} is as short as 0.3 ps. The gain saturation coefficients ($\tilde{\alpha}_i^{(3)}$ and $\tilde{\alpha}_{i(j)}^{(3)}$ in (2.38)) are proportional to the square of the carrier density N_c^2. In addition, when N_c decreases by the transition from the conduction to valence bands, as shown by (2.39), there is also a gain in saturation because the linear gain $\alpha_i^{(1)}$ depends on N_c. The time constant of this relaxation as given by τ_s ($\cong 3$ ns) is much longer than τ_{in}. However, the characteristics of the mode-hopping and mode-partition phenomena described later depend mainly on the intraband relaxation. That is, they are the quantum mechanical phenomena driven by the spontaneous emission fluctuations coupled to each longitudinal mode and based on the gain saturation due to the intraband relaxation of carriers.

The characteristics of an index-guided laser, rather than a longitudinal mode-controlled laser, are discussed to simplify the analysis. The linear gains of the two longitudinal modes can be set almost equal to each other (i.e., $\tilde{\alpha}_1^{(1)} \approx \tilde{\alpha}_2^{(1)}$) by adjusting the injection current and temperature. Figure 2.21(a) shows time dependence of each mode power observed under this condition, which shows a clear switching phenomenon [41]; this is called *mode hopping*. This is attributed to the suppression of one mode by the decrease in carrier density because it is spent lasing the other mode. Because this phenomenon is driven by the randomly generated spontaneous emission that works as the triggering force for lasing the other mode, intensity fluctuations (IM noise) follow the statistics of a Poisson process. Therefore, as is shown by Figure 2.22(a), the profile of the power spectral density of the IM noise can be approximated as Lorentzian [42]. The cutoff frequency of this Lorentzian spectral shape represents the average frequency of mode hopping. It has been confirmed experimentally that the cutoff frequency decreases exponentially as the normalized bias level I/I_{th} increases, as is shown by Figure 2.22(b) [42].

On the other hand, nearly single longitudinal-mode oscillation can be realized—that is, the linear gain of one mode can be fixed far larger than that of the others ($\tilde{\alpha}_1^{(1)} \gg \tilde{\alpha}_2^{(1)} > \alpha_{th}$)—by fixing the injection current and temperature at other values. Figure 2.21(b) shows the time dependences of the two mode powers [41]. The transient decrease in the main mode power is called a *power dropout*. The power exchange between the main and submodes, shown in this figure, is called *mode partition*. These IM noises emanate from the same origin as that of the mode hopping: the gain of the main mode decreases with the decrease in the carrier density due to the transient increase in the submode power driven by the spontaneous emission [41]. The power spectral density of the IM noise is also Lorentzian. Figure 2.23 shows a relation between the threshold setting ϵ and the power dropout probability P_e of the main mode. Here, P_e was measured based on the definition

$$P_e = \sum_i t_i / T_m \tag{2.62}$$

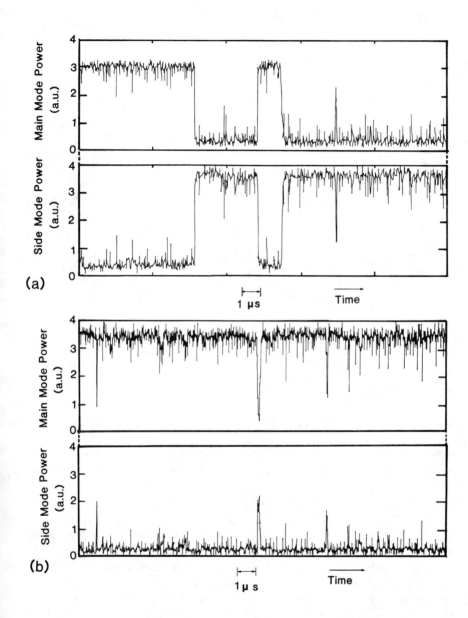

Figure 2.21 Measured results of temporal variations of the mode powers of the AlGaAs laser when two longitudinal modes oscillate (from [41] © 1989 IEEE): (a) mode hopping; (b) mode partition.

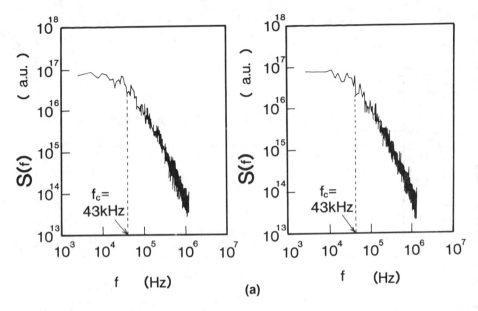

Figure 2.22 (a) Power spectral density of the IM noise of each mode of the AlGaAs laser measured during mode hopping (from [42] © 1989 IEEE). (b) Relation between the normalized injection current I/I_{th} and the cutoff frequency f_c of the curves of (a). The solid line is a least-square fit to the experimental values [42].

where t_i is a time period in which the ratio between the average CW power $\langle I_1 \rangle$ of the main mode and the magnitude of deviation of the main mode power $I_1 - \langle I_1 \rangle$ exceeds the value ϵ (i.e., $|I_1 - \langle I_1 \rangle|/\langle I_1 \rangle > \epsilon$). The term T_m represents the total time of measurement. This figure shows that P_e decreases by increasing E and that P_e decreases by increasing I/I_{th}, which means that the mode power fluctuations are less sensitive to agitation by spontaneous emission at a higher bias level.

Figure 2.24(a) shows the magnified pulsive waveforms of power fluctuations of the main and side modes observed during a power dropout [41]. The dependence of the duration time t_d of the power dropout on the bias level is shown by Figure 2.24(b) [41]. We can see that t_d decreases exponentially with an increasing of I/I_{th}. A noticeable increase in t_d observed around the threshold in Figure 2.24(b) corresponds to the slowing down [43] around the critical point in the phase transition phenomenon. To clarify this correspondence, the cutoff frequency f_c of the Lorentzian power spectral density of the power fluctuations was measured and presented by curve A in Figure 2.25 as a function of I/I_{th}. This cutoff frequency corresponds to the inverse of the correlation time of power fluctuation characteristics; that is, an inverse of t_d. Note, from this figure, that f_c decreases with a decreasing of I/I_{th}. The variance σ_1^2 of the power fluctuations of the main mode is shown by curve B of Figure 2.25. This curve

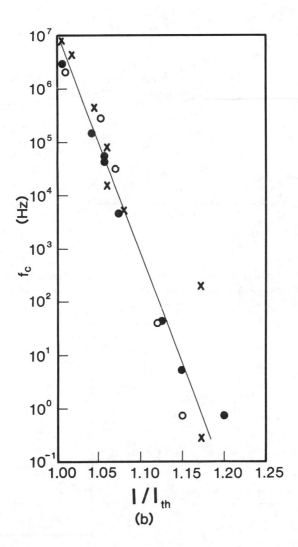

Figure 2.22 continued

shows that the value of σ_1^2 increases with a decreasing of I/I_{th}. The decrease in f_c and increase in σ_1^2 around the threshold shown in this figure are evidence that the behavior of power fluctuations corresponds to the critical slowing down.

Furthermore, the ratio of the average CW power of the main and side modes, $\langle I_1 \rangle / \langle I_2 \rangle$, was changed by changing the temperature while the bias level was maintained. Mode hopping was observed at $\langle I_1 \rangle / \langle I_2 \rangle \cong 1$. Curve A of Figure 2.26 shows a relation between $\langle I_1 \rangle / \langle I_2 \rangle$ and the cutoff frequency f_c. Curve B of this figure shows

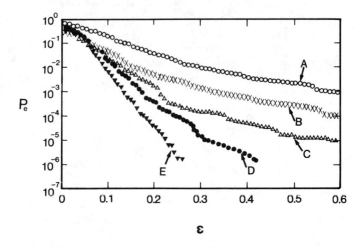

Figure 2.23 The relation between the threshold setting ϵ and the power dropout probability P_e of the main mode estimated using eq. (2.62) (from [41] © 1989 IEEE). The values of I/I_{th} are 1.070, 1.072, 1.075, 1.078, and 1.082, for $A-E$, respectively.

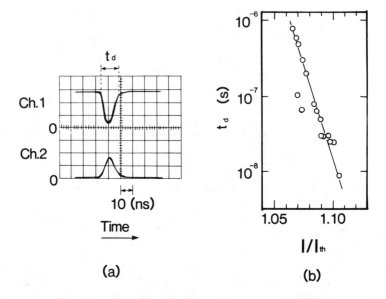

Figure 2.24 (a) Oscilloscope traces of the waveforms of power fluctuations of the main and side modes during a power dropout: Ch. 1 is the main mode, 20 mV/div.; Ch. 2 is the side mode, 10 mV/div. The duration time t_d of power dropout is defined by the width of the pulse-shaped waveform indicated in this figure (from [41] © 1989 IEEE). (b) The relation between the normalized bias level I/I_{th} and the duration time t_d (from [41] © 1989 IEEE).

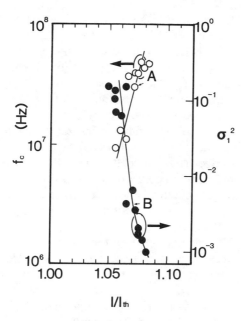

Figure 2.25 Curve A (○) is a measured relation between the bias level I/I_{th} and the cutoff frequency f_c of the Lorentzian power spectral density of power fluctuations of the main mode. Curve B (●) is a measured relation between the bias level and the variance σ_1^2 of the power fluctuations of the main mode (from [41] © 1989 IEEE).

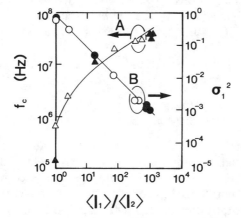

Figure 2.26 Curve A (△, ▲) is a measured relation between the ratio of average CW mode power $\langle I_1 \rangle / \langle I_2 \rangle$ and the cutoff frequency f_c of the power spectral density of the power fluctuations of the main mode. Curve B (○, ●) is a measured relation between the ratio of average CW model powers and the variance σ_1^2 of the power fluctuations of the main mode (from [41] © 1989 IEEE).

a relation between $\langle I_1 \rangle / \langle I_2 \rangle$ and σ_1^2. Note, from this figure, that the cutoff frequency f_c decreases with a decreasing of $\langle I_1 \rangle / \langle I_2 \rangle$; that is, by the conversion from mode partition to mode hopping. Also note that the value of σ_1^2 increases with a decreasing of $\langle I_1 \rangle / \langle I_2 \rangle$. At $\langle I_1 \rangle / \langle I_2 \rangle = 1$, the value of σ_1^2 takes unity, which is a specific value of σ_1^2 for the previously mentioned Poisson process.

A unified stochastic model for describing both the mode-hopping and mode-partition phenomena has been developed by comparison with the experimental results given earlier. This stochastic model is based on the rate equations eqs. (2.38) and (2.39) for the amplitudes of electric fields of the two modes E_i ($i = 1, 2$) and for the carrier density N_c. Because each coefficient in these equations is calculated by using the structural and material constants of the semiconductor laser, quantitative comparisons between the theoretical and experimental results are possible.

Noise terms are added to eq. (2.38) for E_i to represent the contribution from spontaneous emission fluctuations that work as random triggers for mode hopping and mode partition. Here, we assume that the carrier density fluctuations are negligible and the value of the carrier density can be approximated to its stationary value N_c^s, because the total stimulated emission rate can be kept constant. This assumption is based on the experimental observation that total power was maintained through time even though mode power fluctuated in an anticorrelated fashion due to mode hopping and partition. The validity of this assumption is confirmed in [42] and [44] for mode hopping and partition, respectively, by comparison and theoretical results. Therefore, the rate equation for carrier density is excluded in the following discussion, and the only equation to be solved is the rate equation for E_i with the noise due to spontaneous emission. In this formulation, we find that mode hopping and partition are caused by fluctuations in spontaneous emission and a nonlinear mode coupling due to spectral hole burning induced by intraband relaxation of the carrier in the conduction band. The value of relaxation time τ_{in} has been reported as about 0.1–0.3 ps [45].

By normalizing the rate equations for E_i, a set of nonlinear Langevin equations can be derived, expressed as [42, 44]

$$\frac{d\hat{E}_i}{d\tau} = (a_i - |\hat{E}_i|^2 - \xi|\hat{E}_j|^2)\hat{E}_i + q_i(t) \qquad (i, j = 1, 2; i \neq j) \tag{2.63}$$

where $\hat{E}_i$ is the normalized amplitude of the electric field of the ith mode, τ is the normalized time. The quantity a_i is the pump parameter corresponding to the stationary mode power normalized to the rms of the power fluctuations of spontaneous emission. Therefore, the pump parameter a_i is proportional to the small signal gain and depends on the bias level and temperature. The quantity ξ represents the mode coupling constant between the two modes, expressed as

$$\xi = \frac{4}{3} \bigg/ [1 + (2\pi c\tau_{in}\Delta\lambda/\lambda^2)^2] \tag{2.64}$$

where λ is the wavelength, $\Delta\lambda$ is the wavelength separation between the two modes. Substituting $\Delta\lambda = 0.79$ nm, $\lambda = 783$ nm, and $\tau_{in} = 0.2$ ps into the equation gives the value of the mode-coupling constant ξ as 1.08, which is larger than unity and represents a strong coupling between the two modes [2]. The quantity $q_i(\tau)$ is a Langevin noise term that represents the fluctuations of spontaneous emission. These are supposed to be delta-correlated Gaussian random processes with the zero mean and

$$\langle q_i^*(\tau) \cdot q_i(\tau')\rangle = 4\delta_{ij} \cdot \delta(\tau - \tau') \qquad (i, j = 1, 2) \qquad (2.65)$$

where * means the complex conjugate, δ_{ij} is the Kronecker delta, and $\delta(\tau - \tau')$ is the delta function.

If $1/\xi < a_1/a_2 < \xi$, a set of Langevin equations given by eq. (2.63) has two sets of stationary solutions for $(|\hat{E}_1|^2, |\hat{E}_2|^2) = (a_1, 0)$ and $(0, a_2)$. Fluctuations of spontaneous emission drive the two mode powers from one solution to the other at random points of time. Each mode power therefore tends to jump randomly between zero and nonzero values, which corresponds to the mode-hopping phenomenon. If $\xi < a_1/a_2$, on the other hand, these equations have a set of stationarily stable solutions, that is, $(a_1, 0)$, and the two mode powers fluctuate around these values by fluctuation in spontaneous emission. These power fluctuations correspond to the mode-partition phenomenon. Both phenomena therefore can be described by these equations if the values of pump parameters are adjusted appropriately. In experiments, these adjustments were made by changing the bias level and the temperature.

If we express the normalized complex field amplitude $\hat{E}_i$ in terms of real and imaginary parts

$$\hat{E}_k = x_k + i \cdot y_k \qquad (k = 1, 2) \qquad (2.66)$$

the vector $\vec{x} [\equiv (x_1, x_2, y_1, y_2)]$ represents the state of the laser, and its components obey a set of coupled Langevin equations given by (2.63). These multidimensional nonlinear Langevin equations can be transformed to the linear Fokker-Planck equation describing the probability $p(\vec{x},\tau)$, which is expressed as [46]

$$\frac{\partial}{\partial \tau}p(\vec{x}, \tau) = \sum_{i=1}^{2}\left[-\frac{\partial}{\partial x_i}A_i^{(x)}p - \frac{\partial}{\partial y_i}A_i^{(y)}p + \left(\frac{\partial^2}{\partial x_i^2} + \frac{\partial^2}{\partial y_i^2}\right)p \right] \qquad (2.67)$$

where

$$A^{(\eta)} = [a_i - (x_i^2 + y_i^2) - \xi(x_j^2 + y_j^2)]\eta_i \ (i, j = 1,2; i \neq j, \eta = x,y) \qquad (2.68)$$

The steady-state solution, $p(\vec{x}, \infty)$, is given by [46]

$$p(\vec{x}, \infty) = B^{-1} \exp[- U(\vec{x})] \qquad (2.69)$$

where B is the normalization constant. The quantity $U(x)$, called a *potential,* is expressed as

$$U(x) = \tfrac{1}{4}(I_1^2 + I_2^2 + 2\xi I_1 I_2) - \tfrac{1}{2}(a_1 I_1 + a_2 I_2) \tag{2.70}$$

where I_i is the normalized mode power given by $x_i^2 + y_i^2$ ($\equiv |\hat{E}_i|^2$). Forms of the potential are shown in Figure 2.27(a) and (b) for two values of a_1/a_2. The potential has two minima at points M_1 and M_2 in Figure 2.27(a) for $1/\xi < a_1/a_2 < \xi$ and one minimum at the point M_1 in Figure 2.27(b) for $\xi < a_1/a_2$. These minima correspond to the stationarily stable solutions of eq. (2.63). Therefore, mode hopping and mode partition can be described by the potential of Figures 2.27(a) and (b), respectively. The shape of a potential can be changed continuously from one to the other by changing the injection current or temperature. Therefore, this unified stochastic model can describe both mode hopping and mode partition. Also, we can see from these figures that a relation between a_1/a_2 and ξ is important for single-frequency operation. The values of a_1/a_2 can be controlled by controlling the injection current and temperature. The value of ξ can be controlled by controlling τ_{in} at the stage of laser device fabrication, as can be confirmed by eq. (2.64).

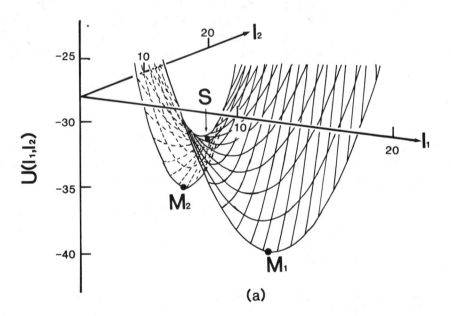

(a)

Figure 2.27 Forms of the potential $U(x)$ (from [41] © 1989 IEEE): (a) for mode hopping, $a_1 = a_2 = 12$, that is, $1/\xi < a_1/a_2 < \xi$. (b) for mode partition, $a_1 = 10$ and $a_2 = 7$, that is, $\xi < a_1/a_2 \angle e$ points M_1 and M_2 represent the positions of the minima of the potential.

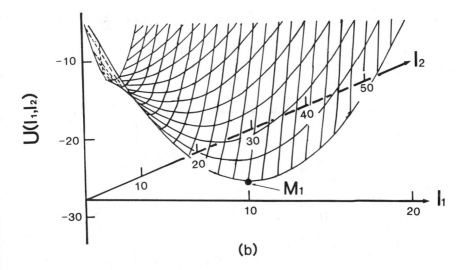

(b)

Figure 2.27 continued

The time-dependent solution of the Fokker-Planck equation is expressed as [46]

$$p(\vec{x},\tau) = p(\vec{x}, \infty) \cdot \sum_{n1,n2,m1,m2} C_{n1,n2,m1,m2}$$
$$\cdot \exp(- g_{n1,n2,m1,m2}\tau) \cdot V_{n1,n2,m1,m2}(\vec{x}) \qquad (2.71)$$

where the coefficient $C_{n1,n2,m1,m2}$ is determined from the boundary conditions and $V_{n1,n2,m1,m2}(\vec{x})$ is the eigenfunction of the Fokker-Planck operator corresponding to the eigenvalue $g_{n1,n2,m1,m2}$. The eigenvalue is expressed as

$$g_{n1,n2,m1,m2} = 2n_1 \cdot a_1 + (m_1^2/a_1) + (2n_2 + |m_2|)|a_2 - \xi a_1| \qquad (2.72)$$
$$(n_1, n_2, m_1, m_2 = 0, 1, 2, 3, \ldots)$$

The eigenvalue of the lowest-order $g_{0,0,0,0}$ is zero, which means that the Fokker-Planck equation has the steady-state solution given by (2.67). Under the approximation $a_1 = a_2 (\equiv a)$, the lowest nonzero eigenvalue gives the cutoff frequency f_c of the power spectral density of the IM noise for the mode hopping, expressed as [42]

$$f_c = \frac{1}{\pi \zeta_t} a^2 \frac{\sqrt{1 + \xi} - 1}{\sqrt{\pi(1 + \xi)}} \cdot \exp\left[-\frac{a^2(\sqrt{1 + \xi} - 1)^2}{1 + \xi}\right] \qquad (2.73)$$

where ξ_t is a constant for normalizing the time $(= t/\tau)$. Figure 2.28 gives the relation between a and f_c derived by using eq. (2.73). The value of f_c in this figure decreases exponentially with an increase in a, which is consistent with the experimental results shown in Figure 2.22(b) because a is proportional to $\tilde{\alpha}_i^{(1)} - \alpha_{th}$; that is, $I/I_{th} - 1$.

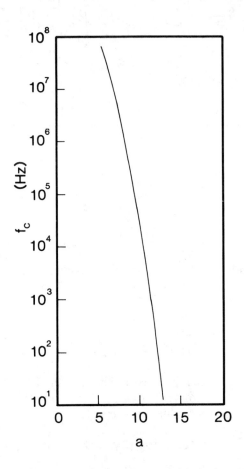

Figure 2.28 A calculated relation between f_c and a given by eq. (2.73) (from [42] © 1986 IEEE).

To derive the probability P_e given by eq. (2.62), the method proposed by Bon ifacio et al. [47] is employed. This method is based on the time-dependent solution given by (2.71). First, we calculate the occupation probability $P(\tau)$, defined as

$$P(\tau) = \int\int_D p(\vec{x}, \tau)dI_1 dI_2 \qquad (2.74)$$

where the region D is bounded by

$$D : \begin{cases} a_1(1 - \epsilon) \leq I_1 \leq a_1(1 + \epsilon) \\ 0 \leq I_2 \end{cases} \qquad (2.75)$$

The quantity ϵ is the threshold setting defined previously. From (2.71), we find that $P(\tau)$ obeys the simple rate equation:

$$\frac{dP(\tau)}{d\tau} = - \gamma[P(\tau) - P(\infty)] \qquad (2.76)$$

where

$$P(\infty) \equiv \int \int_D p(\vec{x}, \infty) \, dI_1 dI_2 \qquad (2.77)$$

Equation (2.76) can be rearranged and expressed in the following form:

$$\frac{dP(\tau)}{d\tau} = - \frac{1}{T_{\text{in}}} P(\tau) + \frac{1}{T_{\text{out}}}[1 - P(\tau)] \qquad (2.78)$$

The state of the laser $\vec{x}$ is either inside region D of the phase space or outside it, and then T_{in} and T_{out} in (2.78) represent the periods of time that the laser is inside and outside D, respectively. The escape probability given by (2.62) is then defined as

$$P_e = T_{\text{out}}/(T_{\text{in}} + T_{\text{out}}) \qquad (2.79)$$

Comparing (2.76) and (2.78), we find

$$\begin{aligned} T_{\text{in}} &= 1/\gamma[1 - P(\infty)] \\ T_{\text{out}} &= 1/\gamma P(\infty) \end{aligned} \qquad (2.80)$$

and therefore

$$P_e = 1 - P(\infty) \qquad (2.81)$$

Figure 2.29 shows the relation between ϵ and P_e calculated by using (2.75), (2.77), and (2.81). Comparison between Figures 2.23 and 2.29 shows that the dependence of P_e on I/I_{th} and ϵ is described well by the present model.

Theoretical expression of the variance σ_1^2 shown in Figures 2.25 and 2.26 can be given by

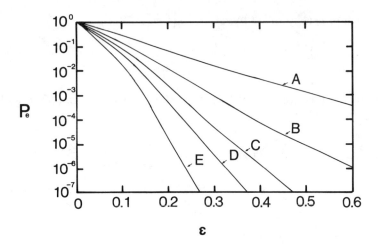

Figure 2.29 A calculated relation between the threshold setting ϵ and the power dropout probability P_e (from [41] © 1989 IEEE). Here, the values of the pump parameters a_1 and a_2 used for calculation are 17.0 and 15.4, 22.0 and 20.0, 26.0 and 24.0, 29.0 and 26.9, 35.0 and 32.4 for curves $A–E$, respectively.

$$\sigma_i^2 = (\langle I_i^2 \rangle - \langle I_i \rangle^2)/\langle I_i \rangle^2 \qquad (i = 1, 2) \tag{2.82}$$

where

$$\langle I_i^n \rangle = \int\int_D p(\vec{x}, \infty) I_i^n \, dI_1 dI_2 \qquad (n = 1, 2) \tag{2.83}$$

Figures 2.30(a) and (b) show calculated results of σ_i^2. Figure 2.30(a) indicates the noticeable increase in the variance σ_1^2 when the bias level approaches the threshold which agrees quantitatively with the experimental result of the curve B of Figure 2.25. We also see that the results of Figure 2.30(b) agree with those of curve B of Figure 2.26.

The cutoff frequency f_c of the power spectral density of power fluctuations corresponds to the inverse of the correlation time of fluctuations. This is given by the lowest nonzero eigenvalue $g_{1,0,0,0}$. Equation (2.72) indicates that $g_{1,0,0,0} = 2\,a_1$, that is, $g_{1,0,0,0}$ is proportional to the bias level, which agrees with the results given by Figure 2.25 that the cutoff frequency f_c decreases with a decreasing of I/I_{th}. In summary, the mode-hopping and mode-partition phenomena are attributed to a strong coupling between the two modes, which is expressed by the fact that the coupling constant ξ is larger than unity. This is due to a very short intraband relaxation constant. In contrast to semiconductor lasers, most gas lasers show weak coupling, that is, $\xi < 1$, which means that each mode lases independently.

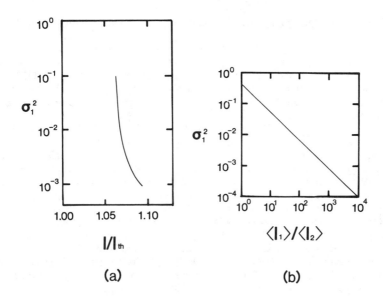

Figure 2.30 (a) A calculated relation between the bias level I/I_{th} and the variance σ_1^2 of the power fluctuations of the main model (from [41] © 1989 IEEE). (b) A calculated relation between the ratio of average CW mode power $\langle I_1 \rangle / \langle I_2 \rangle$ and the variance σ_1^2 (from [41] © 1989 IEEE).

Because the frequency of mode hopping decreases with increases in the magnitude of the cross saturation, use of a saturable absorber has been tried. This was done by doping an impurity (e.g., Te) into the clad layer to form a trap level for the electron; that is, the DX center [48, 49]. An interferometric method of monitoring the mode hopping and, furthermore, a feedback method to maintain the single-mode operation have been proposed for an external cavity semiconductor laser [50, 51].

Power dropout can be observed even in longitudinal-mode controlled semiconductor lasers. That is, stochastic properties of even the DFB and DBR lasers show that they are not single longitudinal-mode lasers in a strict sense. It has been estimated that the ratio between the steady-state intensities of the main and side modes in these lasers should be larger than 40 dB to keep the bit error rate due to the power dropout lower than 1×10^{-9} when these lasers are used in optical communication systems [52, 53]. It has been demonstrated that the side mode power can be decreased by suppressing the spatial hole burning by segmenting the electrodes [54].

REFERENCES

[1] Susskind, J., and J. Glowgower, "Quantum Mechanical Phase and Time Operator," *Physics,* Vol. 1, January 1984, pp. 49–62.

[2]   Sargent, M., III, M.O. Scully, and W.E. Lamb, Jr., *Laser Physics,* Addison-Wesley, Reading, MA, 1974.

[3]   Ohtsu, M., and T. Tako, "Coherence in Semiconductor Lasers," *Progress in Optics,* Vol. 25, ed. E. Wolf, Elsevier, Amsterdam, 1988, pp. 191–278.

[4]   Usami, M., S. Akiba, and Y. Matsushima, "Mode Characteristics of λ/4-Shifted DFB Lasers with the Distrinuted Current Injection Along the Cavity," *Extended Abstracts* (The 49th Autumn Meeting, 1988), Japan Society of Applied Physics, October 1988, paper number 6pZC16 [in Japanese].

[5]   Kotani, Y., M. Matsuda, H. Ishikawa, and H. Imai, "Tunable DBR Laser with Wide Tuning Range," *Electronics Letters,* Vol. 24, No. 8, April 1988, pp. 503–505.

[6]   Mehuys, D., M. Mittelstein, and A. Yariv, "Optimized Fabry-Perot (AlGa)As Quantum-Well Lasers Tunable over 105 nm," *Electronics Letters,* Vol. 25, No. 2, January 1989, pp. 143–145.

[7]   Lau, K.Y., P.L. Derry, and A. Yariv, "Ultimate Limit in Low Threshold Quantum Well GaAlAs Semiconductor Lasers," *Applied Physics Letters,* Vol. 52, No. 2, January 1988, pp. 88–90.

[8]   Itaya, K., G. Hatakoshi, M. Ishikawa, Y. Watanabe, and Y. Uematsu, "High Power Operation of InGaAlP Laser Diode by Broad Stripe Structure," *Extended Abstracts* (The 50th Autumn Meeting, 1989), Japan Society of Applied Physics, September 1989, paper number 28aZG1 [in Japanese].

[9]   Sakamoto, M., D.F. Welch, J.G. Endriz, D.R. Scifres, and W. Streifer, "76 W CW Monolithic Laser Diode Arrays," *Applied Physics Letters,* Vol. 54, No. 23, June 1989, pp. 2299–2300.

[10]   Statz, H., C.L. Tang, and J.M. Lavine, "Spectral Output of Semiconductor Lasers," *J. Applied Physics,* Vol. 35, No. 9, September 1964, pp. 2581–2585.

[11]   Suematsu, Y., S. Akiba, and T. Hong, "Measurement of Spontaneous-Emission Factor of AlGaAs Double-Heterostructure Semiconductor Lasers," *IEEE J. Quantum Electronics,* Vol. QE-13, No. 8, August 1977, pp. 596–600.

[12]   Lamb, W.E., Jr., "Theory of Optical Maser," *Physics Review,* Vol. 134, No. 6A, June 1964, pp. A1429–A1450.

[13]   Yamada, M., and Y. Suematsu, "Analysis of Gain Suppression in Undoped Injection Lasers," *J. Applied Physics,* Vol. 52, No. 4, April 1981, pp. 2653–2664.

[14]   Haug, H., "Quantum-Mechanical Rate Equations for Semiconductor Lasers," *Physics Review,* Vol. 184, No. 2, August 1969, pp. 338–348.

[15]   Haug, H., and H. Haken, "Theory of Noise in Semiconductor Laser Emission," *Z. Physics,* Vol. 204, No. 3, July 1967, pp. 262–275.

[16]   Yamamoto, Y., S. Saito, and M. Mukai, "AM and FM Quantum Noise in Semiconductor Lasers Part II: Comparison of Theoretical and Experimental Results for AlGaAs Lasers," *IEEE J. Quantum Electronics,* Vol. QE-19, No. 1, January 1983, pp. 47–58.

[17]   Ohtsu, M., "Control and Noise in Semiconductor Lasers," *Semiconductor Lasers and Optoelectronics IC's,* ed. Y. Suematsu, Ohmsha Publishing, Tokyo, 1984, Chapter 9, eq. (9.51) [in Japanese].

[18]   Ikegami, T., and Y. Suematsu, "Resonance-like characteristics of the Direct Moulation of a Junction Laser," *Proc. IEEE,* Vol. 55, No. 1, January 1967, pp. 122–123.

[19]   Ohtsu, M., and S. Kotajima, "Derivation of the Spectral Width of a 0.8 μm AlGaAs Laser Considering 1/f Noise," *Japan J. Applied Physics,* Vol. 23, No. 6, June 1984, pp. 760–764.

[20]   Ohtsu, M., H. Fukuda, T. Tako, and H. Tsuchida, "Estimation of the Ultimte Frequency Stability of Semiconductor Lasers," *Japan J. Applied Physics,* Vol. 22, No. 7, July 1983, pp. 1157–1166.

[21]   Henry, C.H., "Theory of the Linewidth of Semiconductor Lasers," *IEEE J. Quantum Electronics,* Vol. QE-18, No. 2, February 1982, pp. 259–264.

[22]   Oshinski, M., and J. Buus, "Linewidth Broading Factor in Semiconductor Lasers—An Overview," *IEEE J. Quantum Electronics,* Vol. QE-23, No. 1, January 1987, pp. 9–29.

[23]   Ohtsu, M., "Light Emitting Devices and Photodetctors for Optical Sensing," Chapter 3 of *Optical Fiber Sensors,* ed. T. Okoshi, Ohmsha Publishing, Tokyo, 1986 [in Japanese].

[24] Welford, D., and A. Mooradian, "Output Power and Temperature Dependence of the Linewidth of Single-Frequency CW (GaAl)As Diode Lasers," *Applied Physics Letters,* Vol. 40, No. 10, May 1982, pp. 865–867.

[25] Okai, M., T. Tsuchiya, and N. Chinone, "Ultra-Narrow Spectral Linewidth (56 kHz) Corrugation-Pitch-Modulated Multi-Quantum-Well Distributed Feedback Lasers," *Technical Digest of Conference on Lasers and Electro-Optics* (CLEO' 91), Baltimore, 1991, paper number CPDP40.

[26] Welford, D., and A. Mooradian, "Observation of Linewidth Broadening in (GaAl)As Diode Lasers Due to Electron Number Fluctuations," *Applied Physics Letters,* Vol. 40, No. 7, April 1982, pp. 560–562.

[27] Elsasser, W., E.O. Gobel, and J. Kuhl, "Coherence Properties of Gain- and Index-Guided Semiconductor Lasers," *IEEE J. Quantum Electronics,* Vol. QE-19, No. 6, June 1983, pp. 981–985.

[28] Vahala, K., and A. Yariv, "Occupation Fluctuation Noise: A Fundamental Source of Linewidth Broadening in Semiconductor Lasers," *Applied Physics Letters,* Vol. 43, No. 2, July 1983, pp. 140–142.

[29] Lang, R., and K. Kobayashi, "External Optical Feedback Effects on Semiconductor Injection Laser Properties," *IEEE J. Quantum Electronics,* Vol. QE-16, No. 3, March 1980, pp. 347–355.

[30] Miles, R.O., A. Dandridge, A.B. Tveten, H.F. Taylor, and T.G. Giallorenzi, "Feedback-Induced Line Broadening in CW Channel-Substrate Planar Laser Diodes," *Applied Physics Letters,* Vol. 37, No. 11, December 1980, pp. 990–992.

[31] Broom, R.F., E. Mohn, C. Risch, and R. Salathe, "Microwave Self-Modulation of a Diode Laser Coupled to an External Cavity," *IEEE J. Quantum Electronics,* Vol. QE-6, No. 6, June 1970, pp. 328–334.

[32] Kobayashi, K., "Improvements in Direct Pulse Code Modulation of Semiconductor Lasers by Optical Feedback," *Trans. IECE Japan,* Vol. E59, No. 12, December 1976, pp. 8–14.

[33] Lenstra, D., B.H. Verbeek, and A.J. den Boef, "Coherence Collapse in Single-Mode Semiconductor Lasers due to Optical Feedback," *IEEE J. Quantum Electronics,* Vol. QE-21, No. 6, June 1985, pp. 674–679.

[34] Berge, P., Y. Pomeau, and C. Vidal, *Orders Within Chaos,* John Wiley & Sons, New York, 1984.

[35] Kawaguchi, H., and K. Otsuka, "A New Class of Instabilities in a Diode Laser with an External Cavity," *Applied Physics Letters,* Vol. 45, No. 9, November 1984, pp. 934–936.

[36] Teramachi, Y., and M. Ohtsu, "Mode-Hopping and Frequency Noise in Semiconductor Lasers," Proc. of US-Japan Seminar on Coherence, Incoherence, and Chaos in Quantum Electronics, Nara, Japan, September 1984, pp. 63–64.

[37] Ohtsu, M., "Noises in Lasers," *Physics Monthly,* Vol. 6, No. 5, May 1985, pp. 297–303 [in Japanese].

[38] Arimoto, A., M. Ojima, N. Chinone, and A. Ohishi, "Optical Videodisc Players Employing a Diode Laser with a High-Frequency Current Superposition Noise-Reduction Method," Technical Digest of Conf. on Lasers and Electro-Optics (CLEO'84), Anaheim, CA, 1984, paper number TUD2, pp. 56–57.

[39] Hayashi, I., K. Matsui, M. Tenetani, S. Yamamoto, M. Yano, and T. Hijikata, "Control of Self-Sustained Oscillation in VSIS Lasers and Noise Reduction," *National Convention Records,* Japan Society of Applied Physics, March 1984, paper number 29pM4 [in Japanese].

[40] Chinone, N., M. Ojima, and M. Nakamura, "Reflection Noise Reduction of a Semiconductor Laser by Adding a RF Oscillator Circuit," Nikkei Electronics, October 10, 1983, pp. 173–194 [in Japanese].

[41] Ohtsu, M., and Y. Teramachi, "Analyses of Mode Paritation and Mode Hopping in Semiconductor Lasers," *IEEE J. Quantum Electronics,* Vol. 25, No. 1, January 1989, pp. 31–38.

[42] Ohtsu, M., Y. Teramachi, Y. Otsuka, and A. Osaki, "Analysis of Mode-Hopping Phenomena in an AlGaAs Laser," *IEEE J. Quantum Electronics,* Vol. QE-22, No. 4, April 1986, pp. 535–543.

[43] Pippard, A.B., *Response and Stability, An Introduction to the Physical Theory,* London, Cambridge University Press, 1985, Chapter 6.

[44] Ohtsu, M., Y. Teramachi, and T. Miyazaki, "Mode Stability Analysis of Nearly Single-Longitudinal-Mode Semiconductor Lasers," *IEEE J. Quantum Electronics,* Vol. 24, No. 5, May 1988, pp. 716–723.

[45] Yamada, M., H. Ishiguro, and H. Nagato, "Estimation of the Intra-Band Relaxation Time in Undoped AlGaAs Laser," *Japan J. of Applied Physics,* Vol. 19, No. 1, January 1980, pp. 135–142.

[46] Hioe, F.T., and S. Singh, "Correlations, Transients, Bistability, and Phase-Transition Analogy in Two-Mode Lasers," *Physics Review A,* Vol. 24, No. 4, October 1981, pp. 2050–2074.

[47] Bonifacio, B., L. Lugiato, J.D. Farina, and L.M. Narducci, "Long Time Evolution for a One-Dimensional Fokker-Planck Process: Absorptive Optical Bistability," *IEEE J. Quantum Electronics,* Vol. QE-17, No. 3, March 1981, pp. 357–365.

[48] Chinone, N., T. Kuroda, T. Ohtoshi, T. Takahasi, and T. Kajimura, "Mode Hopping Noise in Index-Guided Semiconductor Lasers and Its Reduction by Saturable Absorbers," *IEEE J. Quantum Electronics,* Vol. QE-21, No. 8, August 1985, pp. 1264–1269.

[49] Ohtsu, M., Y. Teramachi, and T. Miyazaki, "Analyses of Suppression of Mode Hopping in an AlGaAs Laser by Saturable Absorber," *Optics Communication,* Vol. 61, No. 3, February 1987, pp. 203–207.

[50] Ohtsu, M., K.-Y. Liou, E.C. Burrows, C.A. Burrus, Jr., and G. Eisenstein, "Interferometric Method for Preventing Mode-Hopping in Tunable External-Cavity Semiconductor Lasers," *Electronics Letters,* Vol. 23, No. 21, October 1987, pp. 1111–1113.

[51] Ohtsu, M., K.-Y. Liou, E.C. Burrows, C.A. Burrus, Jr., and G. Eisenstein, "A Simple Interferometric Method for Monitoring Mode Hopping in Tunable External Cavity Semiconductor Lasers," *IEEE J. Lightwave Technology,* Vol. 7, No. 1, January 1989, pp. 68–76.

[52] Linke, R.A., B.L. Kasper, C.A. Burrus, Jr., I.P. Kaminov, J.S. Ko, and T.P. Lee, "Mode Power Partition Events in Nearly Single-Frequency Lasers," *IEEE J. Lightwave Technology,* Vol. LT-3, No. 4, June 1985, pp. 706–712.

[53] Liou, K.-Y., M. Ohtsu, C.A. Burrus, Jr., U. Koren, and T.L. Koch, "Power Partition Fluctuations in Two-Mode-Degenerate Distributed-Feedback Lasers," *IEEE J. Lightwave Technology,* Vol. 7, No. 4, April 1989, pp. 632–639.

[54] Usami, M., S. Akiba, and Y. Matsushima, "Mode Characteristics of λ/4-Shifted DFB Lasers with Distributed Current Injection Along the Cavity," Extended Abstracts of the 49th Autumn Meeting, 1988, Japan Society of Applied Physics, Tokyo, 1988, paper number 6p-ZC-16 [in Japanese].

Chapter 3
OPTICAL FREQUENCY DISCRIMINATORS, DETECTIONS, AND MODULATIONS

We can easily find from eq. (2.57) that there are several methods of reducing FM noise:

1. Reduction of Γ_{ex} by reducing external noise; for example, current fluctuations from the current source, ambient temperature fluctuations, mechanical and acoustic vibrations. In a semiconductor laser, we can easily reach the quantum noise level given by the first term of (2.57) because quantum noise level is fairly high.
2. Control of spontaneous emission. In the near future, spontaneous emission fluctuations, Γ_s may be reduced by introducing a technique of cavity *quantum electrodynamics* (QED).
3. Reduction of the α-parameter. For this, it is effective to introduce the quantum well structure. Here, the α-parameter (see eq. (2.54)) can be reduced to zero because the center frequencies of the spectral profiles of χ' and χ'' coincide with each other due to modification of the energy band structure by the quantum size effect.
4. Reduction of the cavity loss $1/\tau_p$.

These four considerations must be taken into account for the optimum design of laser device fabrications. In addition, a method of active negative feedback can reduce the measured magnitude of the FM noise. Even if the laser devices are fabricated by careful designs based on these methods, they may not always be stable enough. To overcome this difficulty, the following method should be employed:

5. Negative electrical feedback. An electronic servo-control circuit for negative electrical feedback is connected to the laser device to reduce FM noise [1]. Figure 3.1 shows a block diagram of the negative electrical feedback.

This method has been popularly used as the most reliable method for optical application systems. The effect of the negative electrical feedback can be represented by

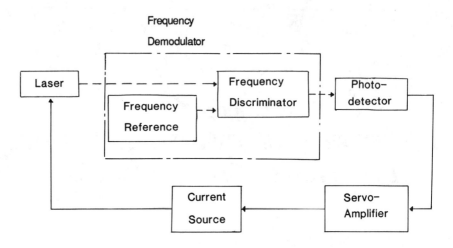

Figure 3.1 A block diagram of a negative electrical feedback system.

$$
\delta v(t) = \frac{1}{2\tau_p} (1 + \alpha^2)\Gamma_s(t) + \Gamma_{ex}(t) - \int_0^\infty h(\tau)\,[\delta v(t - \tau)
$$
$$
+ \Gamma_n(t - \tau)]d\tau \tag{3.1}
$$

The convolution integral represents the effect of negative electrical feedback, and the other terms are the same as those in (2.57). In this integral, $h(\tau)$ is the impulse response function of the feedback loop; $\delta v(t - \tau)$ is the frequency fluctuations measured by the feedback loop; $\Gamma_n(t - \tau)$ is the noise magnitude generated from the feedback loop.

The system represented by Figure 3.1 is composed of three parts: (1) FM noise detection, (2) amplification of the control signal, and (3) frequency modulation. Details of these parts, especially those of (1) together with the noise source limiting FM noise detection sensitivity are described in this chapter.

3.1 OPTICAL FREQUENCY DEMODULATORS

A frequency demodulator, composed of a frequency discriminator and frequency reference providing the stable reference frequency v_r, is required to measure the deviation of the laser frequency v_l from the v_r. Resonance spectral lines in electronic or vibration-rotation transitions in stable atoms or molecules can be used as frequency references. Table 3.1 shows examples of these atoms and molecules. The performances required for these frequency references are the accurately calibrated center frequency of the spectral line and low magnitude of frequency shift induced by various perturbations such as variations in ambient electric or magnetic field, tem perature, gas pressure, and so on; these are needed to assure accuracy and reproducibility, respectively. For the frequency discriminator, the derivative's center slope of atomic or molecular spectral profiles can be used, as long as this slope can be linearly approximated (see Figure 3.2). The derivative can be obtained through phase-sensitive detection by modulating, for example, the laser frequency. FM spectroscopy can be used to measure the derivative profile very sensitively; however, note that this profile can be deformed, if the direct frequency modulation method is employed, by modulating the injection current of the laser, because the intensity is modulated simultaneously. Such deformation can be avoided by employing two-tone modulation [2].

Table 3.1
Atoms and Molecules Used as Frequency References

Laser	Atom, Molecule	Wavelength (μm)
AlGaAs	H_2O	0.83
	Rb	0.78
	Cs	0.85
InGaAsP	H_2O	1.5
	NH_3	1.5
	C_2H_2	1.5
	HCN	1.5
	Kr	1.5
	Ar	1.3
InGaAlP	Li	0.67
	Ca	0.65

The frequency demodulator must have low noise, high sensitivity, and a wide bandwidth. This noise generated from the frequency demodulator could limit the accuracy of finding the center frequency of the spectral line; and the sensitivity could limit the gain of the feedback loop. Because the sensitivity is proportional to the slope of the derivative curve of Figure 3.2(b), it is more advantageous to use a spectral line with a narrower linewidth. The minimum detectable FM noise magnitude is given

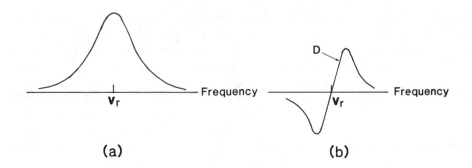

Figure 3.2 (a) Atomic or molecular spectral profile (ν_r is the reference frequency). (b) Derivative of the spectral profile.

by N/D_s, where D_s and N are the magnitudes of the slope and the noise of the frequency demodulator, respectively. The quantum noise limit of the FM noise detection is given if N is due to the shot noise of the photodetector (see Section 3.2). If statistically the FM noise is represented by white noise, the one-sided power spectral density $S_{\nu FB}(f)$ and the square root of the Allan variance $\sigma_y^2(\tau)$ representing this limit are expressed as [3]

$$S_{\nu FB}(f) = 0.08(N/D_s)^2 \tag{3.2}$$

$$\sigma_y(\tau) = \frac{0.2N}{D_s}\tau^{-1/2} = \frac{0.2}{Q(S/N)}\tau^{-1/2} \tag{3.3}$$

where the definitions of the power spectral density and the Allan variance are as given in Appendix II. To derive these expressions, the slope D_s was approximated by $D_s = S/\Delta\nu_r$, and the quality factor of the spectral line was defined by

$$Q = \nu_r/\Delta\nu_r \tag{3.4}$$

where S is the peak-to-peak height of the derivative curve of Figure 3.2(b), and $\Delta\nu_r$ is the FWHM of the reference spectral shape. The signal-to-noise ratio S/N in eq. (3.3) represents the S/N of the spectral measurement of Figure 3.2.

Equations (3.2) and (3.3) show that it is more advantageous to use a spectral line with narrower linewidth, $\Delta\nu_r$, and larger intensity, S. For several decades, researchers have progressed toward successively more narrow spectral lines. The progress, shown in Figures 3.3 and 3.4, has taken the following forms:

1. A linear absorption spectral line (Figures 3.3(a) and 3.4(a)). The laser light power transmitted through a gaseous atomic or molecular cell is measured as a function of the laser frequency (Figure 3.3(a)). The spectral width is deter-

mined by the first-order doppler effect of the thermal motion of low-pressure gaseous atoms or molecules, which can be in the order of 1 GHz.

2. A doppler-free spectral line (Figures 3.3(b) and 3.4(b)). There are, at least, three ways of eliminating the first-order doppler effect to obtain a narrower spectral linewidth (natural linewidth), which is determined by the lifetime of atomic or molecular energy levels. Such a linewidth can be narrower than several MHz. These three approaches are (1) by using an atomic beam—the spectral profile of the atomic beam is measured by radiating the laser light perpendicular to the atomic beam trajectory; (2) by using a saturated absorption spectral line— a high-power pump light is used to excite a group of atoms or molecules having a certain value of thermal velocity to induce absorption of these atoms to saturation (the absorption spectral profile of these saturated atoms or molecules is selectively measured by radiating a probe light); (3) by using a two-photon absorption spectral line (for atoms or molecules moving with a thermal velocity of v, the frequency of the radiated light propagating in the $+z$ direction is $v_t(1 - v/c)$ due to the first-order doppler effect, where c is the speed of light in

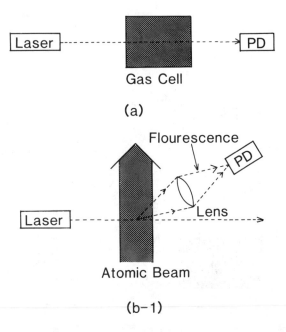

Gas Cell

(a)

(b–1)

Figure 3.3 Schematic explanations of the system for obtaining atomic or molecular spectral lines: (a) a linear spectral line with doppler broadening; (b) a doppler-free spectral line using an atomic beam (1), a saturated absorption spectral line (2), and a two-photon absorption spectral line (3) (the relevant energy levels and optical transitions are shown on the right of this figure); (c) a subnatural linewidth spectral line; (d) the cooling and confinement of atoms; (e) an atomic fountain; (f) an ion trap.

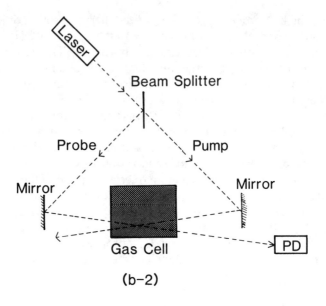

(b-2)

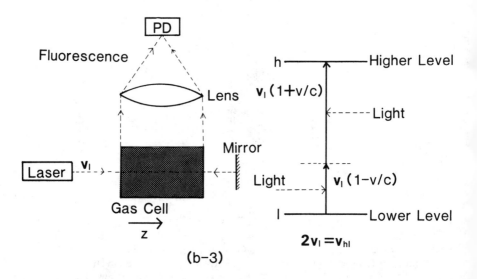

(b-3)

Figure 3.3 continued

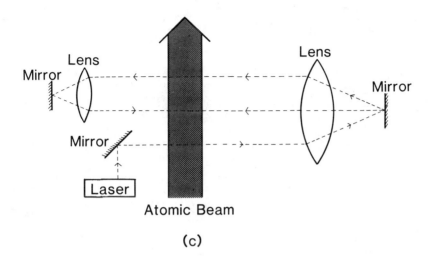

(c)

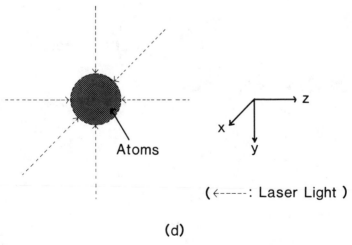

(d)

Figure 3.3 continued

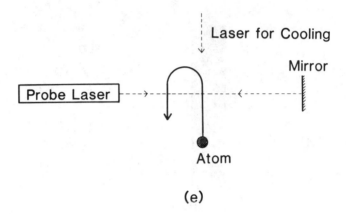

Laser for Cooling

Mirror

Probe Laser

Atom

(e)

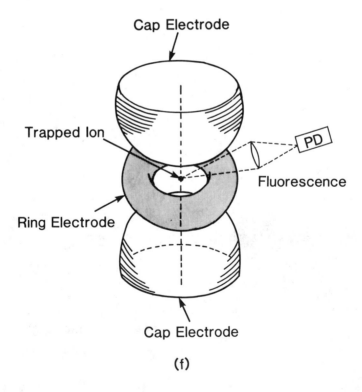

Cap Electrode

Trapped Ion

PD

Fluorescence

Ring Electrode

Cap Electrode

(f)

Figure 3.3 continued

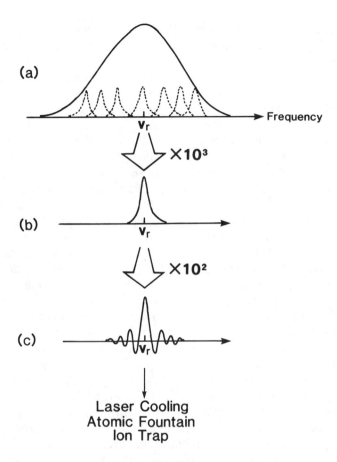

Figure 3.4 Progress of the spectral profiles in atoms and molecules used as the frequency reference and discriminator: (a) spectral profile of atoms or molecules with doppler broadening (the linewidth of the profile is determined by the linewidth of the thermal velocity distribution of the atoms or molecules); (b) a doppler-free spectral profile (the linewidth is determined by the lifetime of each atomic energy level); (c) a spectral profile with a subnatural linewidth (the linewidth is determined by the measurement system, and a linewidth narrower than the natural linewidth is possible).

a vacuum; that of the lightwave running in the $-z$ direction is $\nu_l(1 + v/c)$; therefore, the two-photon absorption process of the atom interacting simultaneously with these two running waves could cancel the doppler-shift of $\pm \nu_l v/c$; as a result, a doppler-free spectral line can be obtained).

3. A subnatural linewidth spectral line (Figures 3.3(c) and 3.4(c)). Even though doppler-free spectral lines are obtained, their minimum linewidth is deter-

mined mainly by the lifetime of the atomic or molecular energy levels and also by the flight time of the atoms or molecules traversing the laser light beam. The former gives the natural linewidth, which depends on the structure of atoms. The latter is the artificial linewidth, which corresponds to the resolution of the laser spectrometer. However, methods of obtaining subnatural linewidths have been proposed. The first such method, the optical Ramsey method [4], is obtained by irradiating three or four spatially separated parallel laser beams on the atomic beam in a direction perpendicular to the atomic beam's trajectory. In this configuration, atoms could suffer a temporally intensity-modulated perturbation from these laser beams. This perturbation could modulate the spectral profile. Such a modulated profile is called an *optical Ramsey fringe.* The width of the main lobe is inversely proportional to the traversing time of the free space between adjacent laser beams. A linewidth of 3 kHz can be obtained when the atomic thermal velocity is 300 m/s and separation between laser beams is 10 cm. This kind of modulation technique has been employed in a variety of microscope application systems to improve the resolution of measurements. For example, it has been used in side-looking radars, *very long baseline microwave interferometers* (VLBI), and microwave Ramsey fringes in cesium-beam atomic frequency standards. Although the technique already is established in the microwave frequency region, several experimental difficulties have occurred in the optical frequency region because of a short optical wavelength. Fortunately, this technical difficulty has been overcome by using at least three laser beams, and optical Ramsey spectral lines having a subnatural linewidth have been successfully obtained [5]. The second method uses the spectral profile from atoms whose lifetimes are longer than those of the ensemble average in the atomic beam. This profile has been obtained by modulating the laser beam phase radiated on the atomic beam [6].

4. Cooling and confinement of atoms (Figure 3.3(d)) [7].
5. An atomic fountain (Figure 3.3(e)) [8].
6. An ion trap (Figure 3.3(f)) [9].

The methods 1 and 2 have been used to obtain a reliable frequency demodulator for laser frequency control. Method 3 is still under development to improve the reliability. Although methods 4 through 6 are still at a preliminary stage of study, their progress is very striking and further developments are expected. Details of 4 through 6 will be described in Section 6.6.

Since the spectral profiles obtained by methods 1 through 6 (corresponding to those in Figure 3.2(a)) cannot be used directly, their derivative (corresponding to the curve in Figure 3.2(b)) should be obtained by frequency modulation and phase-sensitive detection. However, a spectral profile similar to that in Figure 3.2(b) can be alternatively obtained if the frequency dependence of the refractive index, that is, the dispersion characteristics, of the atomic or molecular medium is observed by measuring the phase change in laser light transmitted through this medium. These dis-

person characteristics correspond to the real part of the complex susceptibility χ' of the medium. Meanwhile, the profile of the curve in Figure 3.2(a) corresponds to the frequency dependence of the imaginary part of the complex susceptibility χ''. Although the profile of χ' is similar to that of the curve in Figure 3.2(b), it is not the exact derivative of the curve in Figure 3.2(a). Frequency modulation is not required if this profile is used as a frequency demodulator. An example of measuring χ' is shown in Figure 3.5, where the profile of dispersion of the saturated absorption in CH_4 is given [10].

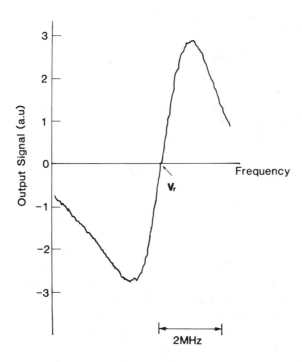

Figure 3.5 Measured result of a saturated dispersion spectral profile of CH_4 (from [10]).

Spectral lines in stable atoms or molecules could provide a high-quality reference frequency v_r, and its value has been calibrated based on a study of atomic or molecular structure. However, if the absolute value of v_r is not required in some application systems, a simpler frequency demodulator can be used. One such demodulator is the Fabry-Perot interferometer shown in Figure 3.6(a). Its resonance characteristics are shown in Figure 3.6(b), in which the resonance frequency of one longitudinal mode works as a reference frequency, v_r. The resonance frequency v_{FPm} of the mth-order longitudinal mode; the frequency separation between the adjacent longitudinal modes, called a *free spectral range* (FSR); and the full linewidth at a half maximum, $\Delta\nu_{FP}$, are given by

$$\nu_{FPm} = m \cdot \frac{c}{2n_{FP}L}$$

$$FSR = \frac{c}{2n_{FP}L} \tag{3.5}$$

$$\Delta\nu_{FP} = \frac{c}{2n_{FP}L} \bigg/ \left(\frac{\pi\sqrt{R}}{1-R}\right)$$

where c is the speed of light in a vacuum, m is an integer ($m \gg 1$), n_{FP} is the refractive index of the medium in the interferometer, L is the length of the interferometer, and R is the power reflectivity of the interferometer mirrors. To derive the expression of $\Delta\nu_{FP}$ given by this equation, the internal loss of the interferometer (α_l of eq. (2.33)) was neglected. Although atomic or molecular spectral profiles sometimes are complicated because of their hyperfine structure, the resonance curve of the Fabry-Perot interferometer is simple. Therefore, it can work as a high-quality frequency reference if the values of n_{FP} and L are stable. Figure 3.6(c) shows a magnified profile of one of the resonance curves in Figure 3.6(b). This profile can be obtained by measuring the light power transmitted through the Fabry-Perot interferometer as a function of the light frequency. The derivative of this curve, shown in Figure 3.6(d), can be obtained by modulating the laser frequency or resonant frequency of the interferometer and can be used as a frequency demodulator. The slope of the curve of Figure 3.6(c) also can be used as a frequency demodulator, by offsetting the output signal of the photodetector used for measuring the transmitted light power. In this case, the laser frequency does not have to be modulated; however, the locked laser frequency is offset from ν_r ($= \nu_{FPm}$). As the sensitivity of the frequency demodulator is proportional to the slope of the curve in Figure 3.6(c) or (d), it is more advantageous to use a Fabry-Perot interferometer with a narrow resonance linewidth $\Delta\nu_{FP}$, because the gain G, of the frequency demodulator is inversely proportional to $\Delta\nu_{FP}$.

In the field of optics, a measure is used to represent the narrowness of this resonance curve, which is called a *finesse*, defined by

$$F \equiv FSR/\Delta\nu_{FP} = \frac{\pi\sqrt{R}}{1-R} \tag{3.6}$$

Although this measure F is almost equivalent to the quality of eq. (3.4), the FSR appears in the nominator of (3.6) instead of the resonance frequency ν_r ($= \nu_{FPm}$). A supercavity with the finesse as high as 1×10^6 has been developed recently. Because the resonance linewidth $\Delta\nu_{FP}$ of such a supercavity can be narrower than 100 kHz (i.e., even narrower than the saturated absorption linewidth of atoms or molecules),

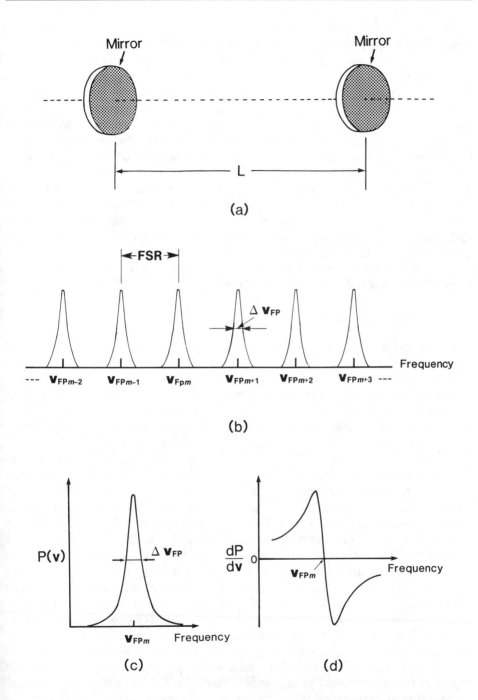

Figure 3.6 (a) The structure of a Fabry-Perot interferometer; (b) the spectral profiles of longitudinal modes; (c) a magnified profile of one of the modes in (b); (d) the derivative of the profile of (c).

it can be used as a highly sensitive frequency demodulator. However, note that fast FM noise components cannot be measured by this highly sensitive frequency demodulator. That is, the bandwidth B of this measurement is proportional to $\Delta \nu_{FP}$, which means that the gain G and bandwidth B are inversely proportional to each other. This relation holds as well for the atomic or molecular spectral lines of methods 1 through 6, which is equivalent to the fact that the gain-bandwidth product GB is a constant for the electronic amplifier. One more important measure to determine the gain is an efficiency η (or so-called throughput), which is defined by the ratio of the input to output laser powers of the interferometer. The η depends on the loss of the interferometer. For the supercavity, it depends mainly on the absorption and scattering loss of the dielectric materials in the high-reflection coating of the interferometer mirrors. A value of η as high as several 10% has been achieved even for such a supercavity. The total gain of the frequency discrimination, therefore, is determined by the values of $\Delta \nu_{FP}$ and η.

To discuss bandwidth B, we must investigate the transfer function of the Fabry-Perot interferometer $H_{FP}(f_m)$, which is defined by

$$H_{FP}(f_m) \equiv \partial P(f_m)/\partial \nu_l(f_m) \tag{3.7}$$

where P is the output laser power from the Fabry-Perot interferometer, ν_l is the frequency of the laser incident into the Fabry-Perot interferometer, and f_m is the modulation frequency for the laser frequency. Although Figure 3.6(c) shows the relation between ν_l and P that is measured for $f_m \approx 0$, that is, by sweeping ν_l adiabatically, a dynamic response of the Fabry-Perot interferometer should be investigated for the present discussion. Because the output $P(t)$ can have a time delay behind the input $\nu_l(t)$, the transfer function $H_{FP}(f_m)$ usually takes a complex value.

Figures 3.7(a) and (b) show the absolute value and phase of the transfer function, obtained by numerical calculation [11, 12]. Curve A is the result for measuring the laser power transmitted through the Fabry-Perot interferometer (called a *transmission mode*). Curve A in Figure 3.7(a) shows that its 3 dB-down cutoff frequency is $\Delta \nu_{FP}/2$. Because the gain G ($= |H_{FP}(0)|$) is inversely proportional to $\Delta \nu_{FP}$, we can confirm that the GB product is independent of $\Delta \nu_{FP}$. In the range of $f_m > \Delta \nu_{FP}/2$, the value of curve A in Figure 3.7(a) exhibits a -40 dB/decade decrease, which is proportional to f_m^{-2}. Curve A in Figure 3.7(b) shows that the phase changes 180° at the limit $f_m \to \infty$. On the other hand, curve B in Figure 3.7(a) represents the result obtained by measuring the power reflected from the Fabry-Perot interferometer (called a *reflection mode*). Although the 3 dB-down cutoff frequency is the same as in curve A, it exhibits a -20 dB/decade decrease at $f_m > \Delta \nu_{FP}/2$; that is, $|H_{FP}(f_m)|$ is proportional to f_m^{-1}. Because the slope of this curve is smaller than that of curve A, a wider bandwidth of frequency demodulation is expected. Furthermore, curve B of Figure 3.7(b) shows that the phase changes only 90° at $f_m \to \infty$, which is more advantageous than the transmission mode in realizing a wider bandwidth of the negative

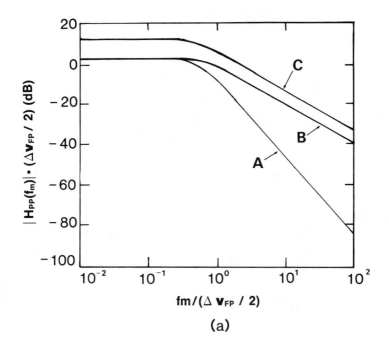

(a)

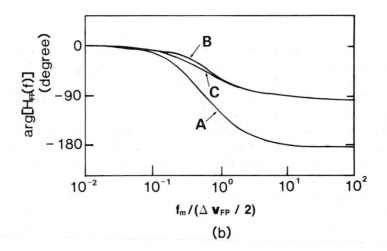

(b)

Figure 3.7 Complex transfer function of the Fabry-Perot interferometer (from [11, © 1990 IEEE 12]), $\Delta\nu_{FP}$ is the FWHM of the resonance curve of the interferometer (see eq. (3.5)): (a) absolute value; (b) phase; (c) measured value of the absolute value. Curve A is the transmission mode; curve B is the reflection mode; curve C is the transfer function of the Mach-Zehnder interferometer in which a Fabry-Perot interferometer is installed (see Figure 3.9).

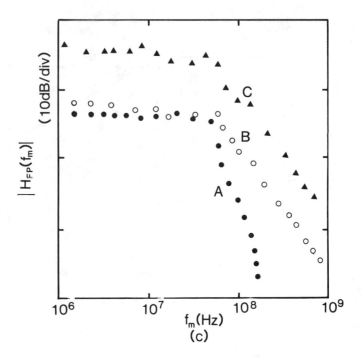

Figure 3.7 continued

electrical feedback. Figure 3.7(c) shows an experimental result to measure the values of $|H_{FP}(f_m)|$ for the transmission and reflection modes [13]. Agreement can be seen between the curves in this figure and those of Figure 3.7(a).

The difference between the transmission and reflection modes can be interpreted as follows. As shown by Figure 3.8, the reflected light contains two kinds of lights: the high-intensity directly reflected light from the input mirror (M1) of the Fabry-Perot interferometer and the light transmitted after the resonance inside the Fabry-Perot interferometer. Because the incident optical frequency varies nonadiabatically in the range of $f_m > \Delta\nu_{FP}/2$, the former bears the present optical frequency $\nu_l(t)$, whereas the latter bears the past averaged optical frequency $\nu_l(t - \tau)$ due to the resonance inside the interferometer, where τ is the average time required to travel inside the interferometer. Therefore, the measurement of the reflection mode corresponds to the measure of the difference between $\nu_l(t)$ and $\nu_l(t - \tau)$, which can be approximated as the differentiation with respect to time:

$$\nu_l(t) - \nu_l(t - \tau) \propto d\nu_l/dt \qquad (3.8)$$

The differential operator in this equation corresponds to $i(2\pi f)$ in the Fourier frequency domain. On the other hand, the transmission mode does not contain the

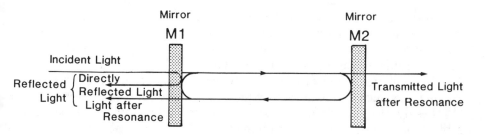

Figure 3.8 Schematic explanation for the property of the transfer function of transmission and reflection modes of a Fabry-Perot interferometer.

directly reflected light from the input mirror (M1), which serves as a reference for the differentiation. Therefore, by the effect of this differential operator, the slope and the maximum phase change of the reflection mode are $+20$ dB/decade larger and $90°$ smaller than those of the transmission mode, respectively, in the range of $f_m > \Delta\nu_{FP}/2$. For these reasons, a wide bandwidth frequency demodulator can be realized by using a reflection mode.

To discuss the difference of the phase delay characteristics between the transmission and reflection modes, the electric field of the incident light is expressed as

$$E(t) = E_0 \exp\{i[2\pi\nu_l t + \phi(t)]\}$$
$$\cong E_0[1 + i\phi(t)] \exp(i2\pi\nu_l t) \qquad (3.9)$$

where the approximation was made by assuming that the fluctuating phase magnitude $\phi(t)$ is small ($|\phi(t)| \ll 1$). The first and second terms in brackets, [ ], of this equation represent the carrier and FM sideband components, respectively. We can see from this equation that the carrier and sideband components have a $90°$ phase difference. On the other hand, note that the complex amplitude transmissivity and reflectivity of the Fabry-Perot interferometer can be expressed as

$$t(\nu_l) = \frac{1}{1 + i2(\nu_l - \nu_{FPm})/\Delta\nu_{FP}} \qquad (3.10)$$

$$r(\nu_l) = \frac{i2(\nu_l - \nu_{FPm})/\Delta\nu_{FP}}{1 + i2(\nu_l - \nu_{FPm})/\Delta\nu_{FP}} \qquad (3.11)$$

respectively, by referring to Figures 3.6 and 3.7. These equations show that the transmitted and reflected sidebands suffer a phase delay of $90°$ and $0°$, respectively, when the detuning of the FM sideband is large; that is, $|2(\nu_{lu} - \nu_{FPm})/\Delta\nu_{FP}| > 1$ or $|2(\nu_{ll} - \nu_{FPm})/\Delta\nu_{FP}| > 1$, where ν_{lu} and ν_{ll} are the frequencies of the upper and lower FM sidebands, respectively. Thus, the total phase delays of the transfer functions of the transmission and reflection modes are $180°$ and $90°$, respectively, at $f_m \to \infty$. As is understood from this discussion, the Fabry-Perot interferometer works as a phase comparator rather than a frequency discriminator in the nonadiabatic region ($f_m > \Delta\nu_{FP}/2$). On the other hand, in the adiabatic region ($f_m < \Delta\nu_{FP}/2$), it works as a frequency discriminator, as shown in Figures 3.6(c) and (d). These characteristics of the Fabry-Perot interferometer can hold as well for general optical band-pass or band-rejection filters, such as resonance spectral lines in atomic or molecular vapors.

The transfer functions of the Fabry-Perot interferometer, qualitatively described earlier, can be derived as follows [12, 13].

The Fourier transform of $E(t)$ of eq. (3.9) yields

$$E_F = E_0[\delta(f - \nu_l) + i\Phi(f - \nu_l)] \tag{3.12}$$

where δ is the delta function, and Φ is the Fourier transform of fluctuating phase $\phi(t)$. The Fourier transform E'_F of the output from the Fabry-Perot interferometer is given by

$$E'_F(f) = E_F(f) \cdot D(f) \tag{3.13}$$

where $D(f)$ represents the Fourier transform of the amplitude transmission or reflection coefficient of the Fabry-Perot interferometer. The autocorrelation function of (3.13) yields the Fourier transform of the output intensity, expressed as

$$I(f) \alpha |D(\nu_l)|^2 \cdot \delta(f) + i\Phi(f)[D^*(f) \cdot D(f + \nu_l) - D(f) \cdot D^*(f - \nu_l)] \tag{3.14}$$

where * represents the complex conjugate, and an approximation $|\Phi(f)| \ll 1$ was used. The second term of this equation represents the fluctuating output intensity that corresponds to the magnitude of the phase fluctuation of the incident light. Thus, the transfer function of the Fabry-Perot interferometer is derived by dividing the second term by the Fourier transform of the fluctuating frequency $if\Phi(f)$, which is expressed as

$$H_D(f) = \frac{D^*(f) \cdot D(f + \nu_l) - D(f) \cdot D^*(f - \nu_l)}{f} \tag{3.15}$$

The transfer functions of the transmission and reflection modes are derived by substituting $t(\nu_l)$ and $r(\nu_l)$ of (3.10) and (3.11) into the $D(f)$ of (3.15). These, respectively, are expressed as

$$H_{FPT}(f) = \frac{-8(\nu_l - \nu_{FPm})/\Delta\nu_{FP}}{\left\{1 + \left[\dfrac{2(\nu_l - \nu_{FPm})}{\Delta\nu_{FP}}\right]^2\right\}\left\{(1 + 2f/\Delta\nu_{FP})^2 + \left[\dfrac{2(\nu_l - \nu_{FPm})}{\Delta\nu_{FP}}\right]^2\right\}} \tag{3.16}$$

$$H_{FPR}(f) = \cfrac{8\left(\cfrac{\nu_l - \nu_{FPm}}{\Delta\nu_{FP}}\right)(1 + i2f/\Delta\nu_{FP})}{\left\{1 + \left[\cfrac{2(\nu_l - \nu_{FPm})}{\Delta\nu_{FP}}\right]^2\right\}\left\{(1 + 2f/\Delta\nu_{FP})^2 + \left[\cfrac{2(\nu_l - \nu_{FPm})}{\Delta\nu_{FP}}\right]^2\right\}}$$

$$(3.17)$$

$|H_{FpT}(f)|$ and $|H_{FPR}(f)|$ take the maximum at $\nu_l = \nu_{FPm} \pm (\sqrt{3}/6)\Delta\nu_{FP}$, and $\nu_{FPm} \mp (\sqrt{3}/6)\Delta\nu_{FP}$, respectively. Equations (3.16) and (3.17) show that the high frequency cutoff (3 dB-down cutoff) of these discriminators is $\Delta\nu_{FP}/2$. Curves A and B of Figures 3.7(a) and (b) are the results calculated using (3.16) and (3.17), respectively.

If both the transmitted and reflected lights from the Fabry-Perot interferometer are utilized, several advantages can be obtained; for example, the output power is increased, which realizes a higher sensitivity. Figure 3.9 shows an example of such a frequency discriminator, composed of a Mach-Zehnder interferometer in which a Fabry-Perot interferometer and two $\lambda/4$ plates are installed, which can be called a *MZ/FP interferometer* [12, 13]. The amplitude transmissivity measured by the photo-detector 1 (D1) in this figure is obtained by using $t(\nu_l)$ and $r(\nu_l)$ of (3.10) and (3.11) and is expressed as

$$t_1(\nu_l) = \frac{r(\nu_l) - t(\nu_l) \cdot \exp(-i2\pi\nu_l l/c)}{\sqrt{2}} \tag{3.18}$$

where l is the optical path difference between the two arms ($l = l_1 - l_2$ in this figure). The amplitude transmissivity measured by the photodetector 2 (D2) is

$$t_2(\nu_l) = \frac{r(\nu_l) + t(\nu_l) \cdot \exp(i2\pi\nu_l l/c)}{\sqrt{2}} \tag{3.19}$$

The output signal from the balanced receiver in this figure is proportional to $|t_1(\nu_l)|^2 - |t_2(\nu_l)|^2$, whose profile is illustrated in Figures 3.10(a) and (b) for the cases $l = \lambda/4$ and $l = L + \lambda/4$, respectively, where L is the length of the Fabry-Perot interferometer. These figures show dispersive shapes, which means that the center slope of these dispersive shapes can be used directly as the frequency discriminator so that the laser frequency is locked to ν_{FPm} without modulation. The transfer function of the MZ/FP interferometer is derived as follows. Because the following approximations hold for $t_1(\nu_l)$ and $t_2(\nu_l)$ around the center frequency ν_{FPm},

$$t_1(\nu_l) \cong \frac{1 + 2(\nu_l - \nu_{FPm})/\Delta\nu_{FP}}{1 + i2(\nu_l - \nu_{FPm})/\Delta\nu_{FP}} \tag{3.20}$$

$$t_2(\nu_l) \cong \frac{1 - 2(\nu_l - \nu_{FPm})/\Delta\nu_{FP}}{1 + i2(\nu_l - \nu_{FPm})/\Delta\nu_{FP}} \tag{3.21}$$

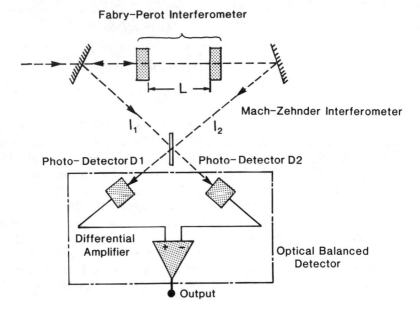

Figure 3.9 A Mach-Zehnder interferometer in which a Fabry-Perot interferometer is installed (from [12, 13]): L is the length of the Fabry-Perot interferometer; l_1 and l_2 are the lengths of the two arms of the Mach-Zehnder interferometer.

substitution of (3.20) and (3.21) into (3.15) gives the transfer functions, which can be expressed as

$$H_1(f) = -\frac{2}{1 + i2f/\Delta\nu_{FP}} \tag{3.22}$$

$$H_2(f) = \frac{2}{1 + i2f/\Delta\nu_{FP}} \tag{3.23}$$

Note that these equations hold for both Figures 3.10(a) and (b) within the vicinity of the resonance frequency ν_{FPm}; that is, $|\nu_l - \nu_{FPm}| < \Delta\nu_{FP}/2$. Thus, the total transfer function $H_{MZ/FP}(f)$ is given by

$$H_{MZ/FP}(f) = H_1(f) - H_2(f) \tag{3.24}$$
$$= \frac{-4}{1 + i2f/\Delta\nu_{FP}}$$

whose 3 dB-down frequency cutoff is $\Delta\nu_{FP}/2$. Curves C of Figures 3.7(a) and (b) show this transfer function. We see that the gain is about 10 dB larger than those of the

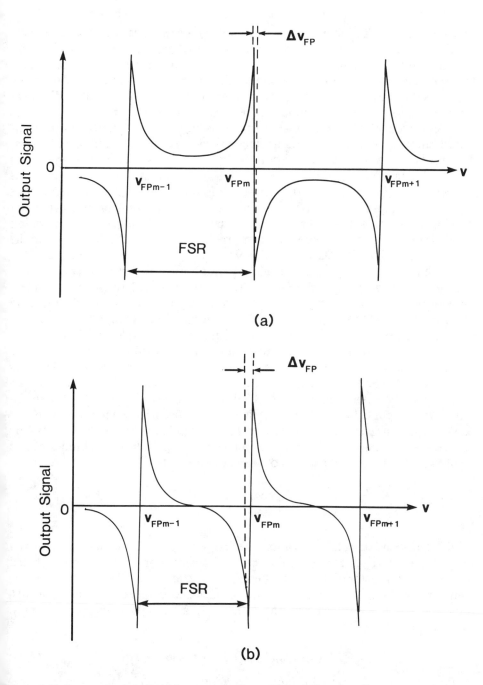

(a)

(b)

Figure 3.10 Output signal profile of the system in Figure 3.9 for (a) $l\,(=l_1-l_2)=\lambda/4$ and (b) $=L+\lambda/4$.

transmission or reflection modes, because two counterpropagating lightwaves in the Fabry-Perot interferometer contribute to the output signal, and the FM discrimination sensitivity is higher at the center of the dispersive profile than on the slope of the resonance curve of the conventional Fabry-Perot interferometer. The phase change is 90°, which is advantageous for wideband negative electrical feedback, as was the case for the reflection mode of the Fabry-Perot interferometer.

A problem of the MZ/FP interferometer is the instability induced by mechanical vibration or ambient temperature fluctuations. It is difficult to maintain the condition of $l = \lambda/4$ or $L + \lambda/4$ required to obtain the dispersive shapes of Figure 3.10(a) and (b). Figures 3.11(a) and (b) show more stable schemes proposed to solve this problem [12, 13]. Ring-resonator and standing-wave Fabry-Perot interferometers are used in Figures 3.11(a) and (b), respectively. These two setups are operated under the same principle as that of the MZ/FP interferometer of Figure 3.9. A polarization rotator is installed in the Fabry-Perot interferometer to remove the degeneracy of the two orthogonal linearly polarized modes of the Fabry-Perot interferometer. In other words, in Figure 3.11(b), the polarization rotator is used to extract the two counterpropagating lightwaves from the Fabry-Perot interferometer. To explain and analyze the basic operation of these modified Fabry-Perot interferometers, consider the setup of Figure 3.11(a). The light emitted from the ring resonator is sent into the analyzer assembly, composed of a $\lambda/4$ plate and a *polarization beam splitter* (PBS). The axis of the $\lambda/4$ plate is rotated by 45° relative to the axis of the PBS. The light intensities I_1 and I_2 at the two output ports of the PBS are monitored by the two photodetectors PD1 and PD2. The electric field vector of the linearly polarized incident beam has an angle θ with the polarization axis of the PBS output port 1. To calculate the amplitude of the output light of the PBS, the light beam is decomposed to the two orthogonal components parallel and perpendicular to the polarization axis of the PBS. By using the Jones matrix similar to that employed in [14], the field amplitudes E_1 and E_2 of the lights at output ports 1 and 2 can be expressed as

$$\begin{pmatrix} E_1 \\ E_2 \end{pmatrix} = \frac{E_0}{\sqrt{2}} \begin{pmatrix} 1,i \\ i,1 \end{pmatrix} \begin{pmatrix} r_{\parallel}, -r_{\perp} \\ r_{\perp}, r_{\parallel} \end{pmatrix} \begin{pmatrix} \cos\theta \\ \sin\theta \end{pmatrix} \tag{3.25}$$

On the right-hand side of this equation, the first, second, and third matrices represent the $\lambda/4$ plate, the ring resonator in which a 90° polarization rotator is installed, and the electric field vector of the incident laser beam, respectively. The $r_{\parallel}$ and $r_{\perp}$ are the complex amplitude reflectivities of the parallel and perpendicular components, respectively, to the incident electric field vector axis at the input of the ring resonator. They can be expressed as

$$r_{\parallel} = \sqrt{R} - \alpha_p RT \cdot \exp(i2\delta)/\{\sqrt{R}[1 - \alpha_p R \cdot \exp(i2\delta)]\} \tag{3.26}$$

$$r_{\perp} = \sqrt{\alpha_p R}\, T \cdot \exp(i\delta)/\{\sqrt{R}[1 - \alpha_p R \cdot \exp(i2\delta)]\} \tag{3.27}$$

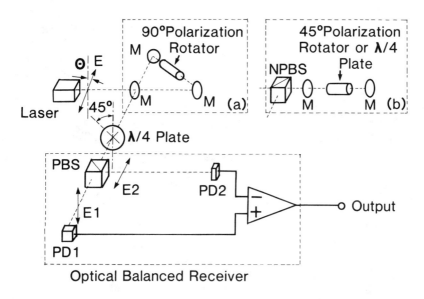

Figure 3.11 Modified configurations of the system in Figure 3.9 (from [12, 13]): (a) a ring-resonator type; (b) a standing-wave type.

where R and T are the power reflectivity and transmissivity of the input mirror M1, respectively. The quantity α_p is the power loss due to the 90° polarization rotator in the resonator, and $\delta = \pi\nu_1/FSR$. The finesse of this interferometer is given by $F = \pi\sqrt{\alpha_p R}/(1 - \alpha_p R)$. The output signal from the differential amplifier is then obtained by (3.25) through (3.27) as

$$
\begin{aligned}
I_0 &= I_1 - I_2 \\
&= 2I(1 + \alpha_p)\sqrt{\alpha_p R}\, T \sin\delta/[(1 - \alpha_p R)^2 + 4\alpha_p R \sin^2\delta]
\end{aligned}
\tag{3.28}
$$

where I is the input power. Note that this expression is independent of θ when a Faraday rotator is used as a polarization rotator. This independence is an advantage of the present setup. The spectral profile is the same as that of Figure 3.10(a). The transfer function can be derived as it was for the previous frequency discriminators, and it is also the same as that represented by curve C of Figure 3.7.

One more advantage of using these frequency discriminators for negative electrical feedback is that the frequency recovering range is wider than those of the transmission or reflection modes Fabry-Perot interferometers. That is, even though some electrical surges unlock it from the center frequency ν_{FPm} of the dispersive shape of Figure 3.10, the laser frequency can be returned to ν_{FPm} because the dispersive shape has far-reaching nonzero wings, as shown in Figure 3.10. Experiments confirmed

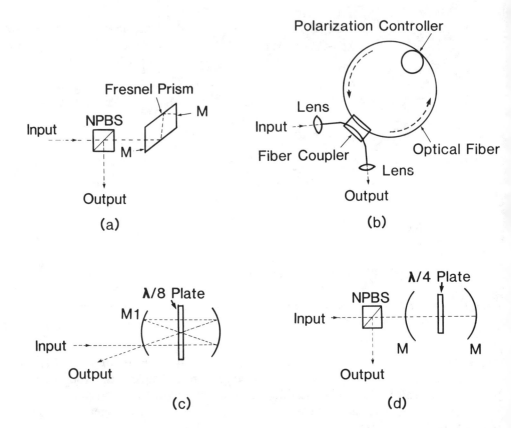

Figure 3.12 Stable configurations of the system in Figure 3.11 (from [13]): (a) a Fresnel prism whose two facets are high-reflection coated; (b) an optical fiber ring resonator that has a polarization controller; (c) a Fabry-Perot interferometer in which a λ/4 plate is installed; (d) a confocal Fabry-Perot interferometer in which a λ/8 plate is installed.

that the recovering range was as wide as twice the free spectral range FSR [12, 13]. Four kinds of practical setups are shown in Figures 3.12(a)–(d) [13]:

1. a Fresnel prism whose two facets are high-reflection coated to form a standing-wave Fabry-Perot interferometer,
2. an optical fiber ring resonator that has a polarization controller,
3. a Fabry-Perot interferometer in which a λ/4 plate is installed,
4. a confocal Fabry-Perot interferometer in which a λ/8 plate is installed.

Figures 3.13(a) and (b) show dispersive shapes for the frequency discriminations obtained by using the setups shown in Figures 3.12 (a) and (c), respectively. It should be pointed out that similar frequency demodulators using a modified Fabry-Perot interferometer have been also proposed [14, 15].

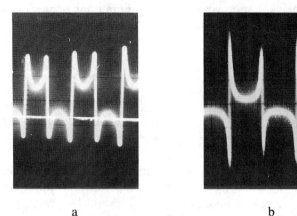

a   b

Figure 3.13 (a) and (b) show dispersive shapes for frequency discriminations obtained by using the setups shown in Figures 3.12(a) and (c).

3.2. NOISE SOURCES IN THE FM NOISE DETECTION SYSTEM

For FM noise detection, a highly sensitive and fast photodiode should be used. A *pin* photodiode is composed of semiconductors of p-type, intrinsic-type, and n-type layers, for which the intrinsic layer is effectively used to decrease the junction capacitance and increase the response speed. The photocurrent at the photodiode is expressed as

$$I_p = e\eta_q P_0 \cdot h\nu_l \tag{3.29}$$

where e is the electron charge, P_0 is the incident laser power, and η_q is the quantum efficiency representing the ratio between the numbers of the generated electrons and the incident photons. The signal-to-noise ratio S/N of the detection is given by

$$S/N = \frac{2I_p^2}{2e(I_p + I_d)B + 4k_B T F_n B/R_l} \tag{3.30}$$

where I_d is the dark current. B is the detection bandwidth, T is the temperature, R_l and F_n are the input resistor and the noise figure of the postdetector amplifier. The nominator of this expression represents the mean square signal current. The first term of the denominator represents the mean square current fluctuations induced by the temporal fluctuations of the electron number generated by the incident photons; that is, the shot noise. The second term is the thermal noise. We can see from this equation that the shot noise can be the dominant noise source if the photocurrent is larger than the following value:

$$I_p = I_d + \frac{2}{e} k_B T F_n / R_l \tag{3.31}$$

The product of the junction capacitance and R_l determines the response speed, which is about several hundred MHz. For higher sensitivity and response speed, the reverse-bias voltage should be increased to decrease the junction capacitance by increasing the thickness of the vacant layer.

An *avalanche photodiode* (APD) amplifies the number of photoelectrons, by which a high sensitivity and response speed are expected. The multiplication rate M for the number of photoelectrons depends on the reverse-bias voltage V, as shown in Figure 3.14(a), where V is normalized to the breakdown voltage V_b. For Si-APD and Ge-APD, the value of M can be increased to as large as 1,000 at $V = 100–150$ volts, and 30–40 volts, respectively. The response time of the APD is limited by the time constant given by the product of the junction capacitance and the load resistor, carrier diffusion time in the diffusion layer, and the rise time of the avalanche multiplication. A bandwidth as wide as several GHz has been achieved. The signal-to-noise ratio of the detection is given by

$$S/N = \frac{2I_p^2 M^2}{2e(I_p + I_d)M^2 M^x B + 2eI_l B + 4k_B T F_n B / R_l} \tag{3.32}$$

where the first term of the denominator represents the shot noise induced by generations of photoelectrons and dark-current electrons, and also by the temporal fluctuations in the avalanche multiplication. The M^x is called an *excess noise factor,* which depends on the device structure. The typical value of x for a Si-APD is about 0.35. The second term represents the shot noise due to the leak current I_l that flows outside the *pn*-junction area. The third term is the thermal noise. The dependence of S/N on M is shown by Figure 3.14(b), from which we find that there is an optimum value of M to maximize the S/N. The bias voltage should be adjusted to realize this optimized condition. Although the APD has a high sensitivity and a wide bandwidth, a stable high-voltage source is required for the reverse bias. To solve this problem, an alternative detector, that is, a stable *pin* photodiode integrated with a postdetector amplifier has been devised, to drive it by a TTL-level bias voltage.

Equations (3.30) and (3.32) represent the signal-to-noise ratio in the direct detection scheme of the signal light power. If the thermal noise, dark, and leak currents are neglected, the minimum detectable light power is estimated by fixing $S/N = 1$, as

$$P_{0,min} = h\nu_l B / \eta_q \tag{3.33}$$

where M^x was fixed to unity in the case of (3.32). This equation represents the quantum detection limit. The FM noise detection limit is given by this quantum detection limit when frequency demodulation is carried out by FM to IM conversion, using the demodulators demonstrated in Section 3.1 (i.e., by using atomic or molecular spectral lines) and by a Fabry-Perot interferometer. However, in these direct detection schemes, the quantum detection limit is not achieved straightforwardly because of technical difficulties in reducing the thermal noise, dark, and leak currents.

To avoid this difficulty, the heterodyne detection schematically explained in Figure 3.15 has been employed. For this detection, a high-power local laser light is incident into the photodetector simultaneously with the signal light. The electric field of the incident lights is expressed as

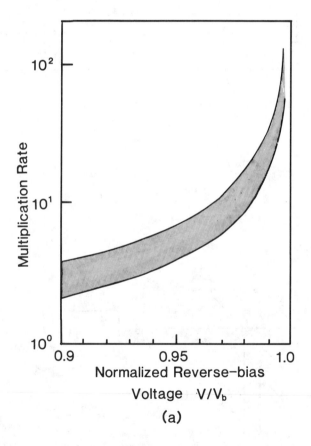

(a)

Figure 3.14 (a) Dependence of the multiplication rate M of an avalanche photodiode on its reverse-bias voltage, V, where V is normalized to the breakdown voltage V_b. (b) Dependence of the relative power levels of signal and noise of the avalanche photodiode on M.

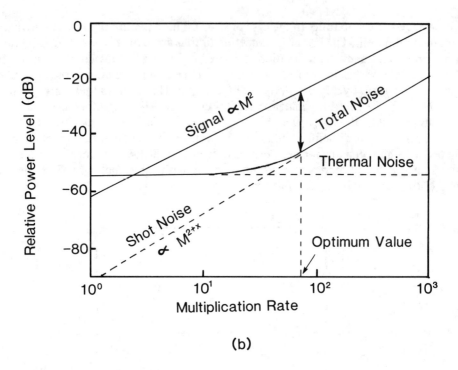

(b)

Figure 3.14 continued

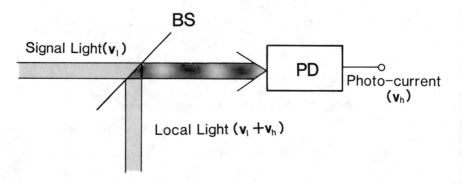

Figure 3.15 Schematic explanation of the heterodyne detection.

$$E(t) = E_s \cos(2\pi v_l t) + E_l \cos[2\pi(v_l + v_h)t] \tag{3.34}$$

where E_s and E_l are the electric field amplitudes of the signal and local light, respectively, and $E_l \gg E_s$. Their frequencies are v_l and $v_l + v_h$, where $v_h \ll v_l$. The photocurrent i_p, being proportional to $[E(t)]^2$, is expressed as

$$i_p(t) \propto E_s^2 + E_l^2 + 2E_s E_l \cos(2\pi v_l t) \tag{3.35}$$

where the higher harmonic components, having the frequencies such as $2v_l$, $2(v_l + v_h)$, $2v_l + v_h$, have been omitted because of the limited bandwidth of the photodetector. This equation can be transformed by replacing E_s and E_l with the light powers P_s and P_l, given by

$$i_p(t) \propto \left(\frac{e\eta_q P_l}{h v_l}\right)[1 + 2\sqrt{P_s/P_l}\cos(2\pi v_h t)] \tag{3.36}$$

We find, by referring to the denominator of (3.32), that the shot noise power induced by this photocurrent is $2e[(e\eta_q P_l/h v_l) + I_d]M^2 M^x$. By noting from (3.36) that the time-averaged signal power is $2(P_s/P_l)(e\eta_q P_l/h v_l)^2 M^2$, the S/N is given by

$$S/N = \frac{2(P_s/P_l)\left(\dfrac{e\eta_q P_l}{h v_l}\right)^2 M^2}{2e\left(\dfrac{e\eta_q P_l}{h v_l} + I_d\right)M^2 M^x B + 2eI_l B + 4k_B T F_n B/R_l} \tag{3.37}$$

Because the second and third terms of the denominator in this equation can be neglected, as compared with the first term, this equation can be reduced to

$$S/N = \frac{P_s}{\dfrac{h v_l B}{\eta_q}M^x} \tag{3.38}$$

which means that the shot noise due to the local laser light is the dominant noise source in this detection scheme. We find from this equation that the quantum detection limit can be achieved if $M^x = 1$, which can realize a highly sensitive detection. This technique has been employed by using a photomultiplier and *pin* photodiode because $M^x = 1$ for these detectors.

If there is a very stable reference laser, the heterodyne technique can be used for the FM noise detection of the laser under test, and the FM noise of the test laser can be reduced by negative electrical feedback. However, because it is not easy, in most cases, to prepare such a highly stabilized reference laser, most of the practical feedback systems have employed the direct detection technique. In this case, an additional noise source for the FM noise detection is the intensity fluctuations (IM noise) of the laser itself. To eliminate the contribution of the IM noise, a balanced receiver, as shown in Figures 3.9 and 3.11 has been employed. By using two photodetectors carefully selected and balanced (not only to balance the detection sensitivities, but also input laser powers, optical and electrical path lengths), the IM noise becomes a common-mode noise for these photodetectors, which can be eliminated by a differential amplifier at the next stage. Figure 3.16 illustrates an example of the IM noise reduction in a 0.8 μm AlGaAs laser by using the balanced receiver [16]. IM noise reduction as large as 40 dB has been achieved. By using this balanced reciever, the quantum detection limited sensitivity can be achieved if the incident laser power is sufficiently high that the magnitude of the shot noise is larger than that of the thermal noise.

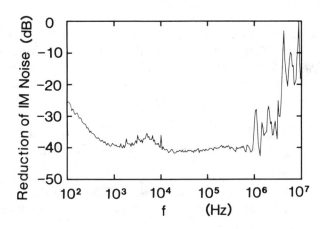

Figure 3.16 IM noise reduction of a 0.8 μm AlGaAs laser by using a balanced receiver (from [16] © 1996 IEEE).

Figure 3.17(a) shows an experimental setup to estimate the frequency dependence of the contribution of laser IM noise to FM noise detection. The correlation coefficient γ between the output signals detected by two well-balanced photodetectors, PD1 and PD2, is measured. Figure 3.17(b) shows the measured result of γ as a function of the Fourier frequency f. The value of γ decreases with an increasing f, which means that the contribution from the IM noise is dominant in the range of low Fourier frequency.

Correlation between the FM and IM noises in a semiconductor laser should be studied to design a high-gain negative electrical feedback loop for FM noise reduc

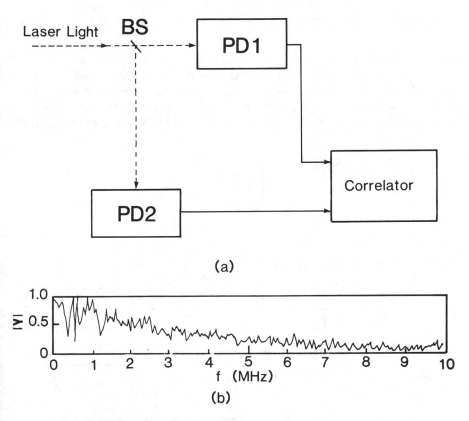

Figure 3.17 (a) Experimental setup to estimate the frequency dependence of the contribution of laser IM noise to FM noise detection. (b) The measured value of the correlation coefficient γ as a function of the Fourier frequency f.

tion by direct FM noise detection and by using the frequency demodulator shown in Section 3.1. Figure 3.18(a) shows the experimental setup [12]. Photodetectors PD1 and PD2 are used to measure the magnitudes of the IM and FM noises, respectively. A Fabry-Perot interferometer is used for direct detection of the FM noise. Figure 3.18(b) shows the measured coherence function $\gamma(f)$, representing the cross-correlation between the IM and FM noises. We see from this figure that $|\gamma| \cong 1$ for $f > 0.5$ MHz, which means that the two noises are correlated. This property is easily understood because the principal quantum noise source of the semiconductor laser is the carrier density fluctuations induced by the spontaneous emission fluctuations. These carrier density fluctuations simultaneously contribute to the IM and FM noises, and the magnitudes of these contributions are represented by the α-parameter defined by (2.54). The values of α and $|\gamma|$ are related to [17]

$$|\gamma| = |\alpha|/\sqrt{1 + \alpha^2} \tag{3.39}$$

With an increase in the carrier density, the laser frequency decreases due to the increase in the refractive index of the active layer. On the other hand, this increase can simultaneously increase the stimulated emission rate, which can increase the lasing power. By these mechanisms, the phase of the coherence function arg[γ] takes π, as is seen from Figure 3.18(b): that is, the IM and FM noises are anticorrelated.

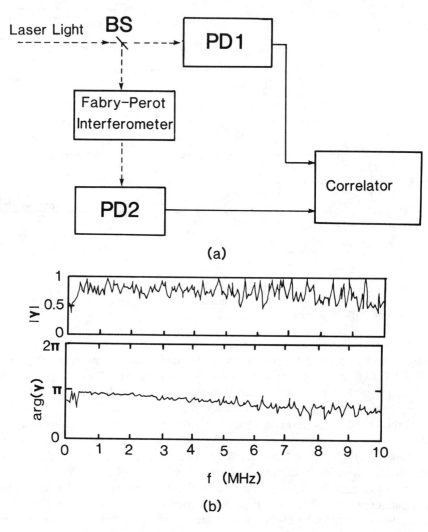

Figure 3.18 (a) Experimental setup to measure the coherence function $\gamma(f)$ between the IM and FM noises (from [12]). (b) Measured result of the coherence function.

3.3. MODULATION CHARACTERISTICS
OF A SEMICONDUCTOR LASER

Modulation of the injection current of a semiconductor laser can directly modulate the intensity (IM) and frequency (FM) simultaneously. If we are interested in modulating only the power or frequency, we should use an external modulator utilizing an electro-optic or acousto-optic effect in some crystals. However, this section concentrates on reviewing the IM and FM characteristics by direct modulation of the injection current.

Although the carrier density in the active layer is clipped to its threshold value (see eq. (AIV.4)) under the dc current operation, the carrier density can be modulated by modulating the injection current, which can modulate the laser power. Because the power is modulated by directly modulating the carrier density in the active layer, we can realize fast and highly efficient modulation. This is a specific property of semiconductor lasers and different from the modulation schemes of other kinds of lasers. Figure 3.19 shows a schematic explanation of the laser IM characteristics. The frequency f_r in this figure represents a relaxation oscillation frequency given by (2.52) and (AVI.13) that limits the modulation bandwidth due to the carrier (τ_s) and photon (τ_p) lifetimes in the cavity. Bandwidths as high as several GHz have been achieved, and several tens of GHz also are possible by employing a quantum well structure.

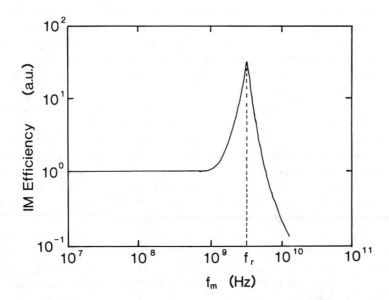

Figure 3.19 Laser intensity modulation (IM) characteristics: f_r is the relaxation oscillation frequency.

The laser frequency also can be modulated directly by injection current, because the longitudinal mode frequency of the cavity is modulated by the change in the refractive index n_i and the cavity length L. The change of the frequency is expressed as

$$\Delta \nu_l = -\nu_l \left[\left(\frac{A_c}{n_i} \right) \cdot \Delta N_c(I) + (\alpha_T + \beta_T) \cdot \Delta T(I) \right] \tag{3.40}$$

where the coefficients in this equation are the same as those of (2.55) (see also Table 2.1). The first term represents the change in the refractive index n_i due to the carrier density change $\Delta N_c(I)$ induced by the change of the injection current. It has been known popularly that the main contribution of the carrier density change to the refractive index change is the plasma effect [18]. The coefficient A_c representing the magnitude of this effect is given by

$$A_c = \left(\frac{e^2 \lambda^2}{8\pi^2 n_i \epsilon_0 c^2} \right) \cdot \left(\frac{1}{m_e} + \frac{1}{m_h} \right) \tag{3.41}$$

where m_e and m_h represent the effective masses of electron and positive hole, respectively. The second and the third terms represent the thermal effect of the cavity length L and the change in refractive index n_i, respectively. Both effects result from the temperature change $\Delta T(I)$ due to the self-heating of the active layer material from a change in the injection current. Figure 3.20 shows FM characteristics for several lasers, which are represented by a transfer function H_L ($\equiv \delta\nu(f_m)/\partial I(f_m)$) [19]. The transfer function usually takes a complex value because of the phase delay in the FM response with respect to the phase of the modulation current with the modulation frequency f_m. Figures 3.20(a) and (b) represent the absolute value and phase angle of H_L for 0.8 μm AlGaAs and 1.5 μm InGaAsP lasers. For the modulation frequency of $f_m <$ several MHz, the thermal effect is dominant for FM because the second and third terms of (3.40) are larger than the first term. The carrier effect becomes dominant for $f_m >$ several MHz because the temperature change of the active layer cannot follow the fast change of the modulation current. The carrier effect has a cutoff frequency determined by the relaxation oscillation frequency f_r. In curves A and B of Figure 3.20, there exist turning points at the f_m of several MHz, and the contributions from the thermal and carrier effects cross at this frequency. The profiles of these curves depend on the waveguide structure, laser materials, and so on. We see by comparing curves A and B that the AlGaAs laser has a homogeneous transfer function compared with the InGaAsP laser, because the thermal effect of the AlGaAs laser is smaller than that of the InGaAsP laser. As a homogeneous profile of this transfer function is advantageous for negative electrical feedback for wideband FM noise reduction, it has been realized for a DFB laser by inhomogeneously distributing the carrier density along the cavity axis. For this purpose, a laser with segmented

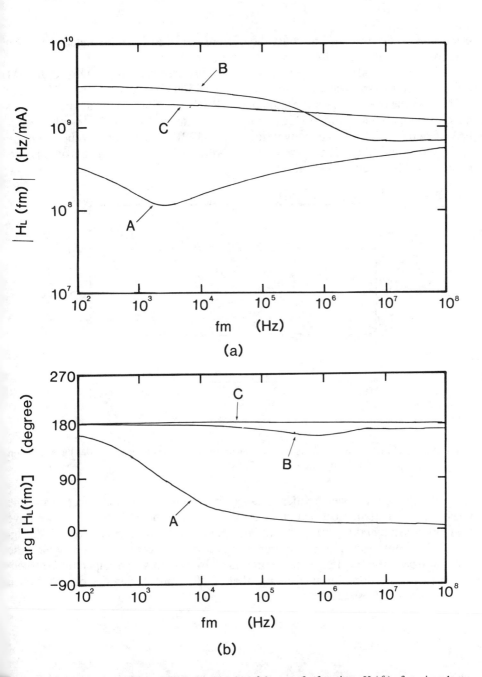

Figure 3.20 (a) Absolute values and (b) phase angles of the transfer functions $H_L(f_m)$ of semiconductor lasers: A is a 1.5 μm InGaAsP laser (from [19]); B is a 0.8 μm AlGaAs laser (from [19]); C is a 1.5 μm InGaAsP laser with segmented electrodes (from [20] © 1987 IEEE).

electrodes was developed to adjust the currents injected into these electrodes. An example of this result is also shown by curve C in Figure 3.20 [20].

Three electrode DFB lasers have been fabricated recently to reduce the FM noise so that field spectral linewidths as narrow as 56 kHz were obtained [21]. Figure 3.21 shows the measured transfer function of this laser, which shows a homogeneous profile of the transfer function [22]. Note that this narrow-linewidth laser has lower FM efficiency $|H_L(f_m)|$ than conventional lasers [22]. This means that the FM noise magnitude and FM efficiency are correlated with each other. Comments on this correlation will be given in Section 7.1.

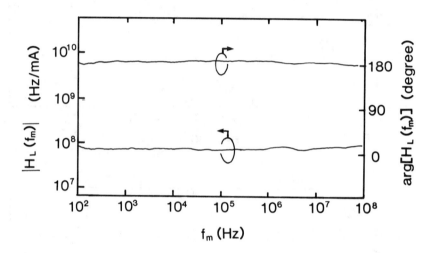

Figure 3.21 Measured transfer function $H_L(f_m)$ of a narrow-linewidth multiquantum-well DFB laser with segmented electrodes (from [22] © 1991 IEEE).

For the low Fourier frequency range, in which the thermal effect cannot be neglected, equivalent electrical circuits for describing the FM characteristics have been proposed by taking into account both the thermal and carrier effects [23]. Figure 3.22(a) illustrates a lumped-parameter equivalent electric circuit in which the heat diffusion characteristics are represented by resistors and capacitors, respectively. Its transfer function is similar to that of a first-order phase-lag compensation circuit, and is expressed as

$$H_L(f) = \frac{g_1 + if g_2/k_1}{1 + ifk_1}$$

(3.42)

where g_1, g_2, and k_1 are constants determined by the circuit parameters of Figure 3.22(a). Figure 3.22(b) illustrates a distributed-parameter equivalent electric circuit in which the transfer function of the thermal effect was derived by using the heat diffusion model [24] and the carrier effect was approximated as independent of the Fourier frequency. Its transfer function is given by

$$H_L(f) = g_3 \frac{\sinh[(1+i)m_f]}{(1+i)m_f \cdot \cosh[(1+i)m_f]} + g_4 \tag{3.43}$$

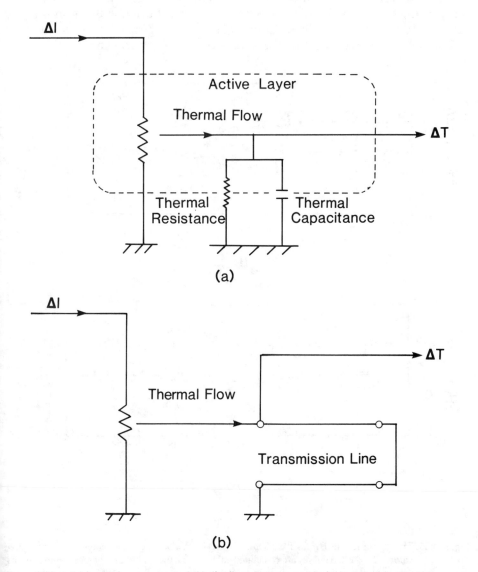

(a)

(b)

Figure 3.22 A (a) lumped-parameter and (b) distributed-parameter equivalent electric circuit for representing the FM characteristics of a semiconductor laser (from [23]).

where

$$m_f = \sqrt{f/2k_2} \qquad (3.44)$$

Here, g_3, g_4, and k_2 are constants. Figures 3.23(a) and (b) show the results of curve fitting by adjusting the parameters of (3.42) and (3.43), respectively, to derive the transfer function of a 0.8 μm AlGaAs laser. Agreement between the measured and calculated curves mean that these equivalent circuits can be used effectively to design an optimal negative electrical feedback loop for FM noise reduction.

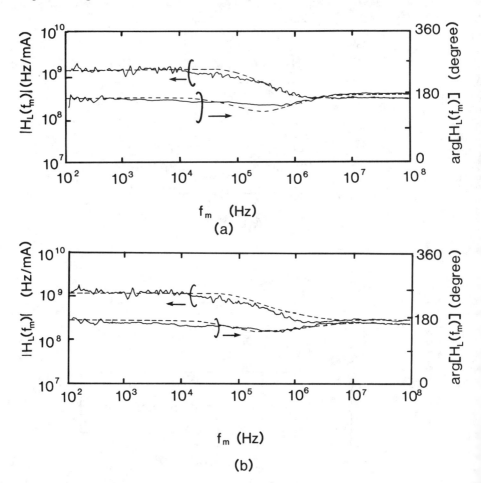

Figure 3.23 Transfer functions $H_L(f_m)$ of a 0.8 μm AlGaAs laser. The solid curve represents the measured value. The dashed curves are calculated values using the (a) lumped-parameter and (b) distributed-parameter equivalent circuits (from [23]).

REFERENCES

[1]   Ohtsu, M., "Realization of Ultrahigh Coherence in Semiconductor Lasers by Negative Electrical Feedback," *IEEE J. Lightwave Technology,* Vol. 6, No. 2, February 1988, pp. 245–256.

[2]   Wang, L.-G., H. Riris, C.B. Carlisle, and T.F. Gallingher, "Comparison of Approaches to Modulation Spectroscopy with GaAlAs Semiconductor Lasers: Application to Water Vapor," *Applied Optics,* Vol. 27, No. 11 June 1988, pp. 2071–2077.

[3]   Kartaschoff, P., *Frequency and Time,* Academic Press, London, 1978.

[4]   Shimoda, K., "Side-Looking Radars and Optical Ramsey Resonances," *Butsuri* (monthly journal of the Physics Society of Japan), Vol. 36, No. 8, August 1981, pp. 590–598 [in Japanese].

[5]   Helmcke, J., J. Ishikawa, and F. Riehle, "High-Constant, High-Resolution Single Recoil Component Ramsey Fringes in Ca," *Frequency Standards and Metrology,* Proc. of the Fourth Symp., Ancona, Italy, September 5–9, 1988, ed. A. De Marchi, Springer Verlag, Berlin, 1989, pp. 270–281.

[6]   Shimizu, F., K. Shimizu, and H. Takuma, "Subnatural-Linewidth Laser Spectroscopy by Phase Switching," *Physics Review A,* Vol. 28, No. 4, October 1983, pp. 2248–2253.

[7]   Phillips, W.D., J.V. Prodan, and H.J. Metcalf, "Laser Cooling and Electromagnetic Trapping of Neutral Atoms," *J. Optics Society of America B,* Vol. 2, No. 11, November 1985, pp. 1751–1767.

[8]   Beausoleil, R.G., and T.W. Hänsch, "Two-Photon Optical Ramsey Spectroscopy of Freely Falling Atoms," *Optics Letters,* Vol. 10, No. 11, November 1985, pp. 547–549.

[9]   Itano, W.M., J.C. Bergquist, and D.J. Wineland, "Laser Spectroscopy of Trapped Ions," *Science,* Vol. 237, August 1987, pp. 612–617.

[10] Ohtsu, M., S. Ohta, and T. Tako, "Frequency Stabilization of a He-^{22}Ne Laser by Intracavity Polarization Spectroscopy of CH_4," *Japan J. of Applied Physics,* Vol. 20, No. 9, September 1981, pp. 1701–1707.

[11] Ohtsu, M., M. Murata, and M. Kourogi, "FM Noise Reduction and Subkilohertz Linewidth of an AlGaAs Laser by Negative Electrical Feedback," *IEEE J. Quantum Electronics,* Vol. QE-26, No. 2, February 1990, pp. 231–241.

[12] Kourogi, M., and M. Ohtsu, "Novel Optical Frequency Discriminator for FM Noise Reduction of Semiconductor Lasers," *Optics Communications,* Vol. 81, Nos. 3 and 4, February 1991, pp. 204–208.

[13] Kourogi, M., and M. Ohtsu, "Genuine Optical Frequency Discriminator with Wide Recovery Range and High-Gain for FM Noise Reduction of Semiconductor Lasers," Proc. Conf. Lasers and Electro-Optics, Baltimore, May 12–17, 1991, paper number CThF4.

[14] Hänsch, T.W., and B. Couillarud, "Laser Frequency Stabilization by Polarization Spectroscopy of a Reflecting Reference Cavity," *Optics Communications,* Vol. 35, No. 3, December 1980, pp. 441–444.

[15] Telle, H.R., "Narrow Linewidth Laser Diodes with Broad Continuous Tuning Range," *Applied Physics,* Vol. B49, No. 3, September 1989, pp. 217–226.

[16] Shin, C.-H., and M. Ohtsu, "Very Precise Phase-Frequency Control of Confocal Fabry-Perot Cavity Coupled Semiconductor Laser," Proc. IEEE/LEOS Summer Topical Meetings on New Semiconductor Laser Devices and Applications, Monterey, CA, August 1990, IEEE/LEOS, Piscataway, NJ, 1990, paper number SCW3.

[17] Kikuchi, K., T. Okoshi, "Estimation of Linewidth Enhancement Factor of AlGaAs Laser by Correlation Measurement Between FM and AM Noises," *IEEE J. Quantum Electronics.* Vol. QE-21, No. 6, June 1985, pp. 669–673.

[18] Nash, F.R., "Mode Guidance Parallel to the Junction Plane of Double-Heterostructure GaAs Lasers," *J. Applied Physics,* Vol. 44, No. 10, October 1973, pp. 4696–4707.

[19] Ohtsu, M., and K. Nakagawa, "Frequency Control of Semiconductor Lasers and Its Applications,"

Oyo-Buturi (Journal of Japan Society of Applied Physics), Vol. 58, No. 10, October 1989, pp. 1428–1444 [in Japanese].

[20] Yoshikuni, Y., and G. Motosugi, "Multielectrode Distributed Feedback Lasers for Pure Frequency Modulation and Chirping Suppressed Amplitude Modulation," *IEEE J. Lightwave Technology,* Vol. LT-5, No. 4, April 1987, pp. 516–522.

[21] Okai, M., T. Tsuchiya, and N. Chinone, "Ultra-Narrow Spectral Linewidth (56 kHz) Corrugation-Pitch-Modulated Multi-Quantum-Well Distributed Feedback Lasers," *Technical Digest of Conference on Lasers and Electro-Optics* (CLEO' 91), Baltimore, 1991, paper number CPDP40.

[22] Kourogi, M., C.-H. Shin, and M. Ohtsu "A 250 Hz Spectral Linewidth 1.5 μm-MQW-DFB Laser Diode with Negative-Electrical-Feedback," *IEEE Photonics Technology Letters,* Vol. 3, No. 6, June 1991.

[23] Kourogi, M., C.-H. Shin, and M. Ohtsu, "Improvement of the Negative Electrical Feedback System for FM Noise Reduction of a Semiconductor Laser," IEICE Tech. Rep., Vol. 89, 1989, paper number OQE89-62, Institute of Electronics, Information and Communication Engineering, Tokyo, 1989 [in Japanese].

[24] Kobayashi, S., Y. Yamamoto, M. Ito, and T. Kimura, "Direct Frequency Modulation in AlGaAs Semiconductor Lasers," *IEEE J. Quantum Electronics,* Vol. QE-18, No. 4, April 1982, pp. 582–595.

Chapter 4

FM NOISE REDUCTION AND IMPROVEMENT OF FREQUENCY ACCURACY

This chapter discusses how to meet the first three of the five requirements for realizing highly coherent semiconductor lasers, as presented in Section 1.2. The methods of meeting the first and third requirements, stabilization of the center frequency of field spectrum and linewidth reduction of the field spectrum, are similar to each other. Their only difference is the bandwidth of the feedback control; that is, a slow, high-gain feedback is required for the former, whereas a wideband feedback is required for the latter. For the second requirement, improvement in accuracy and reproducibility of the stabilized frequency, a low-drift, slow feedback loop must be used. Therefore, the second requirement is similar to the first, except that the second requirement is closely related to system reliability, which is secured by preparing an accurate and reproducible frequency demodulator. All three requirements share a common feature—the FM noise reduction of a single laser—for this reason they are discussed in a single chapter.

4.1 CENTER FREQUENCY STABILIZATION OF THE FIELD SPECTRUM

As was pointed out earlier, because slow, high-grain feedback is required for center frequency stabilization of the field spectrum, the most reliable feedback among the methods 1 through 6, presented at the beginning of Chapter 3, could be negative electrical feedback as represented by eq. (3.1). This is because a low drift servo-control loop can be designed by using electronic circuit devices.

The Fourier transform of eq. (3.1) is

$$F(f) = \frac{1}{2\tau_p} \frac{(1 + \alpha^2)\Pi_s(f)}{1 + H(f)} + \frac{\Pi_{ex}(f)}{1 + H(f)} - \frac{H(f)}{1 + H(f)} \cdot \Pi_n(f) \qquad (4.1)$$

where f, Π_s, Π_{ex}, Π_n, and H represent the Fourier transforms of $\delta\nu$, Γ_s, Γ_{ex}, Γ_n, and h, respectively. This equation shows that the first and second terms approach zero for the infinite gain of the feedback loop ($|H| \rightarrow \infty$); that is, contributions of the quantum noise of the laser device and the external noises can be suppressed. The third term approaches $|\Pi_n|$; that is, the noise magnitude generated from the feedback loop. This means that, if the total system of negative electrical feedback is treated as a quantum system, the quantum noise source in this system is not only the spontaneous emission fluctuations generated in the laser cavity but also the fluctuations represented by Π_n. The most fundamental contribution to Π_n is the shot noise generated from the photodetector used as the first stage in the FM noise detection system; that is, the number fluctuations of the photoelectrons generated from the photodetector as a result of conversion from the optical lightwave to the photoelectrons. Therefore, even though the FM noise magnitude of the laser device is large, the FM noise in the output lightwave from the negatively fed-back laser system can be reduced to the shot noise limit by employing a high-gain negative electrical feedback loop [1]. If a low-noise feedback loop is employed, the magnitude of the reduced FM noise can be suppressed to a value lower than that of the contribution of spontaneous emission fluctuations (see curve A in Figures 2.17 and 2.18). For the linewidth reduction discussed in the Section 4.3, it means that the linewidth can be reduced to a value narrower than the Schawlow-Townes's limit (eq. (2.58) with $\alpha = 0$) of the solitary laser. Because this reduced FM noise magnitude is lower than that of the coherent state of the light, it can be called a *hypercoherent state* [2]. This means that the linewidth can be reduced to a sub-Hz level if the laser frequency is controlled with a sufficiently wide bandwidth and is locked to a stable optical frequency reference. Part of this need has been demonstrated already for the heterodyne optical phase-locked loop, as will be described in Section 5.1.1.

The center frequency fluctuation of the field spectrum can be suppressed by reducing the FM noise at the Fourier frequency range lower than about 1 Hz by employing a slow servo-control loop. Several organic molecular vapors can be used as the frequency references, because there are a great number of absorption lines due to the higher harmonics and combination tones of the vibration-rotation transitions in NH_3 [3], H_2O [4], C_2H_2 [5], HCN [6], in the wavelength region of $0.8-1.6\ \mu m$. The problems in using them include the following: (1) the absorption coefficients are low; (2) the doppler-free narrow linewidth absorption spectra cannot be measured; and (3) spectral assignments are not easy. To solve these problems, Rb [7, 8] and Cs [9] vapors have been used for their strong resonance lines in electronic transitions around the 0.8 μm wavelength region. They hold several advantages: The volume of the experimental setup can be reduced because of their strong absorption; doppler-free saturated absorption spectral lines can be measured; their spectral assignments have been completed; and so forth. Signal strength of the opto-galvanic spectral lines of several inert gases also are large [10]. Although frequency stability is limited by the frequency shift stemming from the plasma instability of the discharge, a simple and practical frequency reference for 1.5 μm InGaAsP lasers has been proposed by using a miniature argon discharge lamp [11].

Because the InGaAsP laser of 1.5 μm wavelength has been used as a key device for optical communication systems, its frequency has been stabilized by using the preceding frequency references. Recently, an advanced method stabilized the frequency by locking the second harmonic frequency generated from its active waveguide layer to a strong absorption spectral line in Rb vapor [12]. Figure 4.1(a) shows the relation between the fundamental power of a 1.56 μm wavelength and its second harmonic power. This figure shows that the second harmonic power is proportional to the square of the fundamental power, as was popularly known. The output second harmonic wave was expected to be generated in the vicinity of the laser facet, because the absorption coefficient of the InGaAsP material is large at the second harmonic wavelength. However, as shown in Figure 4.1(b), temperature dependence of the efficiency of the second harmonic generation is proportional to the square of the sine function ($= [\sin^2(x)]/x^2$). This means, unexpectedly, that the second harmonic generation also follows the conventional phase matching condition [13]. Figure 4.1(c) shows the first derivative of the ^{87}Rb-D_2 absorption spectral lines, measured by using the second harmonic wave [12]. Although the second harmonic power was as low as several pW, a high sensitivity in spectral detection was obtained, as can be seen from this figure. The laser frequency was locked to a center of this spectral line, represented by point A, to achieve the frequency stability of 9.0×10^{-12} at the integration time of 100 s [12].

The sensitivity of this spectral measurement can be improved by heterodyning with a 0.78 μm AlGaAs laser. Furthermore, by using the AlGaAs laser as a pumping source for the Rb vapor, doppler-free optical double resonance spectral lines in Rb can be measured by the second harmonics; and these lines can be used as frequency references [14]. It can be claimed from these results that a low power of the second harmonic wave does not present any essential problem in frequency control of the InGaAsP laser. Nonlinear optical waveguides using organic materials have been fabricated to generate a higher second harmonic power [14]. For a 0.67 μm wavelength InGaAlP laser, resonance spectral lines in several atomic vapors can be used as frequency references; for example, opto-galvanic spectral lines in Li vapor [15].

Figure 4.2 summarizes the experimental results obtained by a pioneering work of frequency stabilization, in which the stability is represented by mean of the square root of the Allan variance [16]. Curve ST_2 represents the result of the frequency stabilization using the Rb atomic vapor as a frequency reference, which is close to the value of curve H of Figure 2.18. As confirmed from the curve ST_2, the frequency stability as high as 2×10^{-12} has been obtained at the integration time of 100 s. Although this value has not yet reached the shot noise limit of the frequency control loop, due to lack of a sophisticated feedback loop design technique in this early stage of research, we expect that the shot noise limit, represented by curve G of Figure 2.18, will be realized as the performance of the feedback loop improves. Curve G of Figure

2.18 shows that the shot noise limit is as high as 2×10^{-15} at the integration time of 100 s. A principal limitation on the frequency stability shown in Figure 4.2 has been the IM noise of the laser, as pointed out in Section 3.2. A balanced receiver, like that in Figure 3.16, can be used effectively to eliminate the contribution from the IM noise.

In a similar frequency stabilization scheme, an absorption cell of Cs vapor was installed in an external cavity-type semiconductor laser (see Section 4.3). In this scheme, the FM noise of the external cavity-type laser was automatically reduced by the nonlinear response of the Cs vapor [17]. The selective reflection associated with a resonant change of the reflectivity in the glass-vapor interface near the resonance

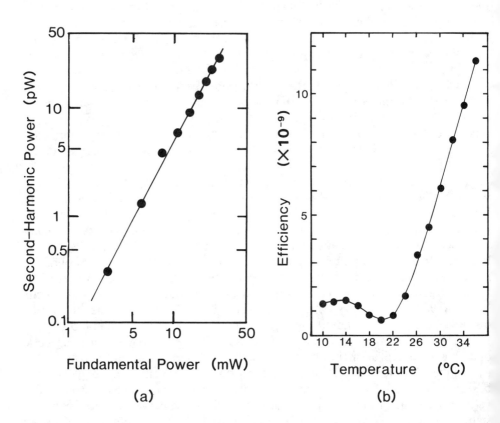

(a)   (b)

Figure 4.1 (a) Relation between the fundamental power of 1.5 μm InGaAsP laser and its internally generated second harmonic power (from [12]). (b) Relation between the 1.5 μm InGaAsP temperature and the efficiency of the second harmonic generation. (c) The derivative of the ^{87}Rb-D_2 absorption spectral lines measured by using the internally generated second harmonic wave (from [12]). The laser frequency was locked to point A of this profile.

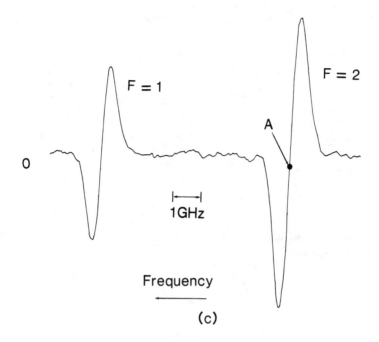

$$F = 1$$

$$F = 2$$

A

0

1GHz

Frequency

(c)

Figure 4.1 continued

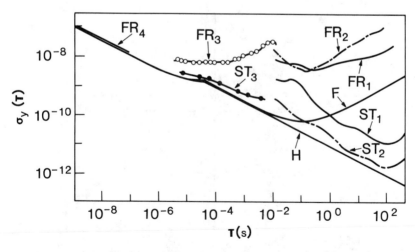

Figure 4.2 Experimental results of the square root of the Allan variance of frequency fluctuations in 0.8 μm AlGaAs lasers (from [16]): FR_1–FR_4 are free-running lasers; ST_1–ST_3 are lasers under negative electrical feedback, for which an absorption spectral line in H_2O vapor, that of Rb vapor, and a Fabry-Perot interferometer were used as frequency references, respectively. Curves F and H of Figure 2.18 are also shown for reference.

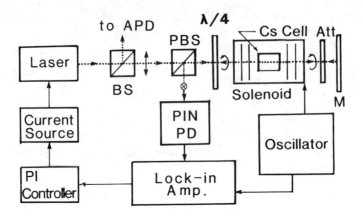

Figure 4.3 Experimental setup of frequency stabilization by using a cesium atomic vapor as a frequency reference (from [20]).

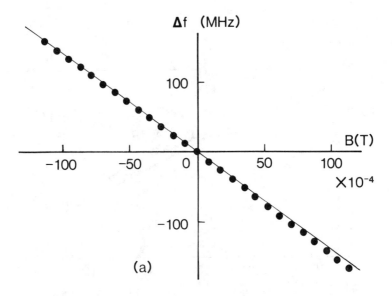

Figure 4.4 (a) Observed magnitude of the Zeeman shift of Cs resonance line as a function of the applied magnetic field [20]. (b) Derivative of the saturated absorption spectral lines of the Cs in the magnetic field, where the magnitudes of the applied magnetic field are represented by those of the current for the solenoid (from [20]).

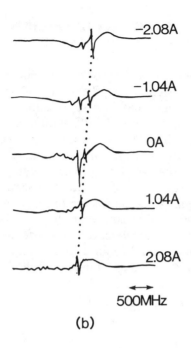

-2.08A

-1.04A

0A

1.04A

2.08A

← →
500MHz

(b)

Figure 4.4 continued

frequency of the alkali vapor has been found to exhibit a dispersive shape [18]. This spectral shape can be used for frequency stabilization of a semiconductor laser without modulating its frequency. Therefore, this stabilization scheme is similar to that using the modified Fabry-Perot interferometer shown in Figures 3.9 and 3.12. This also is similar to that using the saturated dispersion spectral profile of Figure 3.5. Experiments on this selective reflection have been carried out using ^{133}Cs vapor [19].

Another method of obtaining a dispersive spectral profile of the atomic vapor without modulating the laser frequency is to utilize the Zeeman effect of the atoms. An experimental setup using a cesium atomic vapor is shown in Figure 4.3 [20]. An axial ac magnetic field was applied to induce the Zeeman shift of the Cs resonance line. By radiating the circularly polarized laser light to the Cs vapor, the derivative of the saturated absorption lines can be obtained through phase sensitive detection. Figures 4.4(a) and (b) show the magnitude of the Zeeman shift and the derivatives of the saturated spectral line, respectively [20]. The laser frequency was stabilized to the center frequency of this spectral line. By this simple setup, the frequency stability of 2.4×10^{-10} has been obtained at the integration time of 1 s [20].

4.2 IMPROVEMENTS IN THE ACCURACY AND REPRODUCIBILITY OF THE STABILIZED LASER FREQUENCY

It is important to improve the accuracy or reproducibility of the laser frequency stabilized by the methods of Section 4.1. The most fundamental factor limiting accuracy is the drift of the reference frequency. For example, the linear absorption spectral frequency of H_2O vapor shifts 3 MHz/K at room temperature and 1 MHz/K at 273 K, which has been attributed to a temperature-dependent pressure shift in water vapor [21]. Frequency shifts of the linear and saturated absorption spectral shapes in Rb vapor (D_2 line at 780 nm wavelength) have been precisely evaluated by measuring the heterodyne frequency shifts of the two semiconductor lasers stabilized independently [22]. Figure 4.5(a) shows the relevant energy levels of Rb. Figures 4.5(b) and (c) show the derivative shapes of the linear and saturated absorption lines, respectively, used as a frequency reference to stabilize the AlGaAs laser. The results for the linear absorption spectral line are shown in Figures 4.6(a) and (b), in which the frequency shift Δf was plotted as a function of the incident laser power P_L and

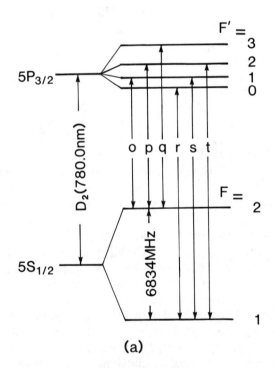

(a)

Figure 4.5 (a) Energy levels of a ^{87}Rb atom. (b) and (c): Derivative spectral shapes of the linear and saturated absorption lines in Rb, respectively (from [22]).

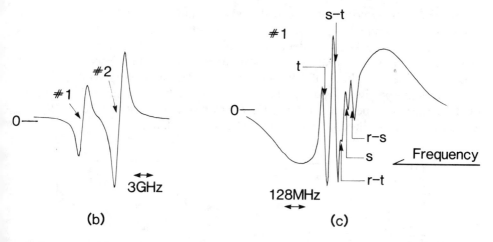

Figure 4.5 continued

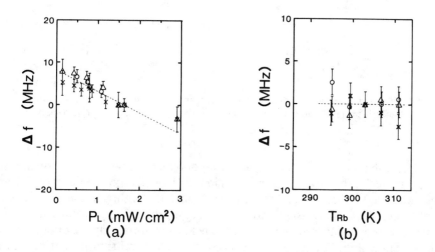

Figure 4.6 Measured frequency shifts of the linear absorption spectral line in Rb as a function of (a) the incident laser power density P_L and (b) Rb vapor temperature T_{Rb}, respectively (from [22]).

the Rb vapor temperature T_{Rb}, respectively. We clearly see from Figure 4.6(a) that Δf decreases with an increasing P_L and this power-induced shift coefficient was estimated as -5 MHz/(mW/cm²), and Figure 4.6(b) shows that Δf was almost independent of T_{Rb}.

The power-induced shift was attributed to the difference in the absorption coefficient and the saturation parameter of each hyperfine transition of Figure 4.5(a). Figures 4.7(a) and (b) show the dependence of the frequency shift Δf of the saturated absorption and cross-resonance spectral lines on P_L and T_{Rb}, respectively, from which we can see that the Δf of these spectral lines is less than 2 MHz/(mW/cm^2) and 0.3 MHz/K, respectively, and that the temperature coefficient is about $\frac{1}{10}$ times that of the absorption spectral line in H$_2$O. These results confirm that the saturated absorption spectral lines in Rb are reliable frequency references.

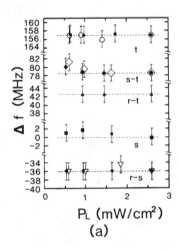
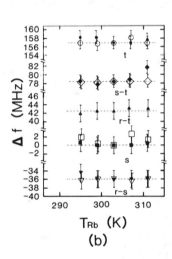

Figure 4.7 Measured frequency shifts of the saturated absorption spectral lines in Rb as a function of (a) the incident laser power density P_L and (b) Rb vapor temperature T_{Rb}, respectively (from [22]).

Opto-galvanic spectral lines in alkali vapors can be a convenient frequency reference. Figure 4.8 shows the spectral lines in the D_1 and D_2 components of Li vapor measured by a 0.67 μm wavelength AlGaInP laser [15]. Although the opto-galvanic spectral lines show a large signal-to-noise ratio, a problem is presented by the frequency shift induced by a strong dc electric field for maintaining the discharge; that is, the dc Stark shift. Due to this dc Stark shift, the spectral splittings of D_1 and D_2 lines can be seen clearly from this figure. The frequency shift of the D_2 line by the unit change of the discharge current is 400 MHz/mA. Although this value shows a complicated dependence on the vapor species, the configuration of the hollow cathode tube, and so on, note that the opto-galvanic spectral lines show larger frequency shift than those of the absorption spectral lines of neutral atomic or molecular vapors.

The frequency shift of the Fabry-Perot interferometer is induced by the changes in the refractive index of the medium in the interferometer and the variation

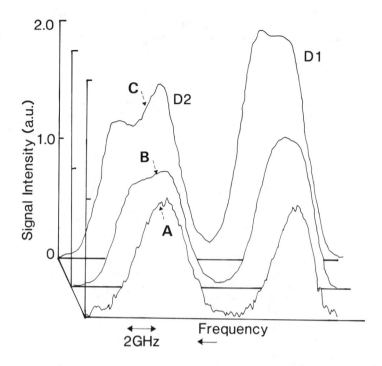

Figure 4.8 Opt-galvanic spectral shapes of D_1 and D_2 lines in Li vapor measured by a 0.67 μm wavelength AlGaInP laser (from [15]). The discharge current for the hollow cathode lamp was 4 (A), 7 (B), and 10 (C) mA.

of the interferometer length. However, the shift due to the variation of interferometer length can be reduced by using a low expansion coefficient material (e.g., Zerodur, a mixture of ceramics and glass manufactured by Schott Optical Glass Inc.) as a spacer to fix two mirrors, by suspending the Fabry-Perot interferometer in a vacuum chamber, or by installing it in an acoustic shield. Furthermore, a glass made by SiO_2 and TiO_2 (ULE, manufactured by Corning Glass Works, with an expansion coefficient of 1×10^{-9}/degree) also has been proposed [23].

The frequencies or wavelengths of these stabilized lasers must be measured as well. Because a practical optical frequency counter has not yet been developed, their wavelengths have been measured by conventional wavemeters. The wavelength of the InGaAsP lasers stabilized to NH_3 and H_2O have been measured with a scanning Michelson interferometer-type wavemeter, as is shown in the Table 4.1. This table shows that their wavelengths have been measured with an inaccuracy of 1×10^{-6} [3]. The wavelengths of AlGaAs lasers stabilized to the H_2O absorption lines also have been measured by the Fabry-Perot interferometer-type wavemeter with an accuracy of 2×10^{-7} [4].

Table 4.1

Wavelengths of the Spectral Lines in NH_3 and H_2O Measured by Using a Scanning Michelson Interferometer-Type Wavemeter (from [3])

	No.	Wavelength in the air (pm)	Wavelength in vacuum (pm)
(NH_3)	1.	1496315.8 ± 0.8	1496311.1 ± 0.8
	2.	1498610.7 ± 0.7	1498605.9 ± 0.7
	3.	1498713.4 ± 0.4	1498708.6 ± 0.4
	4.	1498743.3 ± 0.4	1498738.5 ± 0.4
	5.	1498802.8 ± 0.8	1498798.0 ± 0.8
	6.	1503013.7 ± 0.6	1503008.9 ± 0.6
	7.	1503032.6 ± 1.0	1503027.8 ± 1.0
	8.	1503051.9 ± 1.2	1503047.1 ± 1.2
	9.	1503084.9 ± 0.9	1503080.1 ± 0.9
	10.	1503097.1 ± 0.8	1503092.3 ± 0.8
	11.	1503125.1 ± 0.8	1503120.3 ± 0.8
	12.	1503137.3 ± 0.5	1503132.5 ± 0.5
	13.	1503195.6 ± 1.3	1503190.8 ± 1.3
	14.	1503200.5 ± 1.6	1503195.7 ± 1.6
	15.	1503207.1 ± 0.9	1503202.3 ± 0.9
	16.	1503226.7 ± 1.0	1503221.9 ± 1.0
	17.	1503232.6 ± 0.5	1503227.8 ± 0.5
	18.	1503342.6 ± 0.9	1503337.8 ± 0.9
	19.	1503354.0 ± 1.0	1503349.2 ± 1.0
	20.	1503431.7 ± 0.7	1503426.9 ± 0.7
	21.	1503506.6 ± 1.1	1503501.8 ± 1.1
(H_2O)		1496508.9 ± 0.9	1496504.2 ± 0.9

For improving the frequency reproducibility, it is important to investigate the characteristics of the frequency reproducibility of free-running lasers. Figure 4.9 shows the results of continuous measurements to evaluate the magnitude of frequency drift in free-running AlGaAs lasers [24]. One of the spectral lines in Rb ($F = 1$ component in ^{87}Rb-D_2) was used as a frequency reference for the measurements. The effects of fluctuations in the ambient temperature and injection current were neglected because these were kept as low as 1×10^{-5} K and 0.6 nA/$\sqrt{Hz}$, repectively. We can see from this figure that the laser exhibits a blue shift of 26 MHz/h for 600 h after starting measurements, and a blue shift of 8.6 MHz/h can still be observed six months later. These long-term variations in spectral properties have been attributed to slow temporal decreases of thermal resistance, resulting from oxidation of the indium bonding layer or thermal effects induced by nonradiative carrier recombination near the facets [25]. Reduction and stabilization of the thermal resistance and screening of laser devices are required at the device fabrication stage to limit these uncontrollable variations. The detection and compensation of such long-term variations of spectral properties by a microcomputer has been demonstrated as effective for improving frequency reproducibility [26].

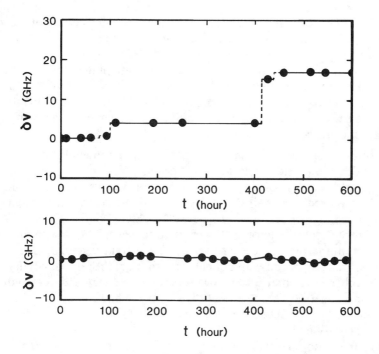

Figure 4.9 The results of continuous measurements to evaluate the magnitude of frequency drift in free-running AlGaAs lasers (from [24]). The lower curve was obtained six months after the upper curve.

4.3 WIDEBAND FM NOISE REDUCTION

For wideband and high gain FM noise reduction, there can be five methods (1 through 5) as were listed at the beginning of Chapter 3. For method 1, we can use a low-noise current source and a highly stabilized temperature controller. Method 2 will be described in Section 6.6 because it is related to the method of cavity QED, which is still in the initial stages of investigation. Method 3 will be described in Section 7.1 because it is related to the fabrication of new semiconductor laser devices. Methods 4 and 5 are described in Sections 4.3.2 and 4.3.1, respectively.

4.3.1 Negative Electrical Feedback

Advantages of the negative electrical feedback method are as follows:

1. The system has high stability and reproducibility.

2. A feedback loop can be designed best by the computer simulation, as in designing conventional analog feedback electronic circuits.
3. The magnitude of the FM noise can be reduced to a value lower than the quantum noise limit of the free-running laser, as was pointed out in Section 4.1.
4. Because very low magnitude FM noise can be realized at the low Fourier frequency range (e.g., $f <$ 100 MHz), this method is useful for a highly sensitive and narrow-bandwidth coherent optical measurements, and high resolution laser spectroscopy.

In this section, we examine how a very low magnitude of FM noise and sub-kHz linewidth of the field spectrum could be achieved. Figure 4.10 shows an experimental setup [27]. An AlGaAs laser of 0.83 μm wavelength (CSP-type, Hitachi HL8314E) was used because it shows flat FM response characteristics in a low Fourier frequency range (see curve B of Figure 3.20). Slopes of resonance curves of two kinds of Fabry-Perot interferometers were used to detect FM noise in the laser. One Fabry-Perot interferometer (FP1) had the free spectral range of 3.45 GHz and the finesse of 25; that is, the full-width of half maximum of the resonance curve was 138 MHz. The other was a confocal Fabry-Perot interferometer (FP2). A cylindrical PZT 2.5 mm long was fixed on one end of the spacer for fine tuning the interferometer length. The FSR of this interferometer was 3GHz. Figure 4.11 shows the measured profile of the resonance curve of FP2. This figure demonstrates a relation between the optical frequency and the light intensity reflected from FP2. The FWHM of the resonance curve was 850 kHz, which corresponds to a finesse of 3500. Efficiency of the transmitted light from the FP2 (the intensity ratio between input and output lights of the FP2) was 4% while that of the reflected light from the FP2 (the depth of the dip of the resonance curve in Figure 4.11 normalized to the input light intensity) was 30%. The reason for the higher efficiency of the reflected light is that the reflected light contained a high intensity light reflected directly from the input mirror of the FP2. High efficiency in the reflected light is advantageous for sensitive FM noise detection. Two optical isolator (Faraday isolator) modules (I1 and I2) were used to suppress the laser oscillation instability, which could be induced by the injections of reflected light from the FP1 and FP2. Optical isolation of each module was 60 dB.

Slow feedback loops were applied to the laser to reduce the drift of the laser frequency. That is, the injection current of the laser was controlled by a PI controller (a proportional amplifier and an integrator) and a P controller (a proportional amplifier). For this control, the transmitted lights from the FP1 and FP2 were detected by *pin* photodiodes, PIN1 and PIN2, respectively. The value of high frequency cutoff of the PI controller and P controller were fixed to 200 Hz.

Faster feedback loops were used as well to reduce wideband FM noise. For this purpose, intensity fluctuations of the reflected lights from the FP1 and FP2 were detected by avalanche photodiodes, APD1 and APD2, respectively. The polarization of the light was controlled by four quarter-wave plates (WP1–WP4) and two polarizing beam splitters (PBS1 and PBS2) to increase the light intensity incident to the

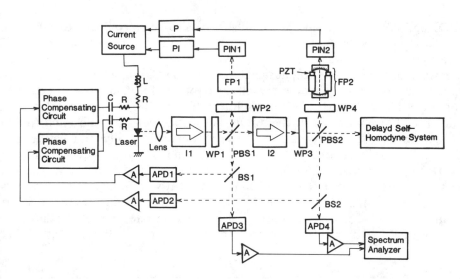

Figure 4.10 The experimental setup of negative electrical feedback to reduce the linewidth of an AlGaAs laser: FP1 and FP2 are Fabry-Perot interferometers; WP1–WP4 are quarter-wave plates; P is a proportional amplifier; PI is a proportional amplifier and an integrator (from [27] © 1990 IEEE).

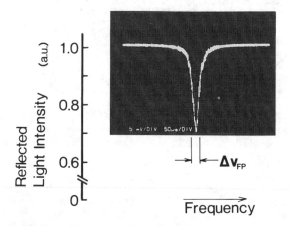

Figure 4.11 The measured profile of the resonance curve of the FP2 of Figure 4.10. This curve represents a relation between the optical frequency and the light intensity reflected from FP2. The FWHM of this curve $\Delta\nu_{FP}$ was 850 kHz (from [27] © 1990 IEEE).

APD1 and APD2. Wideband preamplifiers, passive phase compensating circuits, and bias-T circuits (the circuits composed of C, R, and L as shown in Figure 4.10) were connected in series to the APD1 and APD2, and the injection current of the laser was controlled by the output signals from the bias-T circuits.

About 10% of the light intensity reflected from the FP1 and FP2 were extracted from the feedback loops by the beam splitters BS1 and BS2 to measure the magnitude of the FM noise by using the two avalanche photodiodes (APD3 and APD4) and a microwave spectrum analyzer. The spectrum analyzer allowed measurement of the power spectral density of the FM noise within the Fourier frequency range of $100 \text{ Hz} \leqslant f \leqslant 100 \text{ MHz}$. Curve A of Figure 4.12 shows the measured power spectral density of the FM noise of the free-running laser. Curve D in this figure represents the sensitivity limit of the FM noise detection imposed by the laser IM noise. A part of curve A at $100 \text{ kHz} \leqslant f \leqslant 100 \text{ MHz}$ is composed of white noise, due to the quantum noise induced by spontaneous emission and carrier density fluctuations. Flicker

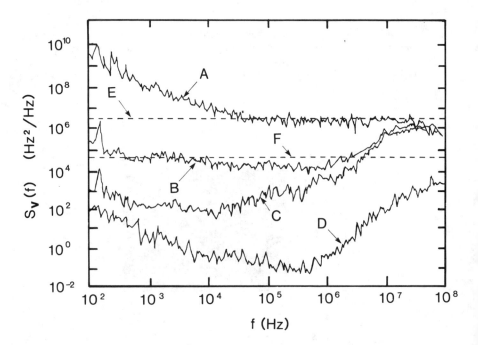

Figure 4.12 The power spectral density of the FM noise of an AlGaAs laser: A is a free-running laser; B and C are under negative electrical feedback using feedback loops 1 and 2, respectively; D is the limit of the residual FM noise detection by FP2 under the auxiliary feedback by the feedback loop 1; E is the magnitude of white noise in curve A, due to the spontaneous emission and carrier density fluctuations; F is the minimum magnitude of quantum FM noise due to spontaneous emission, estimated by using curve E and $\alpha = 9.0$ (from [27] © 1990 IEEE).

noise ($1/f$ noise) can be seen at $f \leqslant 100$ kHz. The profile of the field spectrum $I(\nu)$ of the free-running laser was derived from the power spectral density of curve A by (AII.9) of Appendix II. The result is shown in curve B of Figure 4.13(a), which gives the FWHM ($\Delta \nu_{FR}$) of 4.5 MHz. This value agreed with the directly measured value by the delayed self-homodyne technique.

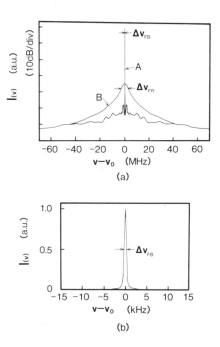

Figure 4.13 Field spectral profile of the AlGaAs laser: (a) A is a free-running laser, B is under negative electrical feedback; (b) magnified profile of curve B (from [27] © 1990 IEEE).

Curves B of Figure 3.20(a) and (b) show the characteristics of direct frequency modulation; that is, the complex transfer function $H_L(f_m)$ of the laser used. We see that the transfer function takes almost constant values for a wide range of f_m, which aids in designing a wideband negative electrical feedback loop for FM noise reduction.

As was discussed in eq. (4.1), the contributions from quantum noise sources in the laser cavity can be suppressed by a high feedback gain and the magnitude of the FM noise ultimately can be reduced to a value limited by the noise generated from the feedback loop. In other words, if a high-gain, low-noise feedback loop is employed, the magnitude of the FM noise can be reduced to a value lower than the quantum FM noise level of the free-running laser.

Preliminary measurements found that the principal noise source generated from the feedback loop in Figure 4.10 was the intensity fluctuation (IM noise) of the laser itself. Here, we assume that the magnitude of the IM noise did not change, even if a negative electrical feedback was applied to the laser for FM noise reduction. The validity of this assumption will be given later. The normalized residual FM noise can be defined as a ratio of the power spectral densities of the free-running laser ($S_{\nu FR}(f)$) to the laser under negative electrical feedback ($S_{\nu FB}(f)$). This is given by [28]

$$\frac{S_{\nu FB}(f)}{S_{\nu FR}(f)} = \left| \frac{1}{1 + H(f)} \right|^2 \tag{4.2}$$

where $H(f)$ represents the open-loop transfer function of the feedback loop in eq. (4.1). To minimize the normalized residual FM noise, the optimum design of the feedback loop must maximize the value of $|H(f)|$. Network analysis is a powerful tool in creating an optimum design, whose details follow.

The loop transfer function $H(f)$ of feedback loop 1 or 2 is given by

$$H = H_T \cdot H_L \cdot H_{FP} \cdot H_A \cdot H_P \cdot H_D \tag{4.3}$$

where H_T, H_L, H_{FP}, H_A, and H_P, and H_D are transfer functions of the bias-T circuit, FM response of the laser, the Fabry-Perot interfermometer, the APD with a preamplifier, the phase compensating circuit, and the delay of signal propagation in the feedback loop, respectively. The transfer function of the circuit composed of the C and R in the bias-T circuit in Figure 4.10 is expressed as

$$H_T(f) = \frac{1}{1 + f_T/if} \tag{4.4}$$

For the feedback loops 1 and 2, the values of f_T in this equation were fixed at 200 Hz This value of f_T gave the 3 dB-down low-frequency cutoff of the feedback loop. The measured values of Figure 3.20 were used as the transfer function of the FM response of the laser $H_L(f)$. The calculated values of Figures 3.7(a) and (b) were used as the transfer functions of the Fabry-Perot interferometers $H_{FP}(f)$. Because the bandwidths of APD1, APD2, and the preamplifier were sufficiently wider than those of the other transfer functions in (4.3), the value of $H_A(f)$ was assumed to be constant at 200 Hz $\leqslant f \leqslant$ 100 MHz. The transfer function of the phase compensating circuit connected to the preamplifier is expressed as

$$H_P(f) = \frac{1 + if/f_1}{1 + if/n_1 f_1} \cdot \frac{n_2 + if/f_2}{1 + if/f_2} \tag{4.5}$$

The first and the second parts of the right-hand side of this equation represent the effect of compensation for phase lag and phase lead, respectively. The values of the parameters f_1, n_1, f_2, and n_2 were adjusted to maximize $|H(f)|$. The transfer function representing the delay of signal propagation in the feedback is expressed as

$$H_D(f) = \exp(-i2\pi f t_D) \tag{4.6}$$

where t_D represents the total delay time, which includes all contributions from the lengths of the electrical cables and optical paths and those of the APD and preamplifier. Measured values of t_D for feedback loops 1 and 2 were 8.4 ns and 10 ns, respectively.

The loop transfer function could be calculated by substituting the value of the transfer function of each servo element into (4.3). This loop transfer function also could be measured directly by inserting a microwave network analyzer between the phase compensating circuit and the bias-T circuit in Figure 4.10. Because these two results agreed well with each other, we concluded that the network analysis was accurate. The validity of this conclusion was proven by comparing curves A (calculated result) and B (measured result) in Figure 4.14. Good agreement actually can be seen between these two curves for the optimized feedback loop 1.

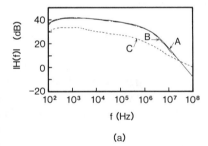 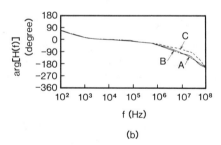

(a)   (b)

Figure 4.14 (a) Absolute value and (b) phase delay of the loop transfer function $H(f)$ of the negative electrical feedback: A and B are the calculated and measured values, respectively, for which the optimally designed phase compensating circuit was used; C is the measured value without any phase compensating circuit (from [27] © 1990 IEEE).

Following these discussions, experiments on the FM noise reduction were carried out by using negative electrical feedback. The reflection mode of the Fabry-Perot interferometer was employed to realize a high loop gain. As will be pointed out later, the reflection mode of the FP2 made an essential contribution to FM noise reduction in the present work. Prior to using feedback loop 2, auxiliary feedback loop 1 was applied to the free-running laser to preliminarily reduce the FM noise. This feedback loop had a wider bandwidth than that of feedback loop 2 because of the larger value of $\Delta\nu_{\text{FP}}$ in the FP1. To maximize the gain of feedback loop 1, the values of the parameters in (4.5) were adjusted optimally. They were $f_1 = 2.5$ MHz, $n_1 = 0.14$, $f_2 = \infty$, and $n_2 = 1$. The 3 dB-down high-frequency cutoff of feedback loop 1 depended on the value of f_1. Curves A and B in Figures 4.14(a) and (b) show the calculated and measured values of the loop transfer function, using the optimized phase compensating circuit, respectively. These two curves agree with each other, which confirms the high accuracy of the network analysis based on eqs. (4.3)–(4.6). Curves C in these figures represent the measured values without using the phase compensating circuit. We see by comparing curves B and C that the loop gain could be increased 10 dB, and it approached as high as 40 dB by using this phase compensating circuit while the loop bandwidth was slightly decreased, from which the usefulness of the phase compensating circuit can be confirmed. Curve B in Figure 4.14(a) shows that the high-frequency cutoff at which the loop gain decreased to 0 dB was 40 MHz. This means that the FM noise could be reduced within the Fourier frequency range as wide as 40 MHz even though the 3 dB-down high-frequency cutoff of the feedback loop was about 200 kHz. This frequency range, 40 MHz, depended on the value of the delay time t_D of signal propagation in feedback loop 1.

Another phase compensating circuit was used for feedback loop 2. The optimized values of the parameters in (4.5) were $f_1 = 20$ kHz, $n_1 = 0.14$, $f_2 = \infty$, and $n_2 = 1$. The 3 dB-down high-frequency cutoff of feedback loop 2 depended on the value of f_1. However, as in feedback loop 1, the loop gain decreased to 0 dB at the Fourier frequency, which was larger than this value of f_1.

Figure 4.12 shows the experimental results of FM noise reduction. Curve B represents the residual FM noise of the laser under auxiliary frequency control by feedback loop 1. This FM noise was measured by using the FP1 and APD3. Curve C results from applying feedback loop 2 to the preliminarily controlled laser. This FM noise was measured by using the FP2 and APD4. Curve D represents the limit of the residual FM noise detection by the FP2 under control of auxiliary feedback loop 1. As described, this limit was estimated from the magnitude of the IM noise of the laser because the main contribution to this limit was found to be the laser's intrinsic IM noise. This IM noise was carefully measured by the APD4 in Figure 4.10. The reason for the increase in the value of curve D at $f > 425$ kHz ($\Delta\nu_{\text{FP}}/2$) resulted from the calibration required to represent the effect of the limited bandwidth of the transfer function of the FP2 used to detect the residual FM noise. Curve D gave the limit of FM noise reduction using both the feedback loops.

We can see by comparing curves A and B that auxiliary feedback loop 1 reduced the FM noise within the range $f < 40$ MHz. This range agreed with that of curve B in Figure 4.14(a), where the gain of feedback loop 1 was larger than 0 dB. We also can see by comparing curves B and C of Figure 4.12 that further reductions in FM noise were realized by feedback loop 2 in the range $f \leqslant 5$ MHz, which mean.

that the gain of feedback loop 2 was larger than 0 dB within this range. Dashed line E represents the magnitude of white noise in curve A, which corresponds to the value of $|(1 + \alpha^2)\pi_s|$ of (4.1), due to the spontaneous emission and carrier density fluctuations. Because the maximum linewidth broadening factor α of the laser used here has been estimated at 9.0 (the open circle in Fig. 4A of [29]), the minimum of $|\Pi_s|$ in (4.1) can be estimated from this value of α and dashed line E. The result is given by dashed line F. The value of curve C was lower than that of line F in the range of 100 Hz $\leqslant f \leqslant$ 4.4 MHz, which means that the magnitude of the FM noise in this range was reduced to a value lower than the quantum FM noise level of the free-running laser. This experimental result supports the validity of the result of theoretical discussion in Section 4.1. Especially at 100 Hz $\leqslant f \leqslant$ 1 kHz, we see by comparing curves A and C that the magnitude of the FM noise was reduced to as low as 1×10^{-7} to 1×10^{-6} that of the free-running laser. At $f <$ 100 Hz, slow frequency fluctuations were also reduced by the **PI** and **P** controls using the transmission modes of the FP1 and FP2. The square root of the Allan variance $\sigma_y^2(\tau)$ of these fluctuations was measured because the Allan variance has been known to be a more accurate measure for evaluating slow frequency fluctuations [30] than the power spectral density. The Allan variance real-time processing system was used for this measurement [31]. The measured value was $1 \times 10^{-12} \leqslant \sigma_y(\tau) \leqslant 1 \times 10^{-11}$ at the integration time of 10 ms $\leqslant \tau \leqslant$ 100 s. Because these slow fluctuations were reduced sufficiently, feedback loops 1 and 2 remained very stable and the very low FM noise level given by curve C was also maintained for more than 3 hours. Furthermore, these slow fluctuations were confirmed to be low enough that the estimated result of the very narrow field spectrum given in Figure 4.13 was independent of them. The gain-bandwidth product of this negative electrical feedback can be estimated to be as large as 40 THz by comparing curves A and C in Figure 4.12.

A very narrow linewidth of the field spectrum of the laser can be expected at such low magnitude FM noise. The FWHM was estimated by calculating the field spectral profile $I(\nu)$ by using curves B and C of Figure 4.12 and eq. (AII.9). The value of FWHM estimated from curve B was 30 kHz. Curve A in Figure 4.13(a) represents the field spectral profile estimated from curve C of Figure 4.12. The unit of vertical axis in this figure is in dB. Curve B represents the profile of the free-running laser. We can see by comparing curves A and B in this figure that the effect of feedback loop appears in the range $|\nu - \nu_0| \leqslant$ 40 MHz, which corresponds to the Fourier frequency range in which the gain of feedback loop 1 was larger than 0 dB. Because the linewidth of curve A is too narrow to measure, its central part was magnified and shown in Figure 4.13(b). A linear scale was employed for the vertical axis of this figure. The value of FWHM of this spectral profile was estimated from this figure as $\Delta\nu_{\mathrm{FB}} =$ 560 Hz.

Curve C in Figure 4.12 has a resonant peak at $f =$ 150 Hz, caused by a low-level residual acoustic vibration and a higher harmonic from the ac electric source. We found that the FWHM of the field spectrum of Figure 4.13(b) was increased slightly by this peak. A narrower linewidth can be expected from a more careful acoustic shield and rejection of the the higher harmonics of the ac source; and finally, the magnitude of the FM noise can be reduced to the value given by curve *D* of Figure 4.12 by further improvements in the performance of the feedback loops.

The 3 dB-down high-frequency cutoff of feedback loop 2 was 20 kHz, determined by the value of f_1 or (4.5). Because this value of a 3 dB-down high-frequency cutoff was smaller than $\Delta\nu_{FP}/2$ (= 425 kHz) of the FP2, we may think that feedback loop 2 did not fully utilize such the advantageous characteristics of the reflection mode as presented in Figure 3.7. However, as shown by curve *C* in Figure 4.12, this feedback loop had a gain larger than 0 dB for the Fourier frequency up to 5 MHz, which was larger than the value of high-frequency cutoff ($\Delta\nu_{FP}/2$) of the transfer function of the FP2. Therefore, when the transmission mode of the FP2 was used in a preliminary experiment, instead of the reflection mode, the excessively increased gain of feedback loop 2 induced instability and oscillation, by which the specific resonant peak appeared in the power spectral density of the FM noise. From comparison between this preliminary experimental result and curve *C* of Figure 4.12, we confirmed that the advantageous characteristics of the reflection mode of the FP2 made an essential contribution to reduce the magnitude of the FM noise to as low as 1×10^{-7} to 1×10^{-6} that of the free-running laser.

For FM noise detection during feedback, the error signals of the feedback loops (i.e., intensity fluctuations of the reflected lights from the FP1 and FP2 induced by the FM noise) were extracted from the feedback loops by using the BS1 and BS2 of Figure 4.10; and they were detected by the APD3 and APD4. Therefore, if the magnitude of the laser's IM noise was increased drastically by the feedback for FM noise reduction, the inaccuracy of the FM noise detection could be increased and the estimated limit of the FM noise reduction may become invalid. To check for this possibility, a simultaneous measurement of the magnitude of the IM noise was carried out under frequency control by using another APD placed between the PBS2 and the delayed self-homodyne system in Figure 4.10. As a result of this measurement, we found that the increase in IM noise under feedback using both feedback loops was within 60% that of the free-running laser. Thus, we confirmed that the increase in the magnitude of the IM noise had no significant effect on FM noise detection. Such a negligible increase in the magnitude of the IM noise has been discussed theoretically in Appendix B of [28]. The validity of this discussion was confirmed by the present experiment.

Recently, a multiquantum-well DFB laser (MQW-DFB laser) of 1.5 μm wavelength was developed that has a corrugation-pitch modulated DFB. The minimum of FWHM of this laser is as narrow as 56 kHz [32]. Furthermore, its FM response is flat for a wide range modulation frequency, as presented by Figure 3.21. Experiments on negative electrical feedback were carried out to reduce the FM noise of this laser by using a reflection mode of a Fabry-Perot interferometer of $\Delta\nu_{FP}$ = 2 MHz as a frequency demodulator and following the design criterion of the feedback loop pre-

sented earlier. The measured value of the power spectral density is shown by curve
B of Figure 4.15(a) [33]. Curve *A* shows the free-running FM noise. Curve *D* shows
the limits of detecting the free-running FM noise imposed by the IM noise of the
laser. Curve *C* shows also the effect of the IM noise on feedback, whose magnitude
was increased due to the negative electrical feedback for reducing the FM noise. By
comparing curves *B* and *C*, we see that the FM noise reduction limit in this case also
is given by the IM noise of the laser. Figure 4.15(b) shows the field spectral profile
obtained by substituting the value of curve *B* in Figure 4.15(a) into eq. (AII.9). We
confirmed that a FWHM as narrow as 250 Hz could be achieved. The power concentration ratio was as high as 98% within the 12 MHz feedback bandwidth,
obtained by using (AII.13). The contribution of IM noise can be reduced by using a
balanced receiver (see Figure 3.16), by which further FM noise reductions can be
expected until it is limited to the shot noise generated by the photodetector used to
detect FM noise.

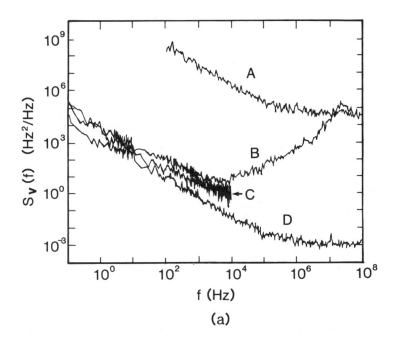

Figure 4.15 (a) Measured power spectral density of the FM noise of a 1.5 μm MQW-DFB laser, which
has a corrugation-pitch modulated DFB: *A* is a free-running laser, *B* is under negative electrical feedback, *C* and *D* are the contributions of laser IM noise to the FM noise detection
under the feedback and free-running conditions, respectively; (b) *A* and *B* are the field spectral profile estimated from curves *A* and *B* of (a), respectively, the inset is a magnified profile
of curve *B* (from [33] © 1991 IEEE). Horizontal axis: 10MHz/div.

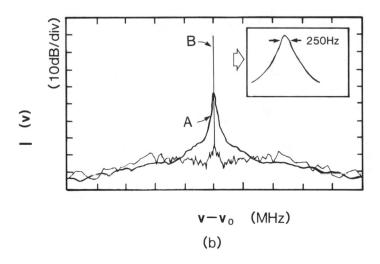

$$\nu - \nu_0 \quad (MHz)$$

(b)

Figure 4.15 continued

4.3.2 Injection Locking and Optical Feedback

FM noise reduction also is possible by reducing the cavity loss, as presented in method 4 at the beginning of Chapter 3. This method has been employed mainly for semiconductor lasers, because their cavity losses are large. One example is optical feedback [34] based on the phenomenon of injection locking shown in Figure 4.16. Injection locking is a nonlinear phenomenon found in general self-sustained oscillators. Its characteristics can be analyzed by using the Van der Pol's equation [35]; that is, the slave laser frequency is pulled to that of the master laser by injecting the master laser light to the slave laser cavity. The locking range, the maximum frequency detuning between the two lasers to realize injection locking, is given by [36]

$$-\frac{1}{4\pi\tau_p} \sqrt{\frac{P_m}{P_s}} \leq \nu_m - \nu_s \leq \frac{1}{4\pi\tau_p} \sqrt{\frac{P_m}{P_s}(1 + \alpha^2)} \qquad (4.7)$$

where P_m, P_s, ν_m, and ν_s are the powers and the frequencies of the master and slave lasers, respectively. Note that P_m and P_s represent the values measured inside the slave laser cavity. The term τ_p is the photon lifetime of the slave laser, and α is the α-parameter of the slave laser. Because this equation demonstrates that the locking range is inversely proportional to the photon lifetime, that is, proportional to the magnitude of the cavity loss, semiconductor lasers can have a wide locking range and are easily injection locked. Figure 4.17 shows a measured result of the locking range of a semiconductor laser [37]. The FM noise of the slave laser can be reduced by injection locking from a stable master laser. The locking range corresponds to the bandwidth of this FM noise reduction. The slave laser frequency can be swept in a stable manner by sweeping that of the master laser within the locking range. However, the accuracy and reproducibility of the frequency sweep usually are lower than that of negative electrical feedback, because injection locking is based on the complicated nonlinear properties of the oscillators.

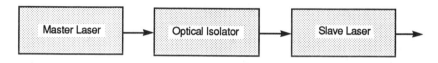

Figure 4.16 Schematic explanation of the injection locking system.

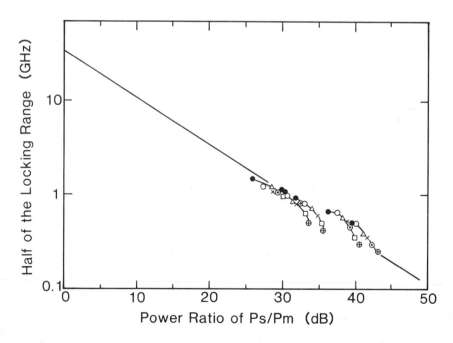

Figure 4.17 Relation of the power ratio P_s/P_m to the injection locking range, where P_m and P_s are the powers of the master and slave lasers, respectively (from [37] © 1981 IEEE).

Optical feedback corresponds to the injection locking by injecting the light reflected back from an external reflection surface to the laser cavity. Although deterministic instabilities usually are induced by injecting this reflected light (see also Section 2.5.1; this instability also has been called *coherent collapse* [38]), stable optical feedback can be realized if the phase of the reflected light is equal to that of the light emitted from the laser cavity (i.e., when the separation between the laser cavity and external reflector is an integer multiple of the half-wavelength) and when the reflectivity of the cavity output mirror is low enough to ensure sufficient power from the reflected light. For actual semiconductor laser devices, the contribution of the α-parameter should be taken into account for the stable optical feedback criterion. Detailed discussion has been given by, for example, [39]. These conditions correspond to form a large laser cavity by using an external reflector (i.e., an external cavity) and to reduce cavity loss. This method is effective especially for semiconductor lasers and has been used for more than 15 years [34]. However, it should be called *opto-mechanical feedback,* because electromechanical elements such as a PZT have been used to control the separation between the laser and the external reflector. For optical feedback semiconductor lasers, frequency modulation efficiency is reduced drastically because the photon lifetime determined by the external cavity becomes very long. Furthermore, the hopping occurs between the external cavity modes because the separation between these modes is much narrower than the gain spectral linewidth. The optical feedback shows a narrow bandwidth because it is inversely proportional to the photon lifetime of the external cavity. A low-loss external cavity has been formed by using a single external reflector to realize a linewidth of about 2 kHz [40]. Although the wavelength sweep is realized by using a diffraction grating as an external reflector, continuous sweep is difficult due to the hopping between the longitudinal modes of the external cavity. Despite these mode hoppings, a total wavelength sweep range over 100 nm has been demonstrated by fabricating the laser device by introducing a quantum-well structure for this optical feedback [41].

A method using a self-pumped phase conjugate mirror (a $BaTiO_3$ crystal) as an external reflector has been proposed to control the phase of the reflected light and realize stable optical feedback [42]. Although this type of optical feedback did not require the phase control of the reflected light, because of the self-aligning nature of the phase conjugate mirror, the jumps between external cavity modes were observed. Furthermore, the built-up time of the phase conjugated wave was too long for this application due to the slow response time of the $BaTiO_3$.

To overcome this difficulty, using a semiconductor laser device as a phase conjugate mirror was proposed; and its reflectivity was measured to be as large as 1×10^3 [43]. Figures 4.18(a) and (b) show the dependence of reflectivity on detuning between the pump and probe beams, which are the measured results for a 0.83 μm AlGaAs laser [44] and 0.67 μm AlGaInP laser [45], respectively. Bandwidths (FWHM) as wide as 6 GHz and 4 GHz can be seen from these figures, which are determined by the intraband relaxation time constant τ_s ($= 1$ ns) of the carrier. The two peaks of these curves originated from relaxation oscillations. Furthermore, the asymmetry of the curves is due to the simultaneously photoinduced gain and index gratings in the active waveguides of the lasers, where the ratio of the magnitudes of the two gratings is represented by the α-parameter. By careful measurement for an AlGaAs laser, it was also found that the low-power phase conjugate wave could be generated even for the detuning as large as 1 THz [44, 46]. The measured result is shown in Figure 4.18(c) [44]. This originated from intraband relaxation of the carrier whose time constant τ_{in} is as short as 0.1 ps. Based on the characteristics just reviewed, stable optical feedback can be expected by using this type of efficient and fast phase conjugation mirror. This novel mirror can be advantageous, especially for the pulsed semiconductor laser whose linewidth is drastically broadened due to chirping in the refractive index of the active waveguide. If chirping can be suppressed by the optical feedback from a wideband phase conjugate mirror, a Fourier limited, narrow-linewidth pulsed laser can be expected.

An alternative and stable optical feedback method using an external confocal Fabry-Perot interferometer has been proposed [47]. The experimental setup is

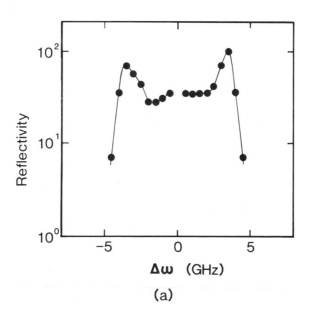

(a)

Figure 4.18 (a) and (b): Measured dependence of the reflectivity of the phase conjugated mirror on the detuning $\Delta\omega$ between the pump and probe beams of AlGaAs lasers (from [44]) and AlGaInP lasers (from [45]), respectively. (c) The measured dependence when the detuning $\Delta\omega$ is as large as 1 THz (from [44]).

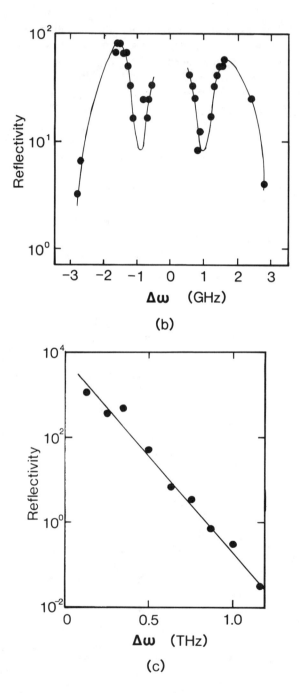

Figure 4.18 continued

shown in Figure 4.19, by which a linewidth of about 10 kHz has been obtained. In this method, the light transmitted from the Fabry-Perot interferometer after resonance is injected into the laser (i.e., the Fabry-Perot interferometer worked as a frequency-dependent reflector), and through it this laser frequency is pulled into the resonance frequency of the Fabry-Perot interferometer so that the FM noise of the laser is reduced. In a weaker feedback level, the optical feedback effect cannot be observed; that is, the linewidth was not reduced from that of a free-running laser. In a moderate feedback level, linewidth reduction factor is nearly inversely proportional to the actual feedback power into the laser cavity, as expected by theoretical analysis for all the types of optical feedback systems. In a stronger feedback level, optical feedback becomes unstable because deterministic instability can be induced (use Section 2.5.1).

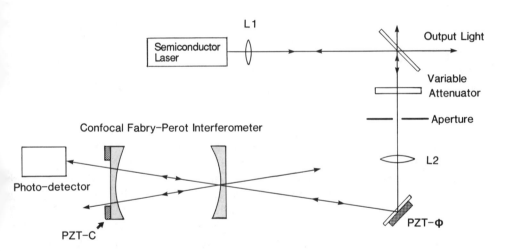

Figure 4.19 Experimental setup of optical feedback using a confocal Fabry-Perot interferometer as an external reflector (from [47]).

The field spectral profile of the laser under this optical feedback condition was observed with 2.2 GHz span to confirm the suppression of external cavity modes, which can originate from the external cavity formed by a laser facet and one mirror of the Fabry-Perot interferometer or by the Fabry-Perot interferometer itself. The result is shown in Figure 4.20 [48]. Any external cavity modes must show up in this span, because the external cavity mode spacing (i.e., the free spectral range) is 1.5 GHz; however, no side modes could be observed. From this measurement, it was confirmed that the side-mode suppression ratio of this laser system was at least 50 dB, proving reliable single-mode oscillation.

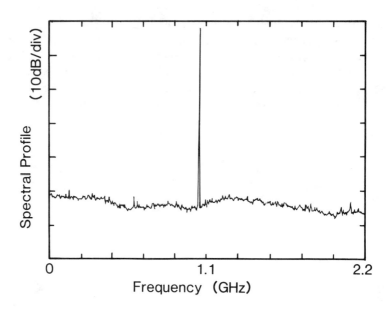

Figure 4.20 Field spectral profile of the heterodyne signal between two lasers optically fed back by the method of Figure 4.19 (from [48]).

Figure 4.21(a) shows the power spectral density of FM noise normalized to that of the free-running laser, which was measured by using the reflection mode of another Fabry-Perot interferometer as a frequency demodulator [48]. The calculated result corresponding to the experiment is shown in Figure 4.21(b). They show a good agreement with each other. The maximum FM noise reduction was 39 dB. The 3 dB-down bandwidth of this optical feedback is given by the photon lifetime of the Fabry-Perot interferometer; that is, half of the Fabry-Perot resonance linewidth $\Delta\nu_{FP}$, as can be seen by this figure. However, we see that the 0 dB bandwidth can be much wider, as wide as about 1 GHz [48]. As we can see in Figure 4.22 [48], using a lower finesse Fabry-Perot interferometer is more advantageous for wideband FM noise reduction if the same feedback gain can be secured. However, note that optical feedback from a higher finesse interferometer gives higher dc gain if the same power from the cavity is fed back to the laser. By decreasing the value of the finesse, oscillation peak at the Fourier frequency corresponding to the resonance frequency of the interferometer, is increased, thereby decreasing the merit of a single external-cavity mode operation.

The accuracy of controlling the separation between the laser and the Fabry-Perot interferometer does not have to be as high as that in conventional optical feedback using a single external reflector [49]. In addition to this, the method has two more outstanding advantages:

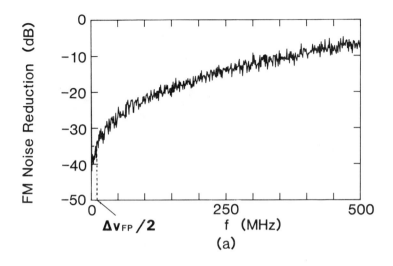

(a)

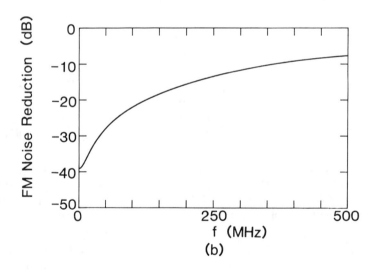

(b)

Figure 4.21 (a) Measured and (b) calculated results of the reduction of a laser's FM noise that was optically fed back by the method of Figure 4.19 (from [48]).

1. A solitary laser cavity structure is preserved because the strong optical feedback is not required, therefore, no mode hopping between external cavities takes place.

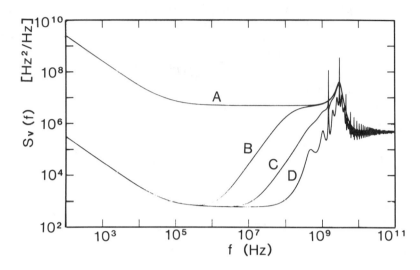

Figure 4.22 Calculated FM noise magnitudes of a semiconductor laser: A is a free-running laser; B, C, and D are under optical feedback by the method of Figure 4.19, where the finesses of the confocal Fabry-Perot interferometer were assumed to be 500, 50, and 5, respectively. Feedback gains were assumed to be the same for these three values of finess (from [48]).

2. Direct frequency modulation is possible by modulating the injection current with the frequencies related by rational fractions to the free-spectral range of the Fabry-Perot interferometer, as shown in Figure 4.23 [50, 51]. This algebraic relation corresponds to the Farey tree and devil's staircase [52], which also can be found in the mode locking of an external-cavity semiconductor laser [53].

The locking range of this optical feedback can be estimated by measuring the resonance spectral profile of the Fabry-Perot interferometer as a function of the injection current of the laser. Figures 4.24(a) and (b) show the results of this measurement under the free-running and optical feedback conditions, respectively [54]. Figure 4.24(a) shows a conventional profile, whereas Figure 4.24(b) shows one deformed because the laser frequency was locked to the center frequency of the Fabry-Perot resonance even though the injection current was swept. The width of this deformed profile corresponds to the locking range, which increases with increasing the power in the reflected light into the laser. A locking range wider than the free-spectral range of the Fabry-Perot interferometer is possible with sufficiently high reflected power. We can see from Figure 4.24(b) that the locking range is asymmetric: that is, the width $\Delta\nu_+$ is narrower than $\Delta\nu_-$ in this figure. This asymmetry corresponds to the asymmetric injection locking range given by (4.7), which depends on the value of the α-parameter of the laser. Therefore, the value of the α-parameter can

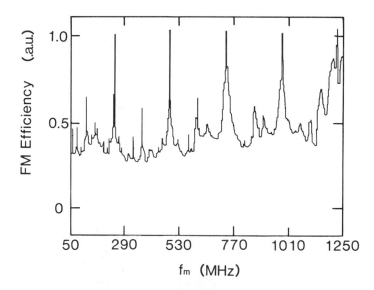

Figure 4.23 The FM efficiency of the optically fed back laser of Figure 4.19, which was measured as a function of the modulation frequency of the injection current (from [50, 51]).

be estimated from this asymmetry. We found by referring to (4.7) that the value of the α-parameter is given by

$$\alpha = \sqrt{\beta} / (1 - \beta) \tag{4.8}$$

where

$$\beta = \frac{\Delta\nu_- - \Delta\nu_+}{\Delta\nu_- + \Delta\nu_+ + \Delta\nu_{FP}} \tag{4.9}$$

The value of the α-parameter of the CSP-type AlGaAs laser was measured to be 3.07 ± 0.26, which showed good agreement with those measured by other methods [29]. We can claim that this method is one of the easiest, most accurate, real-time methods of estimating the value of α-parameter among conventional methods, which sometimes are complicated.

This Fabry-Perot interferometer has been fabricated by employing the techniques of microoptics and fiberoptics to realize a modulatable compact laser module, shown in Figure 4.25 [54]. Because the free-spectral range of the hemispherical microcavity (*HMC* in Figure 4.25(a)) (about 10 GHz) is higher than the relaxation oscillation frequency of the solitary laser, the peak of FM noise at this frequency is

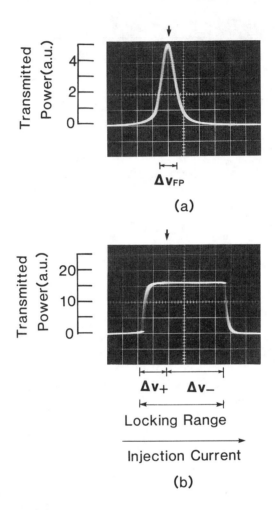

Figure 4.24 Resonance curves of the confocal Fabry-Perot interferometer measured by sweeping the injection current of the laser: (a) free-running; (b) under optical feedback. The scale of the horizontal axis is 0.055 mA/div. The arrows at top of (a) and (b) indicate the resonance frequency of the interferometer (from [54]).

reduced, as we can see by the calculated result in Figure 4.26 [48]. Comparing this result with curve C in Figure 4.22, we confirm that the wideband noise reduction characteristics of this practical HMC-laser module are superior to those of the laser optically coupled with a higher finesse Fabry-Perot interferometer. This method of optical feedback recently was employed in a 0.67 μm wavelength visible AlGaInP laser to reduce the field spectral linewidth to less than 50 kHz (Figure 4.27) [15], where the linewidth under the free-running condition has been as wide as 200 MHz.

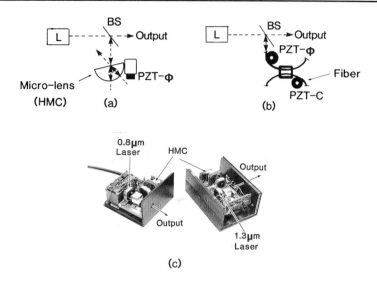

Figure 4.25 (a) A hemispherical microlens interferometer and (b) a fiber-optic interferometer, which were used as the external Fabry-Perot interferometers of compact laser modules; (c) picture of the miniature laser modules assembled by using hemispherical microlens interferometer of 1 cm diameter, the volume of the 0.8 μm wavelength AlGaAs CSP type laser module (left) and 1.3 μm wavelength InGaAsP DFB type laser module (right) are 75 cc and 105 cc, respectively.

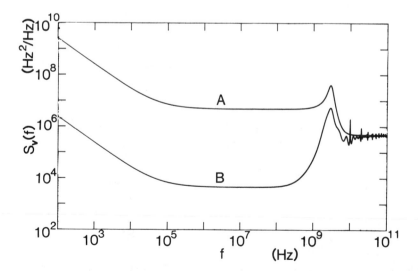

Figure 4.26 Calculated power spectral density of the FM noise of the laser modules in Figure 4.25 (from [48]): *A* is free-running; *B* is under optical feedback.

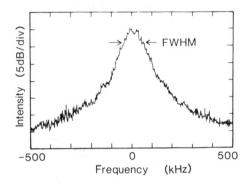

Figure 4.27 Field spectral profile of a 0.67 μm wavelength AlGaInP laser by optical feedback method of Figure 4.19 (from [15]).

Because the optical feedback is destabilized by the change in optical path length between the laser and external reflector, negative electrical feedback has to be used to stabilize the optical path length. For this stabilization and further FM noise reduction, negative electrical feedback was applied to the optical feedback laser, as is shown in Figure 4.28 [49]. A reflection mode of a high-finesse Fabry-Perot cavity ($F = 34,500$) was used as a frequency demodulator for the negative electrical feedback. The feedback signal was applied simultaneously to the injection current of the laser

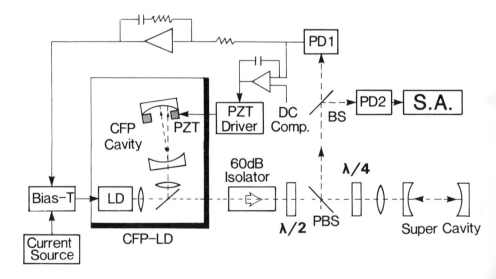

Figure 4.28 Experimental setup of the negative electrical feedback of the optically fedback AlGaAs laser (from [49]).

and the PZT of the Fabry-Perot interferometer used for the optical feedback. Note for the optimum design of a negative electrical feedback loop that the FM efficiency of the laser was reduced as a result of this optical feedback. As is seen from Figure 4.29 [55], the bandwidth of this decrease was given by half the resonance linewidth of the Fabry-Perot interferometer; that is, $\Delta\nu_{FP}/2$. By taking into account this decrease in FM efficiency, the negative electrical feedback loop with a gain of 50 dB and 0 dB-bandwidth wider than 1 MHz was designed.

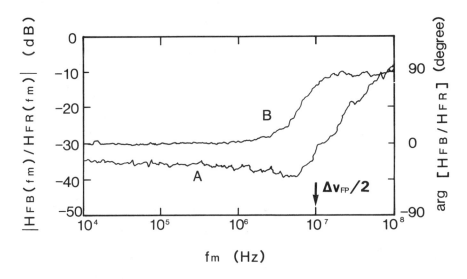

Figure 4.29 Measured FM transfer function $H_{FB}(f_m)$ of an optically fedback laser by the method of Figure 4.19, normalized to that of the free-running laser $H_{FR}(f_m)$ (from [55] © 1990 IEEE).

Figure 4.30 shows the experimental results [49]. The power spectral density of the FM noise was measured down to a Fourier frequency range of 50 mHz for accurate evaluation of low FM noise components; the results are shown separately in Figures 4.30(a) and (b). Comparison of curves A and B in Figure 4.30(a) shows that the negative electrical feedback could realize a maximum FM noise reduction as high as 50 dB at the Fourier frequency of 10 kHz. Although the IM noise of the laser still formed the FM noise reduction limit (curve C), we can confirm that a very low FM noise was obtained, and the optically fed-back laser remained very stable. Figure 4.31 represents the square root of the Allan variance calculated by substituting the values of the curves in Figure 4.30 into eq. (AII.8) [49]. Curves A, B, and C are for the free-running laser, optically fed-back laser, and optically and electrically fed-back laser, respectively. Comparison of curves B and C shows a large improvement in frequency stability after adding a negative electrical feedback loop to the optically fed-back laser.

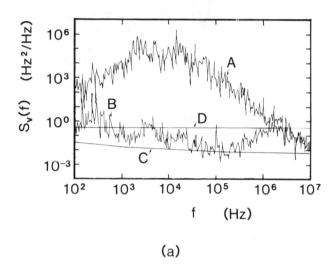

(a)

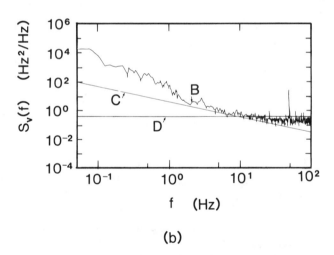

(b)

Figure 4.30 Power spectral density of the FM noise of the optically fedback laser of Figure 4.19: A is the optically fedback laser, B is the optically fedback laser with a negative electrical feedback, C is the contribution of the laser's IM noise to limit FM noise detection, D is the FM noise level of a 1-Hz linewidth Lorentzian field spectrum; (a) and (b) represent the noise magnitude for the Fourier frequencies of 100 Hz $\leqslant f \leqslant$ 10 MHz and 50 mHz $\leqslant f \leqslant$ 100 Hz, respectively (from [49]).

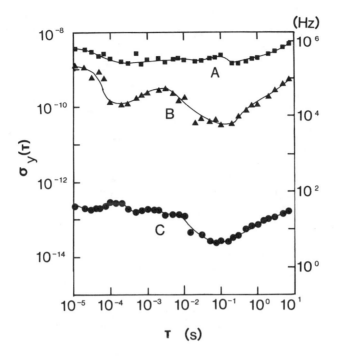

Figure 4.31 The square root of the Allan variance: *A* is a free-running laser, *B* is an optically fed-back laser, *C* is the value estimated by using curves *B* of Figures 4.30(a) and (b) (from [49]).

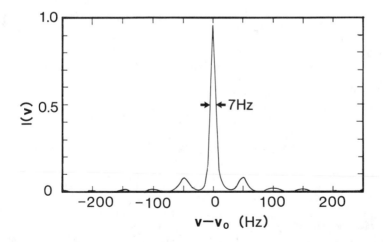

Figure 4.32 Field spectral profile estimated by curves *B* of Figures 4.30(a) and (b) (from [49]).

Figure 4.32 shows the field spectral profile of the optically fed-back laser under negative electrical feedback. This profile was obtained by substituting the value of curve *B* in Figure 4.30 into (AII.9). The FWHM of this profile is as low as 7 Hz with a power concentration ratio as high as 98% within the feedback bandwidth. This narrow linewidth is comparable to carefully stabilized gas or solid-state lasers. Lines *D* in Figures 4.30(a) and (b) represent the FM noise magnitude corresponding to the 1 Hz Lorentzian field spectral profile, which was estimated by using (AII.9). We see that the FM noise magnitude given by curve *B* is lower than that of line *D* for the Fourier frequency range of 10 Hz $\leq f \leq$ 1 MHz. This means that the field spectral profile can be regarded as subHertz if this laser system is used for applications that operate within the frequency range 10 Hz $\leq f \leq$ 1 MHz. Further FM noise reduction is expected by suppressing the contribution of the laser's IM noise by using a balanced receiver.

REFERENCES

[1] Ohtsu, M., "Realization of Ultrahigh Coherence in Semiconductor Lasers by Negative Electrical Feedback," *IEEE J. Lightwave Technology,* Vol. 6, No. 2, February 1988, pp. 245–256.
[2] Ohtsu, M., "Realization of Hyper-Coherent Light," *Science,* March 1989, pp. 64–73 [in Japanese].
[3] Ohtsu, M., H. Kotani, and H. Tagawa, "Spectral Measurements of NH_3 and H_2O for Pollutant Gas Monitoring by 1.5 μm InGaAsP/InP Lasers," *Japan J. of Applied Physics,* Vol. 22, No. 10, October 1983, pp. 1553–1557.
[4] Fukuoka, K., M. Ohtsu, and T. Tako, "Accurate Wavelength Measurements of the Absorption Lines in H_2O Vapor by a 0.8 μm AlGaAs Laser," *Japan J. of Applied Physics,* Vol. 23, No. 2, February 1984, pp. L117–L120.
[5] Kinugawa, S., H. Sasada, and K. Uehara, "Detection of C_2H_2 Absorption Lines with 1.5 μm DFB Lasers," Extended Abstracts, 49th Autumn Meeting, 1988, Japan Society of Applied Physics, October 1988, paper number 6pQ12 [in Japanese].
[6] Sasada, H., "1.5 μm DFB Semiconductor Laser Spectroscopy of HCN," *J. of Chemistry and Physics,* Vol. 88, No. 2, January 1988, pp. 767–777.
[7] Tsuchida, H., M. Ohtsu, T. Tako, M. Kuramochi, and N. Oura, "Frequency Stabilization of AlGaAs Semiconductor Laser Based on the [85]Rb-D_2 Line," *Japan J. of Applied Physics,* Vol. 21, No. 9, September 1982, pp. L561–L563.
[8] Hashimoto, M., and M. Ohtsu, "Laser Spectroscopy and Frequency Stabilization of a Semiconductor Laser for a [87]Rb Atomic Clock," *Trans. IEE Japan,* Vol. 108-C, No. 9, September 1988, pp. 706–712 [in Japanese].
[9] Yabuzaki, T., A. Ibaraki, H. Hori, M. Kitano, and T. Ogawa, "Frequency-Locking of a GaAlAs Laser to a Doppler-Free Spectrum of the Cs-D_2 Line," *Japan J. of Applied Physics,* Vol. 20, No. 6, June 1981, pp. L451–L454.
[10] Yamaguchi, S., and M. Suzuki, "Frequency Stabilization of a Diode Laser by Use of the Optogalvanic Effect," *Applied Physics Letters,* Vol. 41, No. 7, October 1982, pp. 597–598.
[11] Chung, Y.C., "Frequency-Locking of a 1.3 μm DFB Laser Using a Miniature Argon Glow Lamp," *IEEE Photonics Technology Letters,* Vol. 1, No. 2, February 1989, pp. 135–136.
[12] Ohtsu, M., and E. Ikegami, "Frequency Stabilization of 1.5 μm DFB Laser Using Internal Second Harmonic Generation and Atomic [87]Rb Line," *Electronics Letters,* Vol. 25, No. 1, January 1989, pp. 22–23.

[13] Baldwin, G.C., *An Introduction to Nonlinear Optics,* Plenum Press, New York, 1969.

[14] Ikegami, E., H. Kusuzawa, K. Nakagawa, and M. Ohtsu, "Nonlinear Organic Waveguides for a LD-based Optical Sweep Generator I (Frequency Tracking)," Extended Abstracts, 50th Autumn Meeting, 1989, Japan Society of Applied Physics, September 1989, paper number 28pZP16 [in Japanese].

[15] Ohtsu, M., H. Suzuki, K. Nemoto, and Y. Teramachi, "Narrow-Linewidth Tunable Visible InGaAlP Laser, Application to Spectral Measurements of Lithium, and Power Amplification," *Japan J. of Applied Physics,* Vol. 29, No. 8, August 1990, pp. L1463–L1465.

[16] Ohtsu, M., "Frequency Stabilization in Semiconductor Lasers," *Opt. Quantum Electronics,* Vol. 20, No. 4, July 1988, pp. 283–300.

[17] Belenov, M.E., V.L. Velichanskii, A.S. Zibrov, G.T. Pak, T.V. Petrakova, N.V. Senkov, V.A. Sautenkov, A.V. Uskov, and A.K. Chernyshev, "Spectral Characteristics of an Injection Laser with an Intracavity Absorption Cell," *Soviet J. of Quantum Electronics,* Vol. 18, No. 9, September 1989, pp. 1076–1080.

[18] Schuurmans, M.F.H., "The Fluorescence of Atoms near a Glass Surface," *Contemporary Physics,* Vol. 21, No. 5, September/October 1980, pp. 463–482.

[19] Velichanskii, V.L., A.S. Zibrov, V.V. Nikitin, V.A. Sautenkov, V.K. Malyshev, and G.G. Kharisov, "Semiconductor Laser with ^{133}Cs Vapor External Selective Mirror," *Soviet J. of Quantum Electronics,* Vol. 8, No. 7, July 1979, pp. 836–839.

[20] Ikegami, T., S. Ohshima, and M. Ohtsu, "Frequency Stabilization of Laser Diodes to the Cs-D_2 Line with the Zeeman Modulation Method," *Japan J. of Applied Physics,* Vol. 28, No. 10, October 1989, pp. L1839–L1841.

[21] Pevtshin, V., and S. Ezekiel, "Investigation of Absolute Stability of Water-Vapor-Stabilized Semiconductor Laser," *Optics Letters,* Vol. 12, No. 3, March 1987, pp. 172–174.

[22] Furuta, H., and M. Ohtsu, "Evaluation of Frequency Shift and Stability in Rubidium Vapor Stabilized Semiconductor Lasers," *Applied Optics,* Vol. 28, No. 17, September 1989, pp. 3737–3743.

[23] Hils, D., and J.L. Hall, "Ultra-Stable Cavity-Stabilized Lasers with Sub-Hertz Linewidth," *Frequency Standards and Metrology,* Proc. of the Fourth Symp., Ancona, Italy, September 5–9, 1988, ed. A. De Marchi, Springer Verlag, Berlin, 1989, pp. 162–173.

[24] Ohtsu, M., M. Hashimoto, and H. Ozawa, "A Highly Stabilized Semiconductor Laser and Its Application to Optically Pumped Rb Atomic Clock," Proc. 39th Annual Symp. Frequency Control, May 1985, Philadelphia, pp. 43–53.

[25] Favre, F., and D. Le Guen, "Emission Frequency Stability in Single Mode-Fibre Optical Feedback Controlled Semiconductor Lasers," *Electronics Letters,* Vol. 19, No. 17, August 1983, pp. 663–665.

[26] Okazaki, H., M. Ohtsu, and T. Tako, "Frequency Control of Semiconductor Laser Using a Microcomputer," *Trans. IECE,* Vol. J67-C, April 1984, pp. 651–655.

[27] Ohtsu, M., M. Murata, and M. Kourogi, "FM Noise Reduction and Subkilohertz Linewidth of an AlGaAs Laser by Negative Electrical Feedback," *IEEE J. Quantum Electronics,* Vol. QE-26, No. 2, November 1990, pp. 231–241.

[28] Ohtsu, M., and N. Tabuchi, "Electrical Feedback and Its Network Analysis for Linewidth Reduction of a Semiconductor Laser," *IEEE J. Lightwave Technology,* Vol. 6, No. 3, March 1988, pp. 357–369.

[29] Osinski, M., and J. Buus, "Linewidth Broadening Factor in Semiconductor Lasers—an Overview," *IEEE J. Quantum Electronics,* Vol. QE-23, No. 1, January 1987, pp. 9–29.

[30] Allan, D.W., "Statistics of Atomic Frequency Standards," *Proc. IEEE,* Vol. 54, No. 2, February 1966, pp. 221–230.

[31] Kuboki, K., and M. Ohtsu, "The Allan Variance Real-Time Processing System for Frequency Stability Measurement of Semiconductor Lasers," *IEEE Trans. on Instruments and Measurements,* Vol. 39, No. 4, August 1990, pp. 637–641.

[32] Okai, M., T. Tsuchiya, and N. Chinone, 'Ultra-Narrow Spectral Linewidth (56 kHz) Corrugation-

Pitch-Modulated Multi-Quantum-Well Distributed Feedback Lasers," *Technical Digest of Conference on Lasers and Electro-Optics* (CLEO '91), Baltimore, 1991, paper number CPDP40.

[33] Kourogi, M., C. -H. Shin, and M. Ohtsu, "A 250 Hz Spectral Linewidth 1.5 μm-MQW-DFB Laser Diode with Negative-Electrical Feedback," IEEE Photonics Technology Letter, Vol. 3, No. 6, June 1991, in press.

[34] Mooradian, A., "High Resolution Tunable Infrared Lasers," *Laser Spectroscopy,* ed. R.G. Brewer and A. Mooradian, Plenum Press, New York, 1973, pp. 223–236.

[35] Shimoda, K., T. Yajima, Y. Ueda, and T. Kasuya, *Quantum Electronics,* Syokabo Publishing, Tokyo, 1972 [in Japanese].

[36] Lang, R., "Injection Locking Properties of a Semiconductor Laser," *IEEE J. Quantum Electronics,* Vol. QE-18, No. 6, June 1982, pp. 976–983.

[37] Kobayashi, S., and T. Kimura, "Injection Locking in AlGaAs Semiconductor Laser," *IEEE J. Quantum Electronics,* Vol. QE-17, No. 5, May 1981, pp. 681–689.

[38] Lenstra, D., B.H. Verbeek, and A.J. den Boef, "Coherence Collapse in Single-Mode Semiconductor Lasers due to Optical Feedback," *IEEE J. Quantum Electronics,* Vol. QE-21, No. 6, June 1985, pp. 674–679.

[39] Tromborg, B., J.H. Osmudsen, and H. Olessen, "Stability Analysis for a Semiconductor Laser in an External Cavity," *IEEE J. Quantum Electronics,* Vol. QE-20, No. 9, September 1984, pp. 1023–1032.

[40] Olsson, N.A. and J.P. Van der Ziel, "Performance Characteristics of 1.5 μm External Cavity Semiconductor Lasers for Coherent Optical Communication," *IEEE J. Lightwave Technology,* Vol. LT-5, No. 4, April 1987, pp. 510–515.

[41] Mehuys, D., M. Mittelstein, A. Yariv, R. Sarafaty, and J.E. Unger, "Optimized Fabry-Perot (AlGa)As Quantum-Well Lasers Tunable over 105 nm," *Electronics Letters,* Vol. 25, No. 2, January 1989, pp. 143–145.

[42] Vahala, K., K. Kyuma, A. Yariv, S.K. Kwong, M. Cronin-Golomb, and K.Y. Kau, "Narrow Linewidth, Single Frequency Semiconductor Laser with a Phase Conjugate External Cavity Mirror," *Applied Physics Letters,* Vol. 49, No. 23, December 1986, pp. 1563–1565.

[43] Ohtsu, M., I. Koshiishi, and Y. Teramachi, "A Semiconductor Laser as a Stable Phase Conjugate Mirror for Linewidth Reduction of Another Semiconductor Laser," *Japan J. of Applied Physics,* Vol. 29, No. 11, December 1990, pp. L2060–L2062.

[44] Suzuki, H., Master thesis, Tokyo Institute of Technology, 1991.

[45] Awaji, A., Bachelor thesis, Tokyo Institute of Technology, 1991.

[46] Provost, J.G., and R. Frey, "Cavity-Enhanced Highly Nondegenerate Four-Wave Mixing in GaAlAs Semiconductor Lasers," *Applied Physics Letters,* Vol. 55, No. 6, August 1989, pp. 519–521.

[47] Dahmani, B., L. Hollberg, and R. Drullinger, "Frequency Stabilization of Semiconductor Laser by Resonant Optical Feedback," *Optics Letters,* Vol. 12, No. 11, November 1987, pp. 876–878.

[48] Shin, C.-H., Ph.D. thesis, Tokyo Institute of Technology, 1991.

[49] Shin, C.-H., and M. Ohtsu, "Stable Semiconductor Laser with 7 Hz Linewidth by an Optical-Electrical Double Feedback Technique," *Optics Letters,* Vol. 15, No. 24, December 1990, pp. 1455–1457.

[50] Ohtsu, M., "A Frequency Modulatable Narrow-Linewidth Semiconductor Laser," Tech. Rep IEICE of Japan, Tokyo, December 1987, paper number OQE87-135 [in Japanese].

[51] Hollberg, L., and M. Ohtsu, "Modulatable Narrow-Linewidth Semiconductor Lasers," *Applied Physics Letters,* Vol. 35, No. 11, September 1988, pp. 944–946.

[52] Baums, D., W. Elsasser, and E.O. Gobel, "Farey Tree and Devil's Staircase of a Modulated External-Cavity Semiconductor Laser," *Physics Review Letters,* Vol. 63, No. 2, July 1989, pp. 155–158.

[53] Fujii, H., T. Shiragaki, M. Morimoto, T. Kobayashi, and T. Sueta, "Sub-harmonic Mode Locking of a Semiconductor Laser," Extended Abstracts, 36th Spring Meeting, 1989, Japan Society of Applied Physics, Related Soc., paper number 2pX1 [in Japanese].

[54] Shin, C.-H., M. Teshima, and M. Ohtsu, "Novel Measurement Method of Linewidth Enhancement Factor in Semiconductor Lasers by Optical Self-Locking," *Electronics Letters,* Vol. 25, No. 1, January 1989, pp. 27–28.

[55] Shin, C.-H., M. Teshima, M. Ohtsu, T. Imai, J. Yoshida, and K. Nishide, "FM Characteristics and Compact Modules for Coherent Semiconductor Lasers Coupled to an External Cavity," *IEEE Photonics Technology Letters,* Vol. 2, No. 3, March 1990, pp. 167–169.

Chapter 5

OPTICAL PHASE LOCKING AND FREQUENCY SWEEP

Optical frequency-phase synchronization (i.e., the optical frequency locking or *optical phase locking* (OPLL)), of several lasers is essential in realizing a chain of the highly coherent lasers that can be used for various applications. The frequency sweep of a coherent laser also is essential for a light source emitting light in various colors, from infrared to ultraviolet wavelengths. This chapter reviews the use of these two techniques in semiconductor lasers.

5.1 OPTICAL-PHASE AND FREQUENCY-LOCKED LOOPS

Optical phase locking is an important basic technology for achieving the following applications [1]:

1. Coherent optical communication systems employing coherent homodyne-heterodyne detection of *phase shift keying* (PSK) and *amplitude shift keying* (ASK) modulation (homodyne and heterodyne OPLLs).
2. Precise optical measurements such as spectroscopy, frequency chain for frequency measurements [2], interferometric measurements [3], and so forth (heterodyne and homodyne OPLLs).
3. Optical frequency sweep generator (optical frequency synthesizer) with very precise frequency tracking performance (heterodyne OPLL).
4. Frequency stabilization of a laser by locking it to a stable master laser (homodyne and heterodyne OPLLs).
5. Timing stabilization of a mode-locked laser [4] (pulsed OPLL).
6. Coherent combination of two mutually heterodyne phase-locked laser beams to be used as a two-frequency coherent light source for optical measurements [5].
7. The multiple heterodyne OPLLs with an offset frequency to generate coherent optical pulses [6–8] (heterodyne OPLL).

The pioneering work in optical phase locking was carried out in the 1960s by using He-Ne lasers [9] (and listed in Ref. 4 of [10]). In the 1980s, extensive experimental studies began on homodyne and heterodyne optical phase locking for application in coherent optical communication and high resolution spectroscopy. In this section, we review the basic operating principles and the status of research in optical phase-locked loops.

In a *phase-locked loop* (PLL), as shown in Figure 5.1(a), the phase of the output signal of the slave oscillator, that is, a *voltage controlled oscillator* (VCO), is locked to that of the input signal from a master oscillator. These two signals are phase compared with each other by a phase detector whose output signal is proportional to the phase difference between them. This phase error signal is low-pass filtered by a loop filter and then applied to the frequency modulation input of the VCO. Thus, the output phase of the VCO follows the phase of the input signal. The OPLL shown in Figure 5.1(b) works under the same operating principle except that the phase detector, VCO, and input and output signals are replaced by the photo detector, the slave

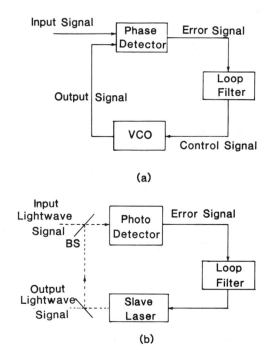

(a)

(b)

Figure 5.1 Block diagrams of phase-locked loops to explain the differences between (a) a conventional microwave standard PLL and (b) an optical PLL: *Bs* is a beam splitter; the signal paths represented by solid lines and dashed lines are for electrical signals and lightwave signals, respectively.

laser, and input and output lightwave signals from the master and slave lasers. Figure 5.1 presents a homodyne PLL, because the frequency of the output signal from the VCO is exactly the same as that of the input signal. By this OPLL, the slave laser can be frequency or phase locked to a frequency or phase-stable master laser. Although injection locking [11–14] can be used for phase locking as well, this technique requires a high-power master laser. Therefore, OPLL can be a better solution to synchronize the master and slave lasers. Note that the power of the highly stable master laser is generally weak, as a considerable portion of power is used for frequency stabilization (e.g., for the optical frequency discrimination at the optical frequency reference) and multistage optical isolation from back reflection from external reflectors. In particular, the power of the master laser (signal power) in coherent optical communication receivers usually is very low after the long transmission through an optical fiber.

Experiments on homodyne OPLL have been carried out by using He-Ne lasers [9], CO_2 lasers [15], free-running semiconductor lasers [16, 17], semiconductor laser-pumped Nd:YAG lasers [18, 19], optically frequency-stabilized semiconductor lasers [20], a He-Ne laser and an optically stabilized semiconductor laser [21], and semiconductor lasers by negative electrical feedback [17]. Except for [16] and [17], optical phase locking was achieved by a loop natural frequency smaller than 100 kHz because of low FM noise of the lasers used in the experiments. In using the free-running semiconductor lasers, an employed loop natural frequency was higher than 10 MHz. The maximum loop bandwidth reported so far was 134 MHz [17]. However, even in this case, the phase error variance was considerably large because of the high magnitude of FM noise in free-running semiconductor lasers.

In the heterodyne PLL (see Figure 5.2), the phase difference between the input signal and the output signal from the VCO is locked to a stable reference phase from a highly stable microwave oscillator, by which the VCO can generate the signal with one frequency of (the input frequency ν_M) $\pm$ (the output frequency from the reference oscillator ν_R). For the frequency down-conversion, the heterodyne OPLL employs a photodetector whereas a frequency mixer is used in the microwave PLL. This is the only difference between optical and microwave PLLs. Inserting a frequency divider between the *band pass filter* (BPF) and the phase detector or a frequency multiplier between the VCO and the mixer, the output frequency of the VCO can be selected with a wide variety. Therefore, the heterodyne PLL has been called an *indirect loop*, a *frequency translation loop*, and a *frequency offset-locked loop*. The heterodyne PLL, therefore, is an indispensable tool for frequency synthesis and also important in applications to coherent receivers in communication systems.

Figures 5.2 (a) and (b) represent equivalent systems because the same equations govern their phase locking operations. However, the systems have two main advantages compared with the standard PLL. One is that the phase detector works with signals at the frequency ν_R, which can be far lower than the frequency ν_S of the VCO, as we can see in Figure 5.2. Another is that a narrow bandpass filter can be used (i.e., the loop is ac-coupled), thus improving the signal-to-noise ratio. However, the bandwidth of the bandpass filter must be sufficiently wider than that of the PLL to prevent sacrificing the loop response. In the heterodyne OPLL, shown in Figure 5.2(c), the former is more advantageous because well-developed microwave phase detectors can be employed in phase locking between optical signals.

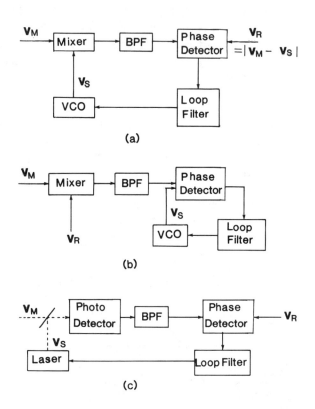

Figure 5.2 Heterodyne phase-locked loops: (a) block diagram of a heterodyne PLL; (b) equivalent model of (a); (c) block diagram of a heterodyne OPLL; *BPF* is a band pass filter.

Experiments on heterodyne OPLL have been carried out by using optically frequency-stabilized semiconductor lasers [22–24], free-running semiconductor lasers [25–28], Nd:YAG lasers [29], He-Ne lasers [10], and a dye laser and a He-Ne laser [30]. The theoretical background of OPLLs is summarized in Appendix V, which can be used as design criteria for heterodyne and homodyne OPLLs.

5.1.1 Heterodyne Optical Phase-Locked Loop

The heterodyne OPLL is known as the frequency offset locking [25–27], translation loop [31], indirect loop [32], and so on. Its advantages include the following [33]:

1. Very precise frequency tracking is possible, which can be superior to a frequency-tracking loop by FM feedback [34].
2. A well-developed microwave phase comparator can be used to detect the phase difference between two lasers at the reference frequency ν_R, which determines the heterodyne frequency.
3. The loop can be coupled to an ac source. This means that a bandpass filter can be used at the input stage of the phase comparator to reject dc drifts at the photodetector and then to increase the signal-to-noise ratio.
4. The slave laser frequency can be swept precisely by sweeping the ν_R, which means that the heterodyne OPLL will be the key technique for an optical-frequency sweep generator in the near future.

Heterodyne Optical Frequency Locking

Figure 5.3 shows an experimental setup using two 0.83 μm AlGaAs lasers [1]. The master laser is a confocal Fabry-Perot cavity-coupled semiconductor laser (CFP-laser) as shown in Figure 4.19, whereas the slave laser is used in a free-running condition. After the heterodyne signal is detected by an *avalanche photodiode* (APD), it is amplified by a wideband ac amplifier. The frequency of the amplified heterodyne signal is divided by a digital frequency divider with a division rate of 10, and the frequency-divided heterodyne signal is phase-frequency compared with a stable microwave signal from a microwave synthesizer by a digital *phase-frequency comparator* (PFC). The maximum operating frequency of the PFC is 30 MHz, which means that the maximum allowable frequency of the heterodyne signal is 300 MHz. This maximum allowable frequency can be increased to the value limited by the response speed of the APD if the heterodyne signal detected by the APD is frequency down-converted to a value less than 300 MHz by heterodyning with another microwave signal (from the Osc. No. 2 of Figure 5.3). The active-phase comparison range of the digital PFC is $\pm 2\pi$ with linearity over the entire range, and the PFC provides sweep-frequency acquisition capabilities if the loop is unlocked [35]. The phase-frequency error signal is passed through a first-order active loop filter whose transfer function is $F(s) = (1 + s/R_2C)/(s/R_1C)$. The injection current of the slave laser was controlled by the low-pass filtered phase-frequency error signal via a current source for slower component of error signal ($f < 1$ kHz) and a bias-T circuit for faster component ($f \geq 1$ kHz).

The performance of the loop was evaluated by measuring the frequency stability of the phase-locked heterodyne signal by the Allan variance real-time process-

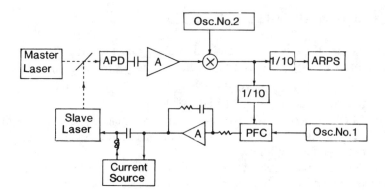

Figure 5.3 Experimental setup of heterodyne OPLL (frequency offset locking): PFC is the phase-frequency comparator, *Osc.* is a microwave oscillator, APD is the avalanche photodiode, *ARPS* is the Allan variance real-time processing system, *A* is a wideband ac amplifier (from [1]).

ing system version 6 (ARPS6 [36], see Appendix III). The linewidth ($\Delta\nu_M + \Delta\nu_S$) of the heterodyne signal was about 15 MHz, which was nearly equal to $\Delta\nu_S$, because $\Delta\nu_s \gg \Delta\nu_M$. The power of the master laser P_M used for phase locking was about 10 μW. From the calculated result of Appendix V and using these values, the optimum natural frequency was found to be larger than 1 GHz. However, it was rather difficult to choose such a high natural frequency because of the loop delay time and the bandwidth of commercially available analog amplifiers.

Comparing the spectral profile of heterodyne signals in a phase-locked condition with that in an unlocked condition, the spectral profile was found considerably cleaned and its center frequency was locked precisely to the frequency of the reference signal; however, its linewidth was not reduced. From this, even though the heterodyne signal was not phase locked, it was confirmed to be successfully frequency locked to the microwave reference signal with a bandwidth much narrower than $\Delta\nu_M + \Delta\nu_S$. To evaluate the frequency tracking capability of the heterodyne frequency-locked loop, the square root of Allan variances $\sigma_y^2(\tau)$ of the heterodyne frequency, unlocked and frequency locked, have been measured by ARPS 6. The measured results are shown in Figure 5.4. The value of $\sigma_y(\tau)$ in a frequency-locked state can be least-square approximated as

$$\sigma_y(\tau) = 3.2 \times 10^{-14}\tau^{-1} \tag{5.1}$$

where τ is the integration time. The minimum value of $\sigma_y(\tau)$ is 6.0×10^{-16} at $\tau = 50$ s. This means that the minimum frequency tracking error was 0.22 Hz at $\tau = 50$ s, because the nominal frequency ν_0 was 3.6×10^{14} Hz.

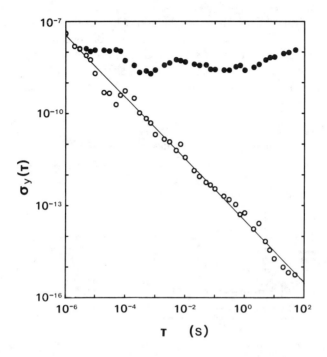

Figure 5.4 Square root of Allan variances of the heterodyne signal under unlocked (closed circles) and frequency-locked (open circles) conditions (from [1]).

Heterodyne Optical Phase-Locked Loop

Figure 5.5 shows an experimental setup of a heterodyne OPLL [33]. The 0.83 μm CFP-lasers are used as master and slave lasers in the experiment. The PZT and the injection current frequency tuning coefficients are 79 MHz/V and 31 MHz/mA, respectively. The spectral linewidth of the heterodyne signal and the heterodyne frequency drift are measured as narrower than 13 kHz and less than 100 kHz/s, respectively.

Two Si-APD's used for detecting the heterodyne signal act only as optical frequency down-converters. However, the shot noise generated by detecting process became a major source of the phase error. The first and second APDs are used for OPLL and for the phase error measurement, respectively. The power of 3.7 μW of each laser is used for the OPLL. The heterodyne signal is phase-frequency compared with the reference microwave signal from a stable RF local oscillator by a digital PFC, which consists of a high-speed voltage comparator and an ECL PFC IC chip. The maximum operating frequency of this PFC is 70 MHz. Figure 5.6 shows the block diagram of the PFC and a first-order active loop filter used in this experiment. The control signal at the output of the loop filter is divided by two and fed back to the slave laser via a PZT driver for slow components of the control signal and injection current for fast components of the control signal. RF attenuators are used for adjusting the balance between the gains of these two control routes.

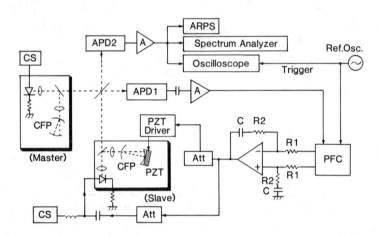

Figure 5.5 Experimental arrangement of the heterodyne OPLL of CFP lasers: *LD* is a semiconductor laser diode, *CS* is the current source, *CFP* is a confocal Fabry-Perot cavity (finesse of 50, free spectral range 1.5 GHz), *APD* is an avalanche photodiode, *A* is an amplifier with 40 dB gain, PFC is a phase-frequency comparator, *ARPS* is the Allan variance real-time processing system (ARPS 8), *Att* is an RF attenuator (from [33] © 1990 IEEE).

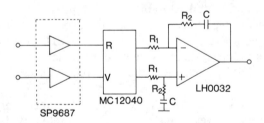

Figure 5.6 Block diagram of the phase-frequency comparator and the loop filter (from [1]).

Figure 5.7 shows a spectral shape of phase-locked heterodyne signal measured by an RF spectrum analyzer. Figure 5.7(a) confirms that the frequency-phase noise components are drastically reduced within the range of about 1 MHz from the center frequency of the spectral shape. Figure 5.7(b) shows the magnified spectral shape observed with a span of 1 kHz and a 30 Hz resolution bandwidth, which is the minimum resolution bandwidth of the spectrum analyzer used in this measurement.

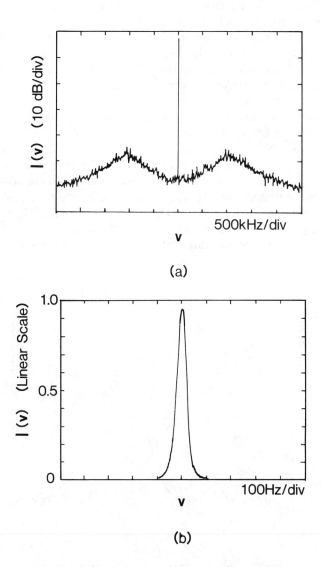

(a)

(b)

Figure 5.7 Field spectral lineshape of the heterodyne signal under phase locking condition. The total frequency span, the sweep time and the resolution bandwidth of (a) are 5 MHz, 15 s and 1 kHz, respectively. Those of (b) are 1 kHz, 15 s and 30 Hz, respectively. The center frequency of the heterodyne signal is 25 MHz (from [33] © 1990 IEEE).

This figure also confirms that its linewidth is maintained to a value nearly equal to this resolution bandwidth. This means that the deconvoluted linewidth of the phase-locked heterodyne signal is nearly equal to that of the microwave reference signal; that is, several mHz. Furthermore, by comparing the spectral shape of the phase-locked heterodyne signal with that of the reference RF signal, we find that both spectral shapes have the same linewidth and S/N ratio as shown in Figure 5.8(a) and (b). This means that the optical phase locking of the heterodyne signal and the reference signal have been carried out successfully by this OPLL. In particular, the same S/N ratio means that the performance of this OPLL reaches the limit determined by the spectral quality of the reference RF signal.

To measure the magnitude of residual phase fluctuations, its waveform is observed by an oscilloscope triggered by the reference signal. This method was first employed to evaluate the performance of a heterodyne OPLL of gas lasers [10], which is an application of measurement method of short-term frequency fluctuations in a laser by an oscilloscope [37]. Comparing Figs. 5.9(a) and (b), we can confirm that the heterodyne signal is successfully phase locked to the reference signal. The rms residual phase fluctuations are estimated to be less than 0.1 rad by measuring the timing jitter of the waveform of the phase-locked heterodyne signal. The phase error variance σ_ϕ^2 was less than 1.0×10^{-2} rad^2 within the bandwidth of the

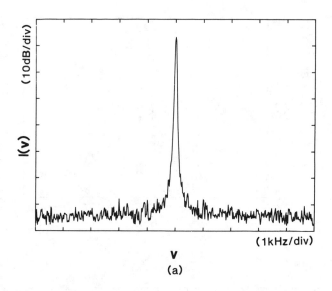

Figure 5.8 Field spectral line shape of (a) the reference signal and (b) the heterodyne signal under phase locking condition. The total frequency span, the sweep time, and the resolution bandwidth are 1 MHz, 10 s and 10 kHz, respectively (from [1]).

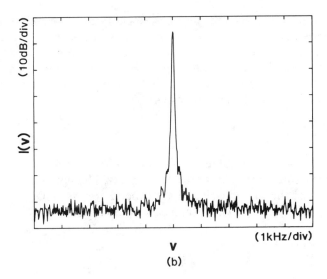

Figure 5.8 continued

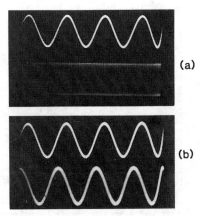

Figure 5.9 The heterodyne signals (lower traces) observed in the time domain by an rf oscilloscope under (a) unlocked and (b) phase-locked conditions; in both, the upper traces are the triggering signals from the reference signal, to which the heterodyne signal was locked (from [33] © 1990 IEEE).

oscilloscope of 150 MHz. However, note that this value does not contain the phase noise of the reference microwave signal because the oscilloscope is triggered by this signal.

To quantitatively evaluate the phase locking performance and frequency-tracking error between two lasers in the time domain, the $\sigma_y(\tau)$ of residual frequency fluctuations of the heterodyne signal, normalized to the nominal laser frequency ν_0, is measured by the *Allan variance real-time processing system, version 8* (ARPS 8, see Appendix III). The measured results are shown in Figure 5.10, approximated by the solid line in this figure and expressed as

$$\sigma_y(\tau) = 6.3 \times 10^{-17}\tau^{-1} \tag{5.2}$$

In particular, the minimum value of $\sigma_y(\tau)$ was 1.1×10^{-18} at $\tau = 70$ s, which corresponds to the frequency tracking error of 0.4 mHz. The stability of the heterodyne signal is at almost the same level as that of the reference signal, as shown by the dashed curve of Figure 5.10, which can be approximated as

$$\sigma_y(\tau) = 3.7 \times 10^{-17}\tau^{-1} \tag{5.3}$$

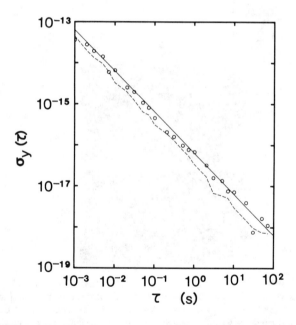

Figure 5.10 Measured values of residual frequency fluctuations of the heterodyne signal: $\sigma_y(\tau)$ and τ are the square root of Allan variance and the integration time, respectively. The values of $\sigma_y(\tau)$ are normalized to the nominal optical frequency ν_0 of the lasers used in this experiment. Open circles and the dashed curve are the measured results for the phase-locked heterodyne and the reference signals, respectively. The solid line is the least-square fitted approximation to the results of the phase-locked heterodyne signal (from [1]).

These results show a very high phase-tracking capability between two lasers by this OPLL.

The phase error variance of the OPLL is estimated by the sum of the following terms:

1. The phase error variance measured by an oscilloscope ($f <$ 150 MHz): 1.0×10^{-2} rad^2.
2. The phase error variance due to the phase noise of the reference microwave signal: 7.0×10^{-3} rad^2.
3. The phase error variance due to residual phase noise of two lasers over the measured bandwidth ($f \geqslant$ 150 MHz): 2.1×10^{-2} rad^2. This value is estimated by eq. (AV.55) of Appendix V.

Figure 5.11 shows the calculated residual phase noise variance. As we can see by this figure, the residual phase error variances for a free-running laser and a CFP laser are almost the same for the Fourier frequency $f >$ 1 GHz. The phase error variance considering the infinite bandwidth therefore is 3.8×10^{-2} rad^2. Using eq. (AII.21), the total phase-locked power of the slave laser is estimated to be about 96% that of the total power. In other words, 96% of the power of the slave laser is a replica of the master laser with respect to temporal coherence.

By comparing these three values, we confirm that the phase error of the OPLL is determined mainly by the laser phase noise and the stability of the reference RF

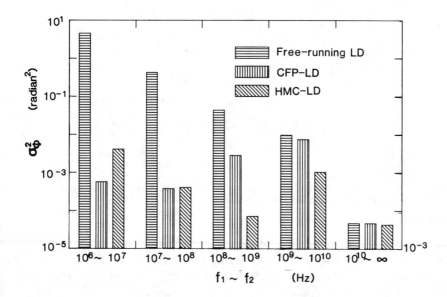

Figure 5.11 Calculated phase-error variances σ_ϕ^2 for a free-running laser, a CFP laser, and a HMC laser (from [1]).

signal. Furthermore, as we can see by Figure 5.11, a low phase error variance (i.e., lower than 1.0×10^{-2} rad^2 with a 1 MHz natural frequency) can be achieved by using *hemispherical microcavity* (HMC) lasers (see Figure 4.25) for a wide Fourier frequency range.

5.1.2 Homodyne Optical Phase-Locked Loop

Figure 5.12 shows an experimental setup [1] in which two 0.83 μm CFP lasers are used as master and slave. The phase error between the two lasers is detected by the optical balanced-phase detector shown in Figure 5.12. This is used to reject the IM noise component of the slave laser by balancing optical and electrical path lengths of two mixed beams at the beam splitter (refer also to Figure 3.16). The two beam powers are balanced by using an optical power attenuator. The detected phase error signal is fed back to the slave laser after low-pass filtering by a standard first-order active loop filter.

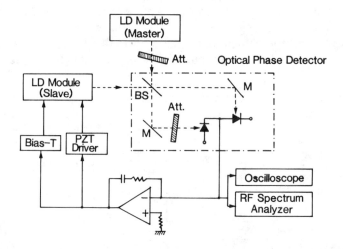

Figure 5.12 Experimental setup for the homodyne OPLL, CFP lasers are used: *BS* is a beam splitter, M is a total reflection mirror, *Att.* is an optical power attenuator (from [1]).

The natural frequency of the loop is fixed at several tens kHz~2 MHz by adjusting the power of the master laser using an optical power attenuator, as shown in Figure 5.12. By this adjustment, the loop gain was changed and the natural frequency and the damping factor of the OPLL were varied.

The output of the optical phase detector is measured by an oscilloscope and an RF spectrum analyzer to evaluate the rms and the power spectral density of phase error, respectively. Figures 5.13(a) and (b) show the output signals from the optical phase detector measured under unlocked and phase-locked conditions, respectively, which were measured by an oscilloscope with a 150 MHz bandwidth. In the unlocked condition, a beat waveform could be seen because of a frequency difference between two lasers. When the slave laser was phase locked to the master, only the phase errors appeared in the output, as shown in Figure 5.13(b), because the frequency difference became zero. The phase error variance under the phase-locked condition is estimated from these figures to be $\sigma_\phi^2 = 2.1 \times 10^{-3}$ rad ^{2}.

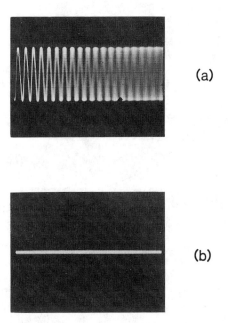

(a)

(b)

Figure 5.13 Output of the optical phase detector under (a) unlocked and (b) phase-locked conditions; the natural frequency of the loop is 1.5 MHz (from [1]).

Figure 5.14(a) shows the power spectral density of phase error of the homodyne OPLL in a phase-locked condition. The breakpoint frequency f_b of the power spectral density is about 1.5 MHz, which is on the order of the natural frequency. The power spectral densities of phase error in a phase-locked condition $S_{PN}(f)$, phase noises of the master laser $S_{PH,M}(f)$, and those of the slave laser $S_{PH,S}(f)$ are related as

$$S_{PN}(f) = [S_{PH,M}(f) + S_{PH,S}(f)] \, |1 - H(i2\pi f)|^2 \qquad (5.4)$$

where $H(i2\pi f)$ is the transfer function of the OPLL given by (AV.21). Figure 5.14(b) shows the calculated values of $[S_{PH,M}(f) + S_{PH,S}(f)]$ (curve A) and $S_{PN}(f)$ (curve

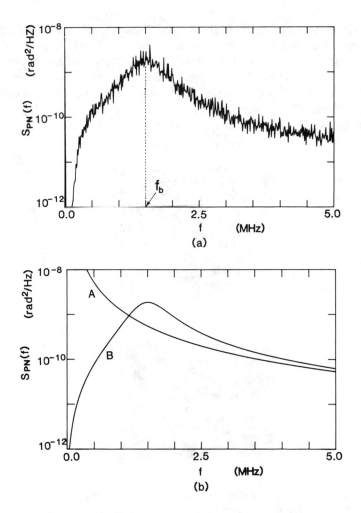

Figure 5.14 Power spectral densities of phase error under phase-locked condition: (a) measured result, (b) calculated result (curve B); curve A in (b) is the sum of power spectral densities of phase noises from the master and slave lasers, f_b is the breakpoint frequency (from [1]).

B). The measured and calculated results show good agreement as we can see by comparing Figure 5.14(a) with curve B of Figure 5.14(b).

Figure 5.15 shows calculated power spectral densities of the sum of phase noises of the master and the slave lasers (curve A) and phase error in a phase-locked condition (curve B). For comparison, the sum of the power spectral densities of phase noises of two free-running lasers (curve C) are also shown. Curves A and B of this figure are equivalent to curves A and B in Figure 5.14(b), respectively. Experi mentally measured parameters are used in the calculations. Dashed line D in this figure represents the phase noise corresponding to a 20 kHz Lorentzian linewidth, which is the estimated sum of the linewidths of the master and the slave lasers. Because the actual spectral profile is considerably different from the Lorentzian, as seen by comparing curves A and D, we can confirm that the actual phase-noise spectrum must be used to evaluate the loop performance.

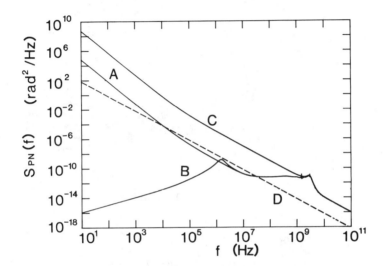

Figure 5.15 Calculated power spectral densities of phase error in a phase-locked condition (curve B) and the sum of power spectral densities of phase noises of the master and slave lasers (curve A). For comparison, the sum of power spectral densities of phase noises of two free-running LDs (curve C) is also shown. Dashed curve D represents the phase noise corresponding to a 20 kHz linewidth, which is the estimated sum of the linewidth of the master and slave lasers (from [1]).

A large amount of phase noise power remains in the range $f > 150$ MHz as can be seen by curve B of Figure 5.15. The phase error variance due to phase noises within that range is calculated as 2.05×10^{-2} rad^2. Then, the phase error variance considering an infinite bandwidth is estimated to be 2.3×10^{-2} rad^2. Using this value and (AII.21), the total phase locked power of the slave laser is estimated to be 98%.

In the preceding discussions, the contribution of shot noise to the phase error is not included because it is negligibly small. This is because the natural frequency is far below the optimal value at which the shot noise magnitude is comparable to the laser phase noise. This is readily confirmed by the calculated results given by (AV.53). The maximum loop bandwidth reported so far is 134 MHz in a homodyne OPLL using a frequency-stabilized laser by negative electrical feedback as the master laser and a free-running laser as the slave [17]. The result is shown in curve B of Figure 5.16 [17]. The phase error variance is 0.15 rad^2.

In the future optical phase locking may realize a long-term locking period by employing long-term stable and low-FM noise lasers and by developing frequency acquisition loops and harmonic locking; for example, optical phase locking between a laser and the second harmonic of another laser for application in a wideband optical sweep generator and frequency measurement systems.

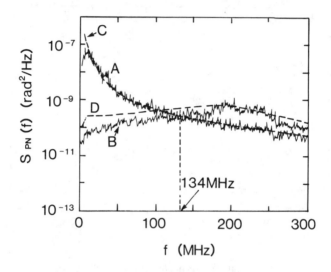

Figure 5.16 Power spectral density of an extremely fast homodyne OPLL; curves A and B show unlocked and phase-locked conditions, respectively; curves C and D are the calculated ones corresponding to curves A and B, respectively (from [17] © 1991 IEEE).

5.1.3 Other Promising Techniques

Frequency-phase locking between two different wavelengths is possible by using the techniques described in Sections 5.1.1 and 5.1.2. However, in this case, one of the lasers should be frequency converted so that the heterodyne signal frequency between the two lasers is sufficiently low to be detected by a conventional photodetector. For this frequency conversion, nonlinear optical techniques can be employed, as in the second harmonics generation of the 1.5 μm InGaAsP laser [38]. However, the frequency-converted light power usually is too low to obtain a sufficiently high heterodyne signal due to the low power of conventional semiconductor lasers. To overcome this difficulty, pump-probe spectroscopy has been employed [38]. Figure 5.17 shows an experimental setup of this spectrometer for Rb vapor by using the low-power second harmonic wave of a 1.56 μm InGaAsP laser as a probe beam and the output from a 0.78 μm AlGaAs laser as a pump beam. Figures 5.18(a) and (b) show the doppler-free spectral shapes of the Rb vapor measured simultaneously by these two beams. The frequencies of these beams were locked to the common hyperfine components of the spectral shapes by using negative electrical feedback control loops, and the frequency fluctuations were reduced, as are shown in Figures 5.19(a) and (b), which means that the two laser frequencies were mutually synchronized. By increasing the second harmonic power, a conventional heterodyne technique described in Section 5.1.1 is employed and more accurate frequency and phase tracking achieved.

The injection locking technique (see Section 4.3.2) is promising in locking the phase of the slave laser to that of the master laser. This technique is effective especially for the multilongitudinal-mode slave laser; that is, injection locking can reduce the side-mode power and enhance the main-mode power, even if the free-running slave laser oscillates with multimodes. Figure 5.20 shows an example of the side-mode suppression of a 1.5 μm InGaAsP laser with power as high as 40 mW [39]. A side-mode suppression ratio and power concentration ratio as high as 31 dB and 99.6%, respectively, were achieved. Figures 5.21(a) and (b) show the power spectral densities of FM noises of the master and the injection-locked slave lasers, respectively. We can see that the magnitudes of these power spectral densities are almost

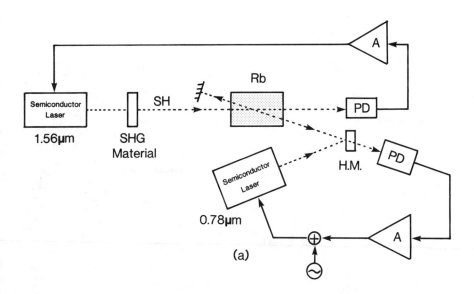

Figure 5.17 Experimental setup for pump-probe spectroscopy for Rb vapor (from [38]).

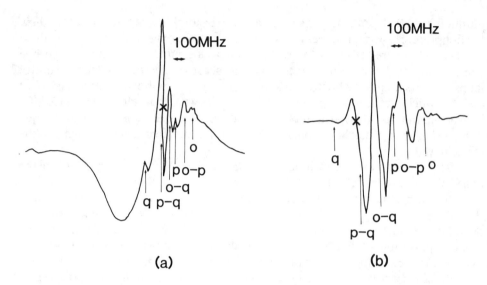

Figure 5.18 The doppler-free spectral shapes of the Rb vapor simultaneously measured by (a) an AlGaAs laser and (b) the second harmonic wave of an InGaAsP laser: x is the frequency at which the two laser frequencies were locked by negative electrical feedback control (from [38]).

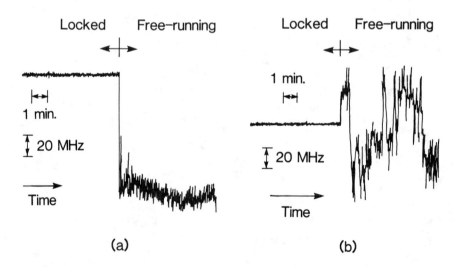

Figure 5.19 Frequency fluctuations of (a) an AlGaAs laser and (b) an InGaAsP laser (from [38]).

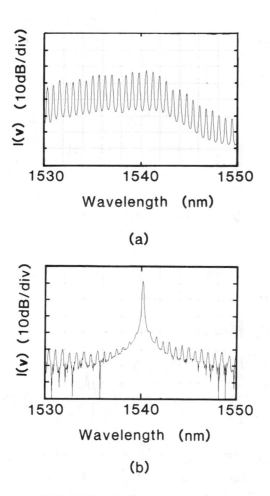

Figure 5.20 Lasing spectral shapes of a multilongitudinal mode InGaAsP laser with 1.5 μm wavelength: (a) a free-running laser, (b) in an injection locked condition (from [39]).

equal with each other, which means that frequency tracking was accurate and a high coherence of the master laser was transferred to the high-power slave laser.

A method of correlated spontaneous emission has been proposed for phase locking between the two modes [40]. This is a method of realizing the correlation between the spontaneous emission fluctuations for the two lasing modes. Until recently this was not thought possible because spontaneous emission can be interpreted as the stimulated emission triggered by random zero-point fluctuations in a vacuum. However, if the upper levels of atoms consist of more than two levels, this correlation can be generated by realizing a quantum correlation between those upper

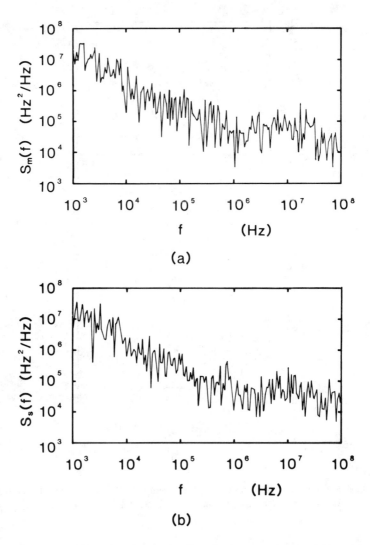

Figure 5.21 Power spectral densities of the FM noises of (a) a master laser and (b) an injection-locked slave laser (from [39]).

levels by an external modulation. Correlations like these have been demonstrated experimentally for a gas laser [41] and an external-cavity semiconductor laser [42]. Confusion between this correlation and the conventional phenomenon of active mode locking should be avoided because the long-term fluctuations of the phase noise of correlated spontaneous emission is similar to those of the active mode locking. The correlated spontaneous emission has been evaluated accurately by measuring the Allan variance of the short-term fluctuations of the phase difference between the two spontaneous emissions [43].

5.2 STABLE, ACCURATE, AND WIDEBAND OPTICAL FREQUENCY SWEEP

5.2.1 Fine Frequency Sweep

For a stable and accurate frequency sweep, a technique of heterodyne frequency tracking has been employed for 0.83 μm AlGaAs lasers [44]. During heterodyne frequency tracking, a fine frequency sweep of the slave laser can be achieved in a stable and accurate manner by sweeping the frequency of the microwave local oscillator. Figure 5.22 shows an example of fine frequency sweep [44]. By this technique, a total sweep range of 64 GHz is achieved. We could confirm that the frequency stability of the slave laser was maintained high while the frequency was swept.

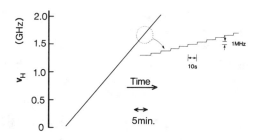

Figure 5.22 Example of fine frequency sweep: the heterodyne frequency was varied by a stepwise sweep of the frequency of microwave synthesizer with 1 MHz interval at every 10 s (from [44] © 1989 IEEE).

The frequency tracking capability of the frequency-locked loop is confirmed for the advanced system shown by Figure 5.3. The master laser frequency is swept by modulating its injection current with a modulation frequency of several 100 Hz. We find by this modulation that the frequency locking of the slave laser is maintained until the FM amplitude of the master laser is increased to 15 GHz. We can expect that this value is extended up to the value limited by the mode-hopping or multimode oscillation phenomenon of the slave and master laser if an amplifier is inserted between the loop filter and the slave laser.

5.2.2 Wideband Coarse Frequency Sweep

A wideband coarse frequency sweep is possible by several methods even though it is a discontinuous sweep. One of the simplest ways is to use the optical feedback method, as shown by Figure 5.23(a), in which an external grating is rotated to sweep the frequency of a 1.3 μm InGaAsP laser [45]. An *antireflection* (AR) coating is added to the output laser facet to suppress multimirror cavity oscillations (i.e., the cavity modes formed by the external grating and the laser facets). Facet reflectivity has been reduced to as low as 0.01–0.1% by this AR coating. Figure 5.23(b) shows spectral profiles of this external-cavity laser to demonstrate the wide range of the frequency sweep. We can see from this figure that a frequency sweep range as wide as 18 THz is achieved. Note that no longitudinal mode of the solitary laser is seen on these spectral profiles, due to the precise and effective AR coating. The field spectral linewidth is reduced drastically due to the cavity loss reduction realized by this AR-coated external-cavity configuration.

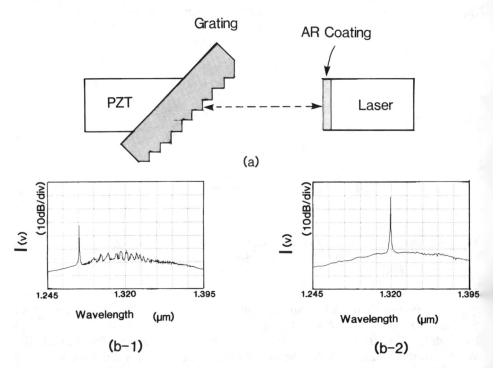

Figure 5.23 (a) Experimental setup of an optically fed-back laser with an external diffraction grating; (b-1)–(b-3) field spectral profiles of the optically fed-back InGaAsP laser with 1.3 μm wavelength (from [45]).

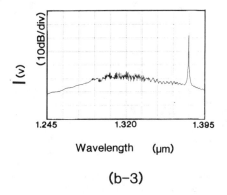

(b-3)

Figure 5.23 continued

By introducing a quantum-well structure to the semiconductor laser device, this external-cavity configuration also realized a range of frequency sweep as wide as 27 THz (i.e., the wavelength tuning range of 105 nm) for a 0.8 μm AlGaAs laser [46]. However, if the AR coating performs poorly, complicated modes originating in the multimirror cavity configuration can oscillate and chaotic instabilities of laser oscillation may be induced, depending on the phase and power of the light injected into the laser after reflection by the external cavity (see Section 2.5.1). To avoid these difficulties, an advanced optical feedback scheme has been demonstrated. Figure 5.24 shows the cavity configuration for a 0.67 μm AlGaInP laser [47]. This configuration is composed of two parts. One part is the optical feedback from a confocal Fabry-Perot interferometer, as demonstrated in Figure 4.19; and the other is that from the external grating. Side modes are sufficiently suppressed by the feedback from the confocal Fabry-Perot interferometer, even though no AR coatings were provided. The laser oscillation was stable because the intrinsic cavity configuration of the solitary laser was maintained due to a weak optical coupling between the laser and the interferometer. By varying the voltage applied to the piezoelectric transducer (PZT-C) attached to the interferometer, the laser frequency was swept in a precise and stable manner. A coarse frequency sweep was achieved by rotating the grating used in the second part of the optical feedback. Although the voltages of the two piezoelectric transducers were controlled to adjust the phase of the light reflected from the interferometer and the grating to maintain a stable optical feedback, total range of the frequency sweep as wide as 3.3 THz was obtained. During the frequency sweep, the field spectral linewidth was maintained narrower than 50 kHz, as shown in Figure 4.27. Figure 4.8 shows the spectral profile of Li vapor measured by using this technique. A high stability and accuracy in the frequency sweep can be confirmed from this figure.

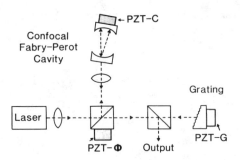

Figure 5.24 Cavity configuration of an AlGaInP laser with 0.67 μm wavelength; optical feedbacks were realized by using an external confocal Fabry-Perot cavity and a diffraction grating simultaneously (from [47]).

A peta-Hz (= 1 × 10^{15} Hz) class coherent optical sweep generator has been proposed to realize a very wideband frequency sweep, ranging from near infrared to ultraviolet (i.e., from 1.56 μm to 0.34 μm wavelengths) [38]. The principle behind the operation of this system will be described in Section 7.2.2.

REFERENCES

[1] Shin, C.H., "Optical Phase-Locking of Semiconductor Lasers," Ph.D. thesis, Tokyo Institute of Technology, 1991.

[2] Telle, B.R., D. Meschede, and T.W. Hänsch, "Realization of a New Concept for Visible Frequency Division: Phase Locking of Harmonic and Sum Frequencies," *Optics Letters,* Vol. 15, No. 10, May 1990, pp. 532–534.

[3] Moran, S.E., R.L. Law, P.N. Craig, and M. Goldberg, "Optically Phase-Locked Speckle Pattern Interferometer," *Applied Optics,* Vol. 26, No. 3, February 1987, pp. 475–491.

[4] Dijaili, S.P., J.S. Smith, and A. Dienes, "Timing Synchronization of a Passively Mode-Locked Dye Laser Using a Pulsed Optical Phase Lock Loop," *Applied Physics Letters,* Vol. 55, No. 5, July 1989, pp. 418–420.

[5] Hercher, M., and G. Wyntjes, "Precision Angle Measurement with a 2-Frequency He-Ne Laser," *SPIE,* Vol. 741, January 1987, pp. 174–185.

[6] Hayes, C.L., and L.M. Laughman, "Generation of Coherent Optical Pulses," *Applied Optics,* Vol. 16, No. 2, February 1977, pp. 263–264.

[7] Ohtsu, M., "Realization of Ultrahigh Coherence in Semiconductor Lasers by Negative Electrical Feedback," *IEEE J. Lightwave Technology,* Vol. 6, No. 2, February 1988, pp. 245–256.

[8] Hagemeier, H.E., and S.R. Robinson, "Field Properties of Multiple Coherently Combined Lasers," *Applied Optics,* Vol. 18, No. 3, February 1979, pp. 270–280.

[9] Enloe, L.H., and J.L. Rodda, "Laser Phase-Locked Loop," *Proc. IEEE,* Vol. 53, No. 2, February 1965, pp. 165–166.

[10] Hall, J.L., L.S. Ma, and G. Kramer, "Principles of Optical Phase-Locking: Application to Internal Mirror He-Ne Lasers Phase-locked via Fast Control of the Discharge Current," *IEEE J. Quantum Electronics,* Vol. QE-23, No. 4, April 1987, pp. 427–437.

[11]   Lang, R., "Injection Locking Properties of a Semiconductor Laser," *IEEE J. Quantum Electronics,* Vol. QE-18, No. 6, June 1982, pp. 976–983.

[12]   Henry, C.H., N.A. Olsson, and N.K. Dutta, "Locking range and stability of injection locked 1.54 μm InGaAsP semiconductor lasers," *IEEE J. Quantum Electronics,* Vol. QE-21, No. 8, August 1985, pp. 1152–1156.

[13]   Spano, P., S. Piazzolla, and M. Tamburrini, "Frequency and Intensity Noise in Injection-Locked Semiconductor Lasers: Theory and Experiments," *IEEE J. Quantum Electronics,* Vol. QE-22, No. 3, May 1986, pp. 427–435.

[14]   Shang, S.Q., and H.J. Metcalf, "Narrowband, High Power Light from Diode Lasers," *Applied Optics,* Vol. 28, No. 9, May 1989, pp. 1618–1623.

[15]   Leeb, W.R., H.K. Phlipp, A.L. Scholtz, and E. Bonek, "Frequency Synchronization and Phase Locking of CO_2 Lasers," *Applied Physics Letters,* Vol. 41, No. 7, July 1982, pp. 592–594.

[16]   Wenke, G., and S. Saito, "Phase Locking of Semiconductor Lasers Using Homodyne Detection and Negative Electrical Feedback," *Japan J. of Applied Physics,* Vol. 24, No. 12, December 1985, pp. L908–L910.

[17]   Kourogi, M., C.H. Shin, and M. Ohtsu, "A 134 MHz Bandwidth Homodyne Optical Phase-Locked Loop of Semiconductor Lasers," *IEEE Photonics Technology Letters,* Vol. 3, No. 3, March 1991, pp. 270–272.

[18]   Kane, T.J., and E.A.P. Cheng, "Fast Frequency Tuning and Phase Locking of Diode-Pumped Nd:YAG Ring Lasers," *Optics Letters,* Vol. 13, No. 11, November 1988, pp. 970–972.

[19]   Kazovsky, L.G., and D.A. Atlas, "A 1320 nm Experimental Optical Phase-Locked Loop," *IEEE Photonics Technology Letters,* Vol. 1, No. 11, November 1989, pp. 395–397.

[20]   Kahn, J.M., B.L. Kasper, and K.J. Pollock, "Optical Phaselock Receiver with Multigigahertz Signal Bandwidth," *Electronics Letters,* Vol. 25, No. 10, May 1989, pp. 626–628.

[21]   Malyon, D.J., D.W. Smith, and R. Wyatt, "Semiconductor Laser Homodyne Phase-Locked Loop," *Electronics Letters,* Vol. 22, No. 8, April 1986, pp. 421–422.

[22]   Steele, R.C., "Optical Phase-Locked Loop Using Semiconductor Laser Diodes," *Electronics Letters,* Vol. 19, No. 2, January 1983, pp. 69–71.

[23]   Harrison, J., and A. Mooradian, "Linewidth and Offset Locking of External Cavity GaAlAs Lasers," *IEEE J. Quantum Electronics,* Vol. QE-25, No. 6, June 1989, pp. 1152–1155.

[24]   Telle, H.R., and H. Li, "Phase-Locking of Laser Diodes," *Electronics Letters,* Vol. 26, No. 13, June 1990, pp. 858–859.

[25]   Kuboki, K., and M. Ohtsu, "Frequency Offset Locking of AlGaAs Semiconductor Lasers," *IEEE J. Quantum Electronics,* Vol. QE-23, No. 4, April 1987, pp. 388–394.

[26]   Kuboki, K., C.H. Shin, T. Kato, and M. Ohtsu, "Performance and Its Evaluation of Optical Tracking Generator/Optical Frequency Synthesizer by Semiconductor Lasers," *Digest 1988 Conf. on Precision Electromagnetic Measurements,* ed. Y. Suematsu, June 1988, pp. 24–25.

[27]   Kuboki, K., and M. Ohtsu, "A Synthesized Method to Improve Coherence in Semiconductor Lasers by Electrical Feedback," *IEEE J. Quantum Electronics,* Vol. 25, No. 10, October 1989, pp. 2084–2090.

[28]   Ishida, O., H. Toba, and Y. Tohmori, "0.04 Hz Relative Optical-Frequency Stability in a 1.5 μm Distributed-Bragg-Reflector (DBR) Laser," *IEEE Photonics Technology Letters,* Vol. 1, No. 12, December 1989, pp. 452–454.

[29]   Kane, T.J., A.C. Nilsson, and R.L. Byer, "Frequency Stability and Offset Locking of a Laser-Diode-Pumped Nd:YAG Monolithic Nonplanar Ring Oscillator," *Optics Letters,* Vol. 12, No. 3, March 1987, pp. 175–177.

[30]   Hall, J.L., M. Zhu, F. Shimizu, and K. Shimizu, "External Frequency Stabilization of a Commercial Dye Laser at the Sub-Hertz Level," *Tech. Digest of the 16th Int. Conf. Quantum Electronics* (IQEC '88), 1989, paper number 19A3-3.

[31]   Gardner, F.M., *Phaselock Techniques,* 2nd Ed., Wiley-Interscience, New York, 1979.

[32]   Blanchard, A., "Phase-Locked Loops: Application to Coherent Receiver Design," John Wiley & Sons, New York, 1976.

[33]   Shin, C.H., and M. Ohtsu. "Heterodyne Optical Phase-Locked Loop by Confocal Fabry-Perot Cavity Coupled AlGaAs Lasers," *IEEE Photonics Technology Letters,* Vol. 2, No. 4, April 1990, pp. 297–300.

[34]   Lowney, S.D., and D.V.L. Marquis, "Frequency Acquisition and Tracking for Optical Heterodyne Communication Systems," *J. Lightwave Technology,* Vol. LT-5, No. 4, April 1987, pp. 538–550.

[35]   Gardner, F.M., "Charge-Pump Phase-Lock Loops," *IEEE Trans. on Communication,* Vol. COM-28, No. 11, November 1980, pp. 1849–1858.

[36]   Kuboki, K., and M. Ohtsu, "An Allan Variance Real-Time Processing System for Frequency Stability Measurements of Semiconductor Lasers," *IEEE Trans. on Instruments and Measurements,* Vol. 39, No. 4, August 1990, pp. 637–641.

[37]   Siegman, A.E., B. Daino, and K.R. Manes, "Preliminary Measurements of Laser Short-Term Frequency Fluctuations," *IEEE J. Quantum Electronics,* QE-3, No. 5, May 1967, pp. 180–189.

[38]   Ohtsu, M., K. Nakagawa, C.-H. Shin, H. Kusuzawa, M. Kourogi, and H. Suzuki, "Progress Toward a 1-PHz Hypercoherent Optical Sweep Generator by Semiconductor Lasers," Conf. on Lasers and Electro-Optics, May 21–25, 1990, Anaheim, CA, paper number CME5.

[39]   Nakagawa, K., M. Teshima, and M. Ohtsu, "Highly coherent and high power diode laser at 1.5 μm wavelength by injection-locking," *Optics Letters,* accepted for publication.

[40]   Scully, M.O., "Correlated Spontaneous Emission Lasers: Quanching of Quantum Fluctuations in the Relative Phase Angle," *Physics Review Letters,* Vol. 55, No. 25, December 1985, pp. 2802–2805.

[41]   Toschek, P.E., and J.L. Hall, "Noise Reduction in the Relative Phase of Two Lasers," *Tech. Digest of 15th Int. Quantum Electronics Conf.* IQEC '87, Baltimore, April–May 1987, Optics Society of America, Washington, DC, 1987, paper number WDD2.

[42]   Ohtsu, M., and K.-Y. Liou, "Correlated Spontaneous Emission Between Two Longitudinal Modes in an Extended-Cavity Semiconductor Laser," *Applied Physics Letters,* Vol. 52, No. 1, January 1988, pp. 10–12.

[43]   Winters, M.P., and J.L. Hall, "Correlated Spontaneous Emission in a Zeeman Laser," *Physics Review Letters,* Vol. 65, No. 25, December 1990, pp. 3116–3119.

[44]   Kuboki, K., and M. Ohtsu, "A Synthesized Method to Improve Coherence in Semiconductor Lasers by Electrical Feedback," *IEEE J. Quantum Electronics,* Vol. 25, No. 10, October 1989, pp. 2084–2090.

[45]   Kourogi, M., and C.-H. Shin, Tokyo Institute of Technology, private communication, January 1991.

[46]   Mehuys, D., M. Mittelstein, and A. Yariv, "(GaAl)As Quantum Well Semiconductor Lasers Tunable over 105 nm with an External Grating," *Proc. Conf. on Lasers and Electro-Optics,* CLEO '89, April 1989, Baltimore, Optics Society of America, Washington, DC, 1989, paper number FL4.

[47]   Ohtsu, M., H. Suzuki, K. Nemoto, and Y. Teramachi, "Narrow-Linewidth Tunable Visible InGaAlP Laser, Application to Spectral Measurements of Lithium, and Power Amplification," *Japan J. of Applied Physics,* Vol. 29, No. 8, August 1990, pp. L1463–L1465.

Chapter 6
APPLICATIONS OF HIGHLY COHERENT SEMICONDUCTOR LASERS

Highly coherent semiconductor lasers are indispensable to many application systems. In this chapter, representative examples are reviewed.

6.1 OPTICAL COMMUNICATION SYSTEMS

Optical communication systems have developed over a long history. Lasers began being suggested and used in optical communication systems soon after their advent [1]. Moreover, the initial motivation behind the invention of lasers was the need to increase the transmission capacity of communication systems. Especially after the development of glass fiber with a transmission loss as low as 20 dB/km and room-temperature and CW semiconductor lasers in 1970, research and development in optical communication systems progressed rapidly. However, because the magnitude of FM noise in the semiconductor lasers was very large at that time, the intensity modulation and demodulation schemes were employed only for signal transmission in practical systems. This scheme, therefore, did not meet the need to increase transmission capacity by utilizing the high optical frequency and high temporal coherence of lasers.

However, as shown in previous chapters, low FM noise semiconductor lasers recently were developed, and the stable modulation of their frequencies or phases became possible. Furthermore, as shown in Figure 6.1, by using a heterodyne or homodyne demodulation scheme, the detection of sensitivity can become much higher than that in a conventional direct demodulation scheme, which also means that the signal transmission span can be increased. In this case, it is advantageous to use a 1.55 μm wavelength laser with an optical fiber showing a minimum transmission loss, as low as 0.2 dB/km. A system employing these modulation and demod-

---

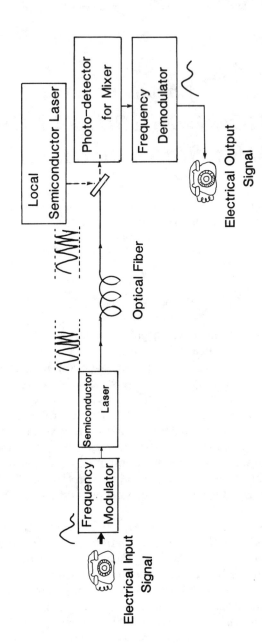

Figure 6.1 Block diagram of a coherent optical communication system.

ulation schemes has been called *coherent optical communication.* Practical systems have been realized using highly coherent semiconductor lasers. Figure 6.2 shows such a coherent optical communication system.

A wider amplifier bandwidth is required for signal demodulation, if the bit rate of the coherent optical transmission is increased. Because it is rather difficult to design a wideband amplifier, one suggestion has been to increase the transmission capacity by increasing the transmission channels instead of the bit rate. For these *frequency division multiplexing* (FDM) systems, numbers of channels can be increased to as large as several thousand with a several GHz channel frequency separation by using the 20 THz-wide low-loss window of the optical fiber around the 1.55 μm wavelength [2]. In this case, the lasers must meet the requirements 1, 2, and 3 of Section 1.2. In this FDM scheme, a large transmission capacity can be expected even though the transmission bit rate of each channel is not very high. Section 4.3.1 showed that a gain-bandwidth product as high as 40 THz could be achieved to reduce FM noise in the feedback loop. We have confirmed that the bit error rate can be kept sufficiently low when this laser is used for low-to-medium bit rate coherent transmission systems [3]. Furthermore, requirement 4 of Section 1.2 should be satisfied for heterodyne or homodyne demodulation. Among the coherent optical communication receivers, homodyne receivers for the modulation format of phase shift keying and amplitude shift keying require optical phase locking, and heterodyne receivers require optical frequency locking and phase locking in the IF frequency. Several kinds of phase-locked loops are used to lock the local oscillator laser to the incoming signal. When the incoming lightwave signal contains the carrier components (i.e., the carrier is not fully suppressed), optical phase locking is achieved directly by using a standard homodyne or heterodyne optical phase-locked loop. However, a nonlinear phase-locked loop is required when the carrier is fully suppressed (i.e., $\pm 90°$ modulated PSK signal); these include the Costas loop [4–7], the decision-driven loop [8], the squaring loop, and their modifications. The squaring loop can not be used in a homodyne receiver but only in a heterodyne receiver. The only difference between the standard optical phase-locked loop and these nonlinear loops is the method of extracting the phase-error signal; that is, the phase-error detection process. Remaining parts operate under the same principles. As the insufficient temporal coherence in lasers can make it difficult to use an optical phase-locked loop in practical systems, an alternative technique of phase diversity has been proposed to relax the requirement of temporal coherence in lasers [9].

Rapid progress also has been seen in coherent optical communication systems in intersatellite or satellite-to-ground communication. As these are similar to the coherent laser radar, 0.8 μm AlGaAs lasers have been used and controlled according to the techniques described in Chapters 4 and 5 [10]. The main problems remaining to be solved are an increase in laser power and improvement in accuracy of laser beam tracking.

176

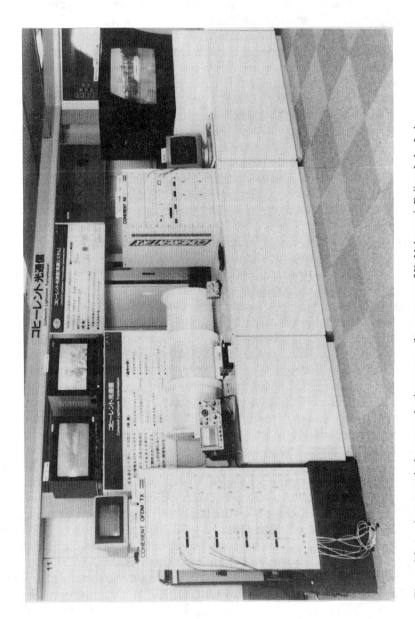

Figure 6.2 A coherent optical communication system (by courtesy of K. Nakagami, Fujitsu Lab., Ltd., 1989).

6.2 OPTICAL MEASUREMENTS

6.2.1 Passive Ring Resonator-Type Fiber Gyroscope

A gyroscope is carried on-board aircraft for inertial navigation and to maintain the correct route. Although conventional mechanical gyroscopes are highly sensitive, they have a short lifetime, are highly sensitive to mechanical shock, and are costly.

Optical gyroscopes tried to overcome these difficulties by using laser and optical fibers. Figure 6.3 shows the block diagram of a fiber gyroscope [11], which is operated based on the Sagnac effect [12]. That is, the phases of two output lights, after traveling in clockwise and counterclockwise directions in the fiber loop, are different from each other if the fiber loop rotates around the axis perpendicular to the fiber loop plane. A rotation rate can be detected by measuring the phase difference between the two traveling lights. This fiber gyroscope has several advantages: its small size, light weight, and long lifetime, for example. The development of a practical apparatus has advanced rapidly.

Figure 6.3 shows one of the most sensitive systems, possibly a promising candidate for the next generation of fiber gyroscopes. A ring Fabry-Perot interferometer was designed with optical fiber and directional couplers for clockwise and counterclockwise ring resonance. The Sagnac effect gives the difference in resonance frequencies between these two running lightwaves. The derivatives of the resonance curves of the interferometer, as shown in Figure 3.6(d), are used as frequency demodulators to measure this difference. In this case, a 1.5 μm wavelength semiconductor laser should be used to reduce the fiber loss. Figure 6.4 shows preliminary experimental results of the relation between the integration time τ of the measurements and the sensitivity of the rotation rate Ω by using a 1.5 μm DFB laser with a 1.3 MHz field spectral linewidth and a fiber loop with the total loss of α_t of 0.8 dB and length of 2.4 m [11]. Sensitivity as high as 1.5°/h was obtained at $\tau = 100$ s even when using a broad linewidth laser. This value is lower than the revolution rate of the earth. Figures 6.5(a) and (b) show calculated results of relations between the integration time and the rotation rate [11]. Five lines are drawn for different values of the laser linewidths and for $\alpha_t = 0.8$ dB and 0.1 dB. Comparison between lines D and E confirms that the laser can work as an approximately FM noise-free light source if its linewidth is narrower than 100 kHz. To realize this narrow linewidth, the compact laser module of Figure 4.25 was fabricated and installed in the fiber gyroscope system, whose appearance is shown in Figure 6.6.

To increase measurement sensitivity, an FM laser spectroscopy technique has been proposed [13]. Figure 6.7(a) shows a fiber gyroscope system employing this technique [14]. Because direct, wideband FM is possible for a semiconductor laser, a very high modulation frequency can be employed for this technique, which also can make the gyroscope system very fast. Furthermore, because the *voltage-controlled oscillators* (VCO) used to drive the frequency shifters (*acousto-optic modu-*

178

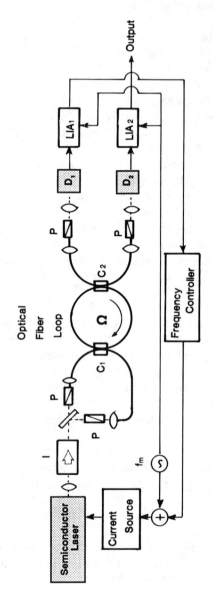

Figure 6.3 Block diagram of a passive ring resonator-type fiber gyroscope (from [11]).

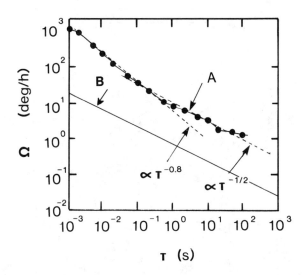

Figure 6.4 Relation between the integration time T of the measurements and the sensitivity of the rotation rate of the fiber gyroscope of Figure 6.3: *A* is the experimental result, *B* is the theoretical shot noise limit (from [11]).

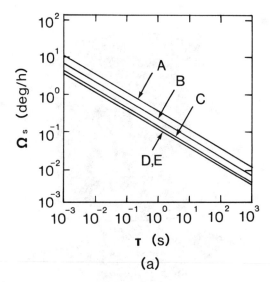

Figure 6.5 Relation between the integration time T and shot-noise limited sensitivity of the rotation rate measurement Ω_s: (a) and (b) are calculated results for the total loss of the fiber loop $\alpha_t = 0.8$ dB and 0.1 dB, respectively. The values of the laser linewidths are (*A*) 13 MHz, (*B*) 5 MHz, (*C*) 1 MHz, (*D*) 100 kHz, and (*E*) 0 Hz.

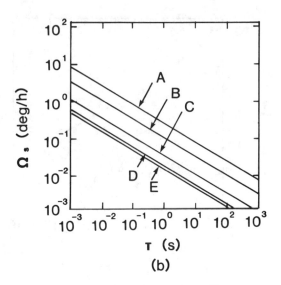

Figure 6.5 continued

Figure 6.6 A passive ring resonator-type fiber gyroscope (by the courtesy of K. Nishide and T. Imai Tokyo Aircraft Instrument Co. Ltd., 1989).

lator, or AOM) are controlled, the output of this system is the frequency difference between the clockwise and counterclockwise ring resonance of the fiber loop. As is popularly known, frequency measurement has a large dynamic range, high linearity, and high accuracy; therefore, a very sensitive gyroscope can be expected from this system. Figure 6.7(b) shows the derivative resonance curve of the Fabry-Perot interfeometer with a loop length of 4.7 m and finesse of 50, where the modulation frequency of the injection current is 10 MHz [14]. The signal-to-noise ratio of this measurement is 30 dB, from which the measurement sensitivity of rotation rate is estimated to be as high as $0.9\ \tau^{-1/2\circ}/h$; that is, $0.09°/h$ at $\tau = 100$ s, which is one of the best results among the passive ring resonator-type fiber gyroscopes documented so far. For complete suppression of the effect of IM induced by direct FM, an external phase shifter like the *electro-optic modulator* (EOM) can be used as an effective tool for this system.

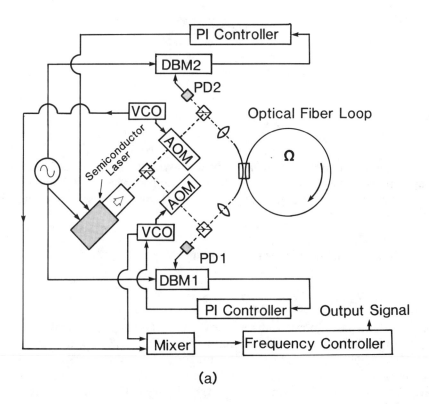

(a)

Figure 6.7 (a) Block diagram of the passive ring resonator-type fiber gyroscope employing the method of FM spectroscopy (from [14]). (b) Derivative resonance curve of the fiber ring Fabry-Perot interferometer with a loop length of 4.7 m and finesse of 50.

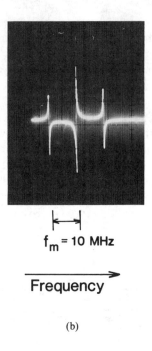

$f_m = 10$ MHz

Frequency

(b)

Figure 6.7 continued

We can expect that these highly sensitive gyroscopes will be used not only for navigation systems but also for geophysics, astronomy, space science, and even prediction of earthquakes by monitoring, for example, the time sequence of the Chandler wobble [15].

6.2.2 Velocity and Displacement Measurements

Two-Frequency Doppler Velocimeter

In a heterodyne laser interferometer, the value of the heterodyne frequency limits the maximum measurable speed of translating objects. A typical system using a commercially available gas laser exhibits a maximum measurable speed of 1.8 m/ because the maximum heterodyne frequency is 20 MHz [16]. However, the heterodyne frequency can be increased to 2 GHz by using the technique described in Section 5.2.1 for master and slave lasers, which can increase the maximum measurable speed to 100 times that obtained by conventional systems. This system could be effectively used to control the speed of a fast stepper machine used in semiconductor factories if the X-ray exposure technique is employed in the future.

Heterodyne Displacement Measurement

For this purpose, a high-power, stable CO_2 laser has been used conventionally. The phase of the output lightwave is modulated by an external phase modulator to measure the displacement and velocity of a moving object. However, the system performance is limited by the speed and efficiency of the phase modulator in the CO_2 laser. Because semiconductor lasers show wideband and highly efficient direct FM characteristics in realizing versatile modulation schemes, we can expect that the performance of this system will improve.

6.3   PHOTON SCANNING TUNNELING MICROSCOPE

After the advent of ultrahigh-resolution *scanning tunneling microscopes* (STM) utilizing the tunneling of electrons between the probe tip and the conductive sample surface [17], a variety of STMs have been developed, such as the atomic force microscope [18]. The *photon STM* (PSTM) is a modification of the STM, a sort of superresolution optical microscope used to measure the topography of three-dimensional samples within the dimensions of an optical wavelength. This can be used advantageously to measure the profiles of a biomembrane, organic ultrathin film and nonconductive materials without contact or destruction of the sample. The PSTM can be considered a version of *near-field microscope* (NFM) [19]; however, conventional NFMs have not shown a sufficiently high performance due to lack of maturity in their basic technology. Although more practical systems have been proposed recently [20], such research is still at a preliminary stage of development. Two directions can be taken in the system's design:

1. A transmission-type PSTM inducing a photochemical reaction in the sample to observe the reaction under high resolution. This typical system is shown in Figure 6.8(a) [21]; it is similar to the systems developed by Oak Ridge National Laboratory [20]. In this figure, a semiconductor laser is used for analytical spectroscopy at each local point on the sample.
2. A reflection-resonance type PSTM could improve resolution without contact or destruction. This system is shown in Figures 6.8(b) and (c) [21, 22].

A transmission-type PSTM picks up evanescent light from the sample surface by a fiber probe with a subwavelength diameter aperture. Because the profile of the evanescent light field depends on the sample's topography, the three-dimensional profile of the sample can be measured. In Figure 6.8(a), an optical fiber tip was used as the aperture. Figure 6.9 shows a SEM picture of the Cr-film coated fiber tip, whose top was sharpened to a curvature radius of 80 nm; in addition, its top has an aperture with a diameter of about 10 nm. Because the picked-up evanescent light can be interpreted as a tunneling photon in the near-field region, that is, in the region where the sample-fiber separation is smaller than the wavelength λ, a photon tunneling probability depends on the height of the potential barrier determined by the ratio between

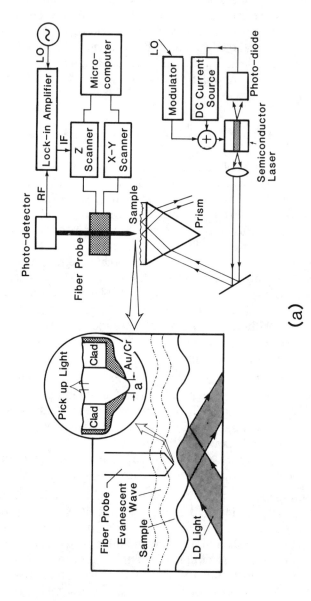

Figure 6.8 Block diagrams of PSTMs: (a) A transmission-type (from [21]); (b) and (c) reflection-type using a fiber Fabry-Perot cavity and a semiconductor laser as a pick-up, respectively.

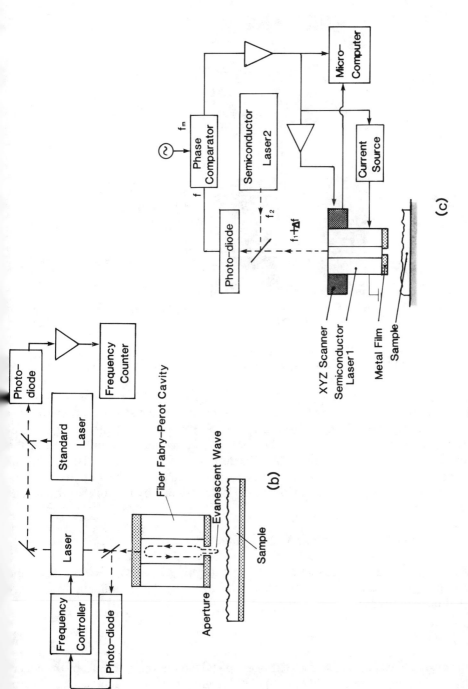

Figure 6.8 continued

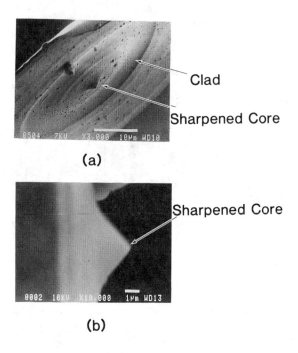

(a)

Clad

Sharpened Core

Sharpened Core

(b)

Figure 6.9 SEM images of a Cr-film coated fiber tip. The profile of the sharpened core of (a) is magnified in (b).

the refractive indices of the sample and air. A high normal resolution is obtained, as the probability of tunneling photons decreases exponentially with increasing sample-fiber separation. Furthermore, as the lightwave is free from the diffraction in the near-field region, the lateral resolution is determined by the aperture diameter a; and as the tunneling photon is detected by destroying the photon field by the fiber tip, uncertainty of the photon momentum Δp is determined by that of the wavelength $\Delta\lambda$, given by

$$\Delta p = p \cdot (\Delta\lambda/\lambda) = (h/\lambda)(\lambda/a) = h/a \qquad (6.1)$$

where h is the Planck's constant, and the relationship $\Delta\lambda/\lambda = \lambda/a$ is used. Thus, the minimum uncertainty of photon Δx is determined by the Heisenberg uncertainty relation, expressed as

$$\Delta x = (h/2\pi)/\Delta p = a/2\pi \qquad (6.2)$$

Although the resolution of a conventional optical microscope is limited by the uncertainty relation imposed by diffraction phenomenon, the PSTM achieves high lateral resolution by position squeezing the photon using a subwavelength aperture. In summary, the high resolution of the PSTM beyond the diffraction limit is due to utilization of evanescent wave, subwavelength aperture, and near-field measurements.

Figure 6.10 shows the relation between the sample-fiber separation and the light power picked up by the transmission-type PSTM [21]. Although the picked-up power is lower than 100 pW, a sensitive detection is carried out by directly modulating the 0.8 μm wavelength AlGaAs laser power and employing phase sensitive detection. Figure 6.11(a) shows an example of measurement by the transmission-type PSTM, where the sample is a prism surface, half of which is coated with a 9 nm thick SiO$_2$ film [21]. This figure was obtained by scanning the fiber tip along the x and y axes. Figure 6.11(b) shows the measured profile of a moth-eye optical disk surface, which has pits with a diameter of 300 nm and a depth of 80 nm [21]. Even though the time constant of the phase-sensitive detection was as short as 1 ms for these measurements, a normal resolution of 1 nm was obtained. Although the lateral resolution has not yet been evaluated accurately, it is roughly estimated to be within 10 nm based on the fiber-tip profile of Figure 6.9(b). Further improvement in resolution is expected through optimization of the modulation-demodulation parameters and the fiber-tip profile.

The transmission-type PSTM detects a very weak evanescent light power, which can limit its resolution. To overcome this difficulty, the reflection-resonance-type PSTM employs a fiber Fabry-Perot cavity (Figure 6.8(b)) or a semiconductor laser (Figure 6.8(c)) as a pick-up. It is also possible to replace the fiber Fabry-Perot cavity with a low-loss dielectric optical waveguide grown on a glass substrate. A subwavelength aperture is made on the pick-up surface of Figures 6.8(b) and (c). Because

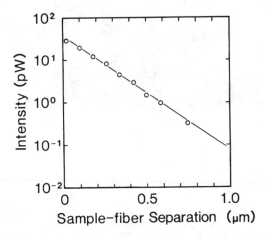

Figure 6.10 Relation between the sample-fiber separation and the evanescent light power picked up by the transmission-type PSTM (from [21]).

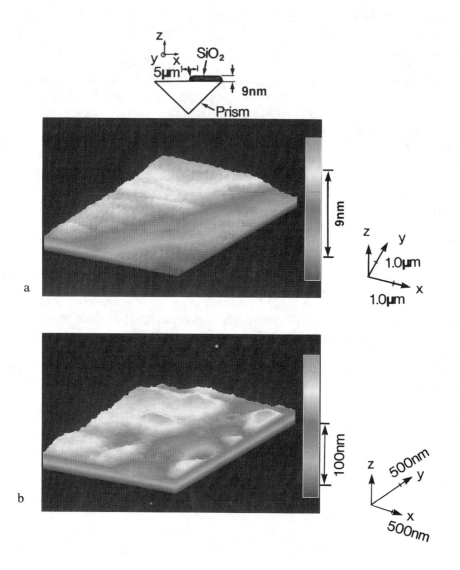

Figure 6.11 (a) Surface profile of the SiO₂ film with a thickness of 9 nm coated on half of the prism surface. The upper part of this figure shows a schematic explanation of the cross section of film; the picture corresponds to the area pointed by an arrow of this figure. (b) Surface profile of a moth-eye optical disk, which has pits with a diameter of 300 nm and a depth of 80 nm. (Both from [21].)

the resonance frequency of the cavity is shifted slightly when the evanescent light is perturbed by the sample, the three-dimensional profile can be measured by measuring this frequency shift. Because the technique of heterodyne optical phase locking can be employed to measure the frequency shift and the residual heterodyne frequency fluctuations have been reduced to as low as 1.1×10^{-18} (see Figure 5.10), a high resolution can be expected without losing the detected laser power.

Figure 6.12 shows a calculated relation between the sample-cavity separation z and the cavity resonance frequency shift Δf, where a flat plane sample surface was assumed [22]. An exponential decrease of Δf in this figure can assure high normal resolution, as in the transmission-type PSTM. The lateral resolution is determined by the diameter of the aperture. Figure 6.13 shows the calculated relation between the aperture diameter a and the frequency shift of the cavity Δf, where the sample-cavity separation z is used as a parameter [22]. Curves $A-D$ represent the shot noise limits of detecting Δf, which depend on the finesse of the cavity F and the laser power incident to the photodetector P. We can see from this figure that a lateral resolution as high as several nm is expected. Recently developed very high finesse supercavity and high-power semiconductor lasers could assure further improvement in resolution.

Figure 6.14 shows the result of a simulation experiment using a 44 mm wavelength microwave instead of using the lightwave. The profile of the measured signal (Figure 6.14(b)) has two peaks, which correspond to the adjacent peaks of the corrugated sample (Figure 6.14(a)). These figures confirm that adjacent corrugation

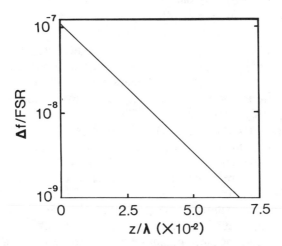

Figure 6.12 Calculated relation between the sample-cavity separation z and the cavity resonance frequency shift Δf, where aperture diameter a is assumed to be 60 nm: λ is the laser wavelength, *FSR* is the free spectral range of the cavity (from [22]).

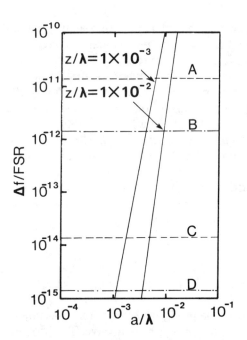

Figure 6.13 Calculated relation between the aperture diameter a and the frequency shift of the cavity Δf, where the sample-cavity separation is used as a parameter. Lines A–D represent the shot noise limits of detecting Δf, where the finesse of cavity F and the laser power incident into the photodetector P are (A) 1×10^2 and 10 mW, (B) 1×10^2 and 1 W, (C) 1×10^5 and 1 mW, and (D) 1×10^5 and 1 W, respectively (from [22]).

peaks are clearly resolved even though the separation between them b is smaller than the aperture diameter a, because the evanescent power is concentrated around the center of the aperture. A series of such simulation experiments, varying the aperture diameter a and the integration time of the measurements τ, achieved the normal and lateral resolutions as high as $5 \times 10^{-3}\lambda$ and $5 \times 10^{-2}\lambda$, respectively [21, 22]. By using a multicore fiber [23], we can measure the dynamic properties of the stimulus propagation on the biomembrane. To fully analyze the performance of the PSTM, a theory of near-field wave optics first should be established.

Furthermore, as a future technique, we can expect that this sort of optical tunnel tip will be used to manipulate the motion of a single atom for crystal growth [21]. This crystal growth technique is composed of three steps. As the first step, thermal velocities of gaseous atoms are decreased by laser cooling and optical molasses (see Section 6.6.3); thus, the atomic temperature is reduced. As the second step, the fiber tips of the reflection-resonance-type PSTM are brought closer to these cold atoms. If one atom falls into the evanescent field of the fiber tip, the atom is trapped by the dipole force of the evanescent wave. Six fiber tips (directing along $\pm x$, $\pm y$

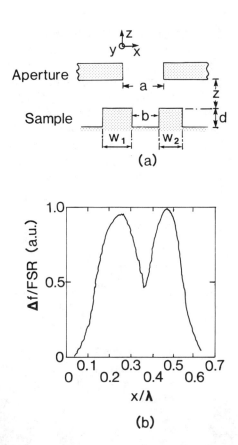

Figure 6.14 Experimental results of a simulation experiment on a reflection-resonance-type PSTM, using a microwave with a wavelength of 44 mm: (a) cross section of the corrugated sample; (b) relation between the displacement of the cavity along the x-axis and the frequency shift of the cavity Δf (from [21, 22]).

and $\pm z$ axes) and a weak dc magnetic field are required for a stable trap; that is, to form a stable potential well for the atom. The position of the trapped atom (i.e., the position of the potential minimum) can be controlled by controlling the magnitude of the cavity frequency shift induced by this atom. The number of trapped atoms is detected by measuring the magnitude of cavity frequency shift. Such control and measurement are possible by using the precise optical phase locking described in Section 5.1. As a final step, the seventh fiber-tip is brought closer to the trapped atom, and by emitting the lightwave from this tip, the atom is heated and pushed down to the cold substrate on which it is fixed. This technique requires determining the input laser power to the fiber-tip needed to obtain sufficiently high evanescent power. Calculation for Cs atoms of 852 nm resonant wavelength show that the input laser power can be as low as 1 mW if the atomic temperature of the optical molasses is 0.1 mK and the aperture diameter is 8 nm [21]. This value of the incident laser power is easily obtained by the commercial semiconductor lasers, which means that this sort of single atom-level crystal growth is possible in the future. Furthermore, by using an appropriate wavelength laser, this technique is applicable as well for As, Ga, Ge, and Si atoms, which are essential elements in the semiconductor industry. As other applications of the PSTM, fabrication of an atomic tower (single-atom-level whisker), local laser annealing, trimming of ULSI, and so on are expected. We can conclude that these advanced PSTM systems will be achieved by fully utilizing highly coherent semiconductor lasers.

6.4 ANALYTICAL SPECTROSCOPY

6.4.1 Laser Radar (Lidar)

Remote sensing of densities and location of pollutant gases can be accomplished by measuring the scattering or absorption of laser light. High power lasers, for example,

Figure 6.15 Appearance of a transmitter head of an AlGaAs laser lidar (by courtesy of N. Takeuchi, The National Institute for Environmental Studies, 1989).

CO_2, YAG, and Ar^+ lasers, have been used in conventional systems. The high-frequency stability of the lasers is needed for a differential absorption lidar system by which the difference in absorption between two wavelengths is measured. To satisfy this requirement, the techniques described in Chapters 4 and 5 are utilized. In a coherent lidar system, further FM noise reduction is required, as in coherent optical communication systems. Although the power in semiconductor lasers is lower than that in these lasers, their small size and low power consumption are advantages that can be used in practical airborne or automobile-borne lidar systems. Furthermore, by utilizing the high efficiency of direct modulation of semiconductor lasers, a pseudo-random modulation technique has been employed to achieve high sensitivity and high spatial resolution in lidar systems. Field tests have confirmed that such pseudo-random modulation CW lidars show a maximum measurable distance of 1 km for aerosols, and 3~5 km for clouds or dust with a spatial resolution of 9 m [24]. Figure 6.15 shows the transmitter head of an AlGaAs laser lidar. In the lidar system used to measure the ozone density in the stratosphere, a heterodyne technique between solar light and lead-salt compound semiconductor lasers (several μm–10 μm wavelength) has been employed. As a result, detection sensitivity as high as the shot-noise level is achieved [25].

6.4.2 Isotope Separation and Analysis of Radicals

Isotope Separation

Lasers have been used for the isotope separation of uranium (U) for laser fusion and several atoms that act as tracers in medical diagnostics. Although the conventionally used gas-diffusion method falls into the category of a statistical separation process, the method using lasers is an individual separation process because the relevant isotopic atom or molecule is selectively excited by the lasers. This isotope can be completely separated from the others by additional techniques, like successive laser excitation; consequently, we can claim that the efficiency of *laser isotope separation* (LIS) is very high. The lasers should be highly stable in frequency and power and tunable to the resonance spectral line of the relevant isotope to develop a practical LIS system.

For the selective excitation of relevant isotopes, an isotope shift in resonant spectral lines of atoms or molecules is utilized. The principal causes of isotope shift in atoms are the mass, volume, and nuclear-spin effects. The mass effect of molecules is larger than that of atoms and the main cause in the isotope shift of molecules. To separate selectively excited isotopes, the techniques of photoionization, photodissociation, infrared multiple-photon dissociation, and photochemical reaction have been employed. Dye lasers or infrared molecular gas lasers have been employed mainly in conventional LIS systems. Because many articles have been published on the subject [26], a new method making use of semiconductor lasers is introduced in the following paragraphs.

For the isotope separations of Rb and Cs atoms, the technique of laser-induced drift has been proposed [27]. However, its separation efficiency is not yet sufficiently high, owing to the deexcitation process associated with optical pumping. Nevertheless, it was found that the separation efficiency could be increased by using semiconductor lasers [28]. Because the direct FM response characteristics of semiconductor lasers exhibit a resonant peak at the relaxation oscillation frequency, a series of FM sidebands appear in the field spectrum of these lasers. By careful adjustment of the bias level, the frequency separation between the optical carrier and the FM sideband of the second order can be made to coincide with the frequency separation between the two hyperfine energy levels of the ground states of these atoms. By simultaneously pumping the atoms with an optical carrier and this FM sideband, a cyclic excitation was realized. Due to this cyclic excitation, for example, most of ^{87}Rb atoms could be maintained in excitation states to achieve a large cross section of the collision with buffer gases. As a result, the drift velocity of ^{87}Rb in buffer gases could become different from that of ^{85}Rb and consequently improve the separation efficiency [29]. For this method, the technique described in Section 4.1 has to be employed to lock the optical carrier frequency of the laser at the ^{87}Rb resonant frequency. As shown in Figure 6.16, a separation efficiency as high as that obtained by

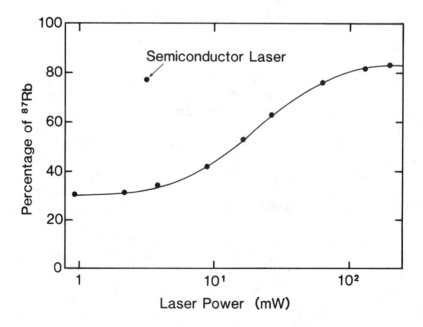

Figure 6.16. Relation between the laser power and the percentage of ^{87}Rb obtained by laser-induced drift. These results were obtained by using a dye laser. The closed circle shown in this figure represents the results by using an AlGaAs laser (from [27]).

using conventionally used dye lasers (150 mW power) can be achieved by an AlGaAs laser with a power of only 3.3 mW [27]. In the isotope separation of Ba and Ga by using the doppler-free two-photon transition process, one dye laser has been replaced by a frequency-controlled semiconductor laser [28]. For these purposes, and especially for the isotope separation of U, we expect that the recently developed visible AlGaInP laser will be used as an efficient pumping source [29]. Its field spectral line-width has been reduced to less than 50 kHz, and its wavelength tuning range was expanded to 5 nm by using the optical feedback technique shown in Figures 4.19 and 5.24 [30]. Its power could be amplified with a 25 dB gain by using a dye solution and optogalvanic spectral shapes of the D_1 and D_2 lines in Li have been observed with a very high signal-to-noise ratio, as shown in Figure 4.8 [30]. We expect that these lasers also can be used as powerful tools for isotope separation of tracers for medical diagnosis.

Analysis of SiH$_x$ Radicals

The fabrication of an amorphous silicon film by chemical vapor deposition has been a key technology in the semiconductor device industry. For accurate control of the thickness of a deposited film, quantitative analyses and the assignment of SiH$_x$ species are required. For example, UV photolysis has confirmed that an SiH$_2$ radical could emit fluorescence due to transitions between vibration energy levels. Therefore, we can expect that visible AlGaInP lasers will be used as a light source for efficient and practical spectral analyses in UV photolysis systems [29], because, due to the excitation by a pulsed ArF excimer laser, the emitted fluorescence spectra are distributed around a wavelength region of 0.6 μm, as shown in Figure 6.17 [31].

6.5   OPTICAL PUMPING OF ATOMIC CLOCKS

Stable frequency microwave oscillators have been used as key devices in microwave communication, broadcasting, navigation, earthquake prediction, astronomy, and so forth. Atomic clocks have been popularly used in these system, because they are the most reliable oscillators. Drastic improvement in the performance of these clocks has been attained by using semiconductor lasers as coherent optical pumping sources. Two examples of these improvements are described in this section.

6.5.1   Cesium Atomic Clock at 9.2 GHz

A cesium (Cs) atomic clock is a microwave oscillator, for which the transition frequency (a Bohr frequency of 9.2 GHz) between two hyperfine levels ($F = 4$, $m_F = 0$ and $F = 3$, $m_F = 0$; see Figure 6.18(a)) in the Cs ground state has been used as the frequency reference to control the frequency of a *voltage-controlled crystal oscillator*

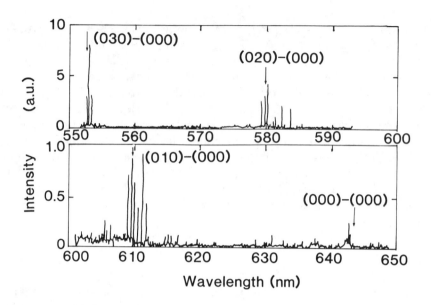

Figure 6.17 Fluorescence spectral lines of the SiH_2 radicals excited by an excimer laser (from [31]).

(VCXO). Because the frequency accuracy of this clock is very high, it has been used as a primary standard of time. This clock has been studied and developed in a number of major research institutes around the world and has been used for time keeping. A compact and portable Cs atomic clock has also been developed for satellite-borne systems.

In a conventional Cs atomic clock, the deflection of a Cs atomic beam by dc magnetic fields is used to select atoms at the energy levels of $F = 4$, $m_F = 0$ and $F = 3$, $m_F = 0$. In such a selection scheme, atoms at the $m_F \neq 0$ levels among the $2F + 1$ magnetic sublevels cannot be used, which limits the efficiency of the state selection. Furthermore, this clock has revealed inherent sources of errors limiting its frequency accuracy, such as the frequency shift induced by magnetic fields used to deflect the atomic beam. To overcome these difficulties, an optical pumping scheme has been proposed [32]. Figure 6.18(b) shows a typical experimental setup of an optically pumped Cs atomic clock. Two 852 nm AlGaAs laser frequencies, ν_1 and ν_2, are tuned to transition frequencies from $F = 4$ to $F' = 4$ and from $F = 3$ to $F' = 4$, respectively, where F' represents the quantum number of the excited state. Following the cyclic transition between the ground and excited states, due to simultaneous optical pumping by the two lasers, all atoms are transferred to the $F = 4$, $m_F = 0$ level of the ground state. Therefore, the efficiency of the state selection is increased to eight times that of the conventional magnetic deflection scheme because the conventional scheme could not utilize the atoms at $m_F \neq 0$ levels. Subsequent to this state selection, atoms pass through the two spatially isolated microwave cavities, from which a fringe-shaped microwave Ramsey spectral profile can be observed. Figure 6.19 shows a typical fringe-shaped Ramsey spectral profile [33]. (The fringe occurs due to the same principle as the optical Ramsey fringe shown in Section 3.1.) The half line-width of the center part of this fringe is very narrow and determined by the inverse of the separation between the two microwave cavities. This narrow spectral line is used as a sensitive and stable frequency demodulator to control the microwave frequency. Because eq. (3.3) shows that a narrower linewidth is a more advantageous frequency demodulator, the Ramsey resonance method has been employed favorably [34].

The third AlGaAs laser is used to measure the Ramsey spectral shape. Its frequency ν_3 is tuned to the transition frequency between $F = 3$ and $F' = 2$ to excite the atoms at the $F = 3$ level that have been deexcited from the $F = 4$ level by the microwave transition. The Ramsey spectral shape can be measured by detecting the

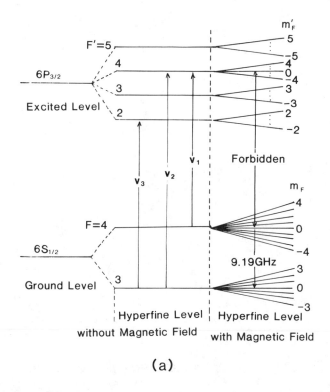

(a)

Figure 6.18 (a) Energy levels of a Cs atom. (b) A typical experimental setup of an optically pumped Cs atomic clock.

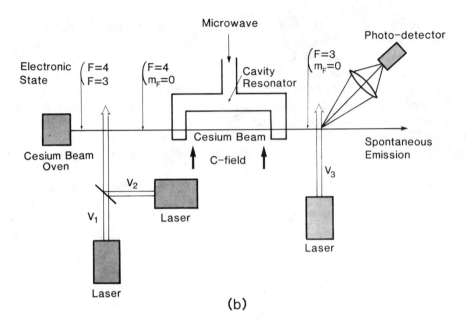

Figure 6.18 continued

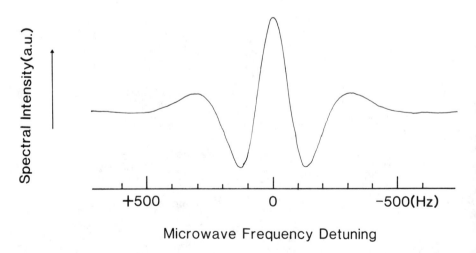

Figure 6.19 Measured Ramsey spectral shape of the microwave transition in Cs atomic clock (from [33] © 1989 IEEE).

fluorescence from the $F' = 2$ level, which is emitted by the optical pumping from $F = 3$ to $F' = 2$ of this laser.

By using these techniques (i.e., state selection by two lasers and Ramsey spectral measurements by a third laser), most problems associated with the magnetic deflection scheme can be solved. Although an optical pumping scheme was proposed over fifteen years ago [32], experiments carried out with this scheme have progressed slowly, owing to the lack of frequency-controlled AlGaAs lasers at an 852 nm wavelength. However, rapid progress in developing highly coherent AlGaAs lasers, as described in Chapter 4, led to a drastic improvement of this scheme [35]. An experimental setup is shown in Figure 6.20. Due to optical pumping, we can expect a frequency accuracy higher than 5×10^{-14} (which is the theoretical limit of conventional Cs atomic clocks) in the near future. The use of a laser cooling technique has been proposed [36] for the further improvement of this optically pumped Cs atomic clock.

Cesium Beam Tube   Semiconductor Lasers

Figure 6.20 An optically pumped Cs atomic clock (by courtesy of Y. Koga, National Research Laboratory of Metrology, 1989).

6.5.2   Rubidium Atomic Clock at 6.8 GHz

A rubidium (Rb) atomic clock has been popularly used as a compact and inexpensive microwave oscillator because its short-term frequency stability is higher than that of Cs atomic clocks, even though its frequency accuracy is lower. As shown in Figure 6.21(a), the transition frequency (a Bohr frequency of 6.8 GHz) between the two hyperfine levels in the ground state ($F = 2$, $m_F = 0$ and $F = 1$, $m_F = 0$) is used as the reference frequency to control the VCXO.

To use this transition spectral line as a frequency demodulator, its spectral profile should be detected with high sensitivity. For this purpose, atoms in the $F = 1$ level of the ground state are pumped by radiating the light tuned to the transition between the ground and the excited states. The excited atoms immediately decay to a $F = 1$ or $F = 2$ level of the ground state. As a result, the population in the $F = 2$ level of the ground state increases whereas that of the $F = 1$ level decreases; and finally, in the steady state, the population difference between these two states approaches a constant value. However, by radiating the microwave resonant to the

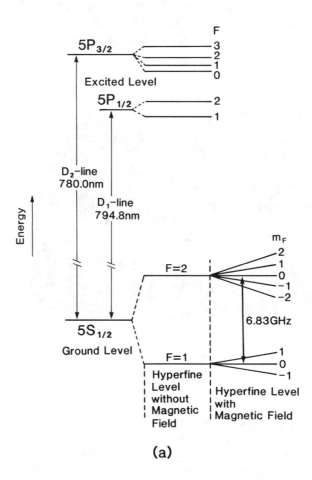

(a)

Figure 6.21 (a) Energy levels of a Rb atom. (b) Block diagram of a semiconductor laser-pumped Rb atomic clock.

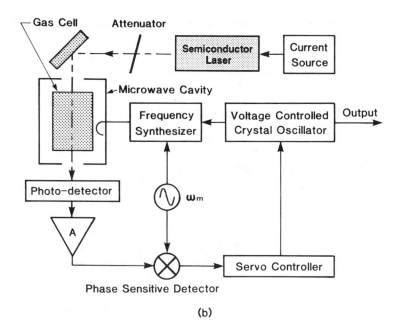

Figure 6.21 continued

Bohr frequency between these levels, this population difference is changed by the stimulated emission and absorption of microwaves. This change also varies the absorption coefficient of the pumping light. Thus, the microwave transition spectral profile can be measured by measuring the light intensity transmitted through the Rb vapor cell as a function of the microwave frequency. This technique of resonating the light and microwave simultaneously to the atoms is called *optical-microwave double resonance.* This technique increases the sensitivity of the microwave resonance spectral profile. This is because the microwave transition is measured by monitoring the optical transition, which realizes an energy amplification of 10^5 corresponding to the frequency ratio of the microwave and the light.

As was shown by eq. (3.3), the double-resonance spectral width should be narrow to detect accurately the FM noise of the microwave. Buffer gases, like Ne, Ar, and N_2, have been used to fill the Rb vapor cell to reduce the spectral width generated by the atomic collisions between Rb and these buffer gas atoms. As a result of this collisional narrowing, a spectral width as narrow as 100–500 Hz is obtained.

Conventional Rb atomic clocks have used an incoherent discharge lamp for optical pumping. However, the center frequency of the double resonance spectral profile could be shifted due to variations in lamp power. This shift, called the *light shift,* is attributed to the spectral profile deformation induced by the optical ac Stark effect. This light shift limits the long-term frequency stability of Rb atomic clocks. Furthermore, the frequency accuracy also is limited by the frequency shift induced by collisions between Rb and buffer gas atoms. For these reasons, the Rb atomic clock has been considered a secondary standard of time.

The Rb atomic clocks have been installed on-board satellites to improve performance in the *global positioning system* (GPS). For this purpose, the optical pumping scheme using a 780 nm wavelength AlGaAs laser is proposed; the system diagram is shown in Figure 6.21(b). In this scheme, using a low FM-noise semiconductor laser, the effect of microwave frequency modulation could be transferred to the optical field of the laser in the Rb vapor cell. This modulation transfer occurs due to the nonlinear susceptibility of the Rb atoms that interact with the optical and microwave fields simultaneously. Because the double-resonance spectral signal is detected by using this modulated laser light, the effect of the modulation transfer induces some sort of interference fringe on the double-resonance spectral profile, as shown in Figure 6.22(a) [37]. The spectral profile in this figure is the first derivative signal. The width of the center part of this fringe-shaped spectral profile is about 5×10^{-2} times that of a conventional lamp-pumped Rb atomic clock. The principle behind obtaining such a fringe-shaped spectral profile is equivalent to that of FM-laser spectroscopy [38]. As shown in Figure 6.22(b), such a specific spectral profile could be accurately reproduced by using the theoretical model based on the density matrix formalism of three-level atoms. It has also been confirmed that the fringe-shaped spectral profile of Figure 6.22 is equivalent to the fringe-shaped Ramsey spectral profile in a Cs atomic clock (see Figure 6.19). In Cs atomic clocks, perturbations from microwave fields are applied to Cs atoms at two separate positions along the spatial axis of the Cs atomic beam trajectory. On the other hand, in Rb atomic clocks, perturbations from optical fields are applied to Rb atoms at separate positions along the optical frequency axis as a result of modulation transfer. The effect of these separate perturbations induce a fringe on the double-resonance spectral shape. By using this narrow linewidth spectral shape as a frequency demodulator, an S/N ratio of microwave FM noise detection as high as 74 dB/$\sqrt{\text{Hz}}$ is obtained. This value corresponds to the square root of the Allan variance representing the stability as low as $7.9 \times 10^{-13}\tau^{-1/2}$ (see eq. (3.3)). This high S/N value is obtained by applying a slow negative electrical feedback to the laser so that the center frequency of the laser field spectrum is locked to the Rb optical resonance frequency [39]. Curve B of Figure 6.23 represents this value whereas curve A is a typical value for a commercially available lamp-pumped Rb atomic clock. Comparison between the curves confirms that the higher short-term frequency stability is realized.

Further improvements in short-term frequency stability are confirmed by reducing the FM noise of the laser at the Fourier frequency of the microwave modulation frequency, because the noise contained in the double resonance originates from the FM noise of the laser [40]. Because Figure 4.12 shows that the FM noise of the laser can be reduced 60 dB at the Fourier frequency of about 1 kHz (the FM

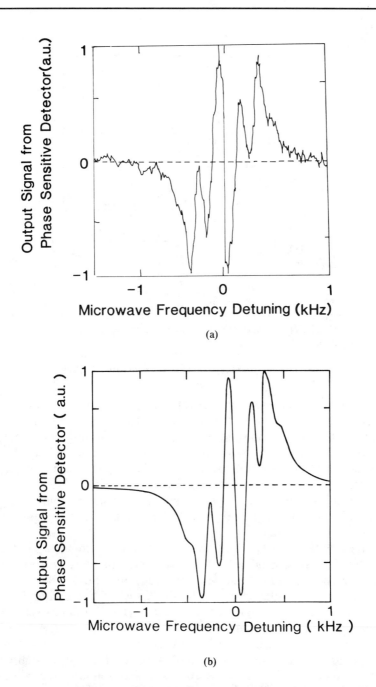

(a)

(b)

Figure 6.22 A double-resonance spectral profile of Rb: (a) measured profile, (b) calculated profile (from [37] © 1987 IEEE).

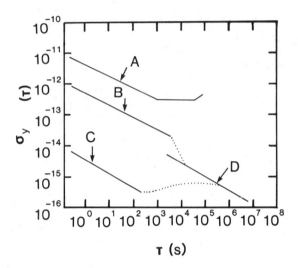

Figure 6.23 The square root of the Allan variance for frequency stabilities of Rb atomic clocks: *A* is a
commercial Rb atomic clock pumped by an incoherent Rb lamp; *B–D* are a semiconductor
laser-pumped Rb atomic clock (*B* is stability by using the spectral profile of Figure 6.22(a);
C is the shot noise limit of the stability by using the spectral profile of Figure 6.22(a); *D* is the
stability by using the self-tuning system of Figure 6.24 (from [39]).

frequency of the microwave for phase-sensitive detection), the S/N value of microwave detection can be increased to 134 dB/$\sqrt{\text{Hz}}$. However, because the actual S/N
value is limited by the shot-noise magnitude generated from the photodetector in
Figure 6.21(b), the maximum S/N value is estimated to 115 dB/$\sqrt{\text{Hz}}$ [39], even
though the laser FM noise is reduced. Equation (3.3) gives this shot-noise-limited
short-term frequency stability as $5.4 \times 10^{-15}\tau^{-1/2}$, which is represented by curve C
of Figure 6.23. It is about 1×10^3 higher than that of a conventional lamp-pumped
Rb atomic clock and even higher than that of a commercially available hydrogen
maser.

The magnitude of the light shift, due to the double-resonance spectral deformation induced by the optical ac Stark effect, can be measured quantitatively by
varying the laser power and frequency; this is shown in Figures 6.24(a) and (b) [37,
41]. A novel computer-aided electrical feedback system (see Figure 6.24(c)) was
developed to control the injection current of the laser and suppress spectral deformation. By this self-tuned system, the light shift was suppressed and the drift in
microwave frequency reduced, the result of which is shown in Figure 6.24(d) [41].
This figure confirms that the drift is reduced 40 times over that of conventional ones
for the measurement time period of 2×10^4 s. This corresponds to the improvement
of the medium-term microwave frequency stability, which can be estimated based
on the results of Figure 6.24(d). Curve D of Figure 6.23 represents the estimated

value expected from the presently developed self-tuned system. This stability could be even higher than that in commercially available portable Cs atomic clocks [39–41].

Replacement of an Rb vapor cell by an Rb atomic beam has been proposed to improve the frequency accuracy and eliminate the atomic collisions with buffer atoms [42]. The experimental setup is shown in Figure 6.25(a). After the Rb atomic beam is optically pumped by a semiconductor laser (LD1), it interacts with the microwave in the microwave cavity. The resultant microwave transition is monitored by detecting the fluorescence from the Rb atomic beam by using another semiconductor laser (LD2). Figure 6.25(b) shows the measured spectral profile, which

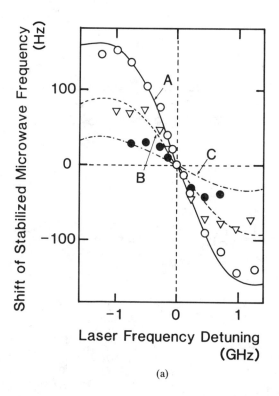

(a)

Figure 6.24 (a) Relation between the laser frequency detuning and the microwave frequency shift induced by the ac Stark effect, curves A, B, and C represent the measured results for the laser power densities $1.00\ \mu W/cm^2$, $0.36\ \mu W/cm^2$, and $0.14\ \mu W/cm^2$, respectively; (b) calculated result of the derivative of double-resonance spectral profiles for the laser frequency detunings of (A) 7.5 GHz, (B) 0, and (C) -7.5 GHz, respectively; (c) block diagram of a self-tuning system to compensate for the light shift; (d) measured microwave frequency shift normalized to the 6.8 GHz microwave frequency, closed circles and triangles are the results with and without using the self-tuning system, respectively (from [37] © 1987 IEEE and [41] © 1990 IEEE).

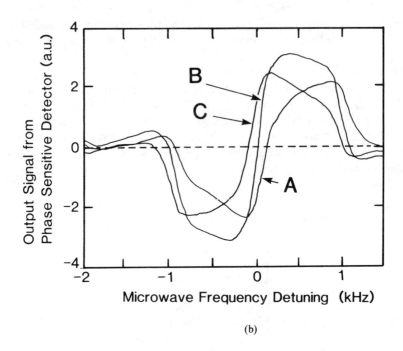

(b)

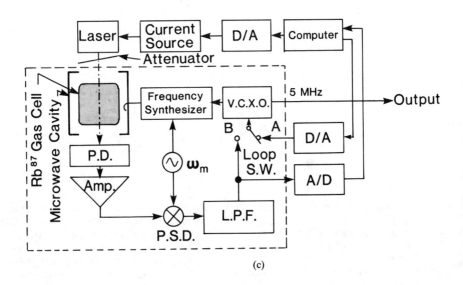

(c)

Figure 6.24 continued

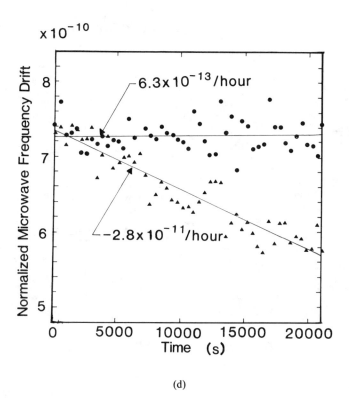

(d)

Figure 6.24 continued

also has a Ramsey-type fringe and is similar to that in Figure 6.22(a). This is due to the spatially inhomogeneous interaction between the Rb atoms and the microwave of the higher-order mode (TE_{012} mode) in the cavity. This profile is reproduced by theoretical analysis using a Bloch equation. The result is shown in Figure 6.25(c), which agrees with the curve of Figure 6.25(b). Because the linewidth of the center part of the spectral profile in Figure 6.25(b) is narrow and obtained in a nearly collision-free condition, we expect high stability and accuracy simultaneously. By substituting the signal-to-noise ratio of the spectral profile of Figure 6.25(b) into eq. (3.3), the short-term frequency stability is estimated to be $7.8 \times 10^{-13}\tau^{-1/2}$ [43]. Furthermore, frequency accuracy is estimated to be 1.3×10^{-12} by taking into account the contributions of the collisions between Rb atoms, frequency pulling of the microwave cavity modes, spatial distribution of the higher cavity modes, and misalignment of the atomic beam trajectory [43]. The principal contribution was confirmed to be from frequency pulling, which can be reduced by more careful cavity tuning.

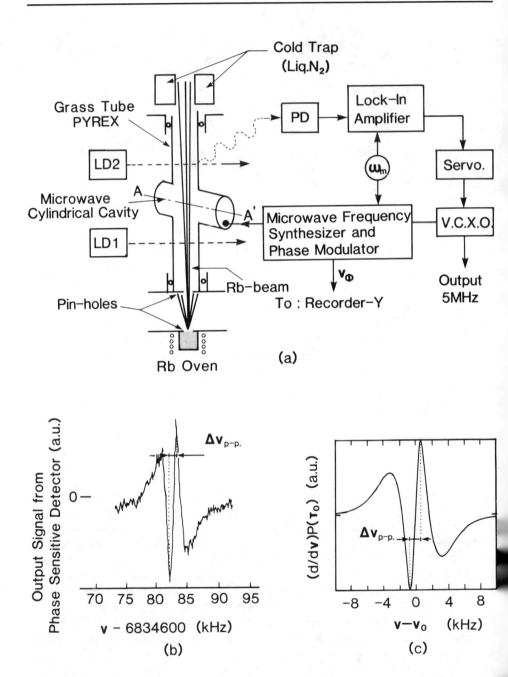

Figure 6.25 A semiconductor laser-pumped Rb atomic beam clock: (a) experimental setup; (b) measured double-resonance spectral profile; (c) calculated double-resonance spectral profile (from [42]).

Based on these experimental results, the achievement of a new primary standard of time is expected in the near future.

As a result of these intensive studies, we expect that a new high-performance, compact, and low-price Rb atomic clock will be developed in the near future and incorporated in key application systems, such as GPS, the *broadband integrated services digital network* (B-ISDN), and in a new primary standard of time.

6.6 QUANTUM OPTICS AND BASIC PHYSICS

6.6.1 High-Resolution Spectroscopy of Atoms and Molecules

High-resolution laser spectroscopy could provide accurate information on the structures and dynamic properties of the excited states of atoms and molecules. The frequency demodulators presented in Section 3.1 used the results of high-resolution spectroscopy obtained by using several low FM-noise lasers. That is, low FM-noise lasers are required to observe the narrow linewidth spectral profiles in atoms and molecules; furthermore, FM noise reduction is possible by using these spectral profiles as a high-quality frequency demodulator. Thus, laser spectroscopy and frequency control are mutually related.

Although wavelength-tunable dye lasers have been used for conventional laser spectroscopy in the visible region, spectroscopic data of atoms and molecules at the near-infrared region of about $0.7-1.6$ μm wavelength have not been documented sufficiently due to the lack of a reliable coherent light source. However, improvements in highly coherent semiconductor lasers have made possible highly sensitive and high-resolution spectroscopy in this wavelength region. The advantage of spectroscopy using these semiconductor lasers is the possibility of obtaining a wideband frequency sweep by varying the temperature or injection current of semiconductor lasers. In addition, improvement in the sensitivity of these spectrometers can be expected by employing FM laser spectroscopy [44], in which the high FM efficiency of semiconductor lasers can be used. The higher harmonics and combination tones of vibration-rotation transitions in organic molecular vapors let us observe many doppler-broadened spectral lines within a wavelength range of $0.7-1.6$ μm. Although their absorption is weak, spectral lines caused by $2\nu_1$, $2\nu_3$, or $\nu_1 + \nu_3$ vibration transitions in NH_3 and $2\nu_2 + \nu_3$ vibration transitions in H_2O have been observed at a wavelength of 1.5 μm with a detection sensitivity of 2.3×10^{-3} Torr per unit optical pass length [45]. Furthermore, those caused by the $2\nu_1 + \nu_2 + \nu_3$ vibration transition in H_2O have been measured at a wavelength range of 0.8 μm [46]. In this case, fairly strong absorptions are observed because the $2\nu_1 + \nu_2 + \nu_3$ band is coupled to the $\nu_2 + \nu_3$ band by Darling-Dennison resonance [47]. The wavelengths of these absorption lines have been calibrated within an error of $1 \times 10^{-7} \sim 1 \times 10^{-8}$. Following such pioneering work, spectroscopic data were accumulated for several organic molecular vapors; for example, spectral lines in C_2H_2 [48] were obtained by sweeping a DFB laser frequency over 1.5 THz. Furthermore, the high-resolution spectroscopy of second-harmonic vibration transitions in HCN [49] and NH_3 [50] also is obtained by DFB lasers.

A recently constructed spectrometer for the wavelength regions of $0.75 \sim 0.88$ μm, 1.3 μm, and 1.5 μm exhibited sensitivity as high as 2×10^{-6} absorption [50]. Using this spectrometer, a systematic study of the characteristics of spectral measurements of the vibration transitions in NH_3 was carried out. Results show that the transfer from normal-mode vibration to local-mode vibration is found with an increase in the vibration quantum number. These experimental data were compared with theoretical analyses and found to be in good agreement. Further improvement in the sensitivity of these spectrometers can be expected from improvement in FM laser spectroscopy [51]. Several experiments in FM laser spectroscopy already have demonstrated such progress [44]. The problem remaining in FM laser spectroscopy by semiconductor lasers is the simultaneous inducement of intensity modulation, which limits the measurement sensitivity. However, it may be possible to reduce the contribution from the IM by using the two-tone FM technique, resulting in 10 times the sensitivity of the conventional technique [52].

Spectral lines due to electronic transition in atomic vapors have been measured in the wavelength region of 0.8 μm. Systematic studies on Rb [53] and Cs [54] have been reported. For rare gases, optogalvanic spectroscopy has been employed because a great number of optogalvanic spectral lines are distributed between the near-infrared and the visible region [55]. Although sufficiently reproducible frequency measurements could be rather difficult to obtain owing to the frequency shift caused by plasma instability and the dc Stark effect, a fairly high sensitivity in measurements is obtained [56].

Because most spectral lines caused by electronic transitions in atomic vapors are distributed within the visible region, short-wavelength lasers are required for these measurements. For this purpose, a second harmonic wave generated from the active layer of an AlGaAs laser has been used to measure the strong spectral lines in K (transitions $5p^2P_{1/2} - 4s^2S_{1/2}$ and $5p^2P_{3/2} - 4s^2S_{1/2}$) and Al (transition $3p^2P_{3/2} - 4s^2S_{1/2}$) vapors at a wavelength range of 0.4 μm [57]. As shown in Figure 4.1(c), similar measurements of Rb lines, using the second harmonic wave generated internally from a 1.56 μm InGaAsP laser, also have been obtained [58]. The recently developed 0.67 μm wavelength visible AlGaInP laser can be used for laser spectroscopy of Li atoms, too. Figure 4.8 shows the optogalvanic spectral profiles of the D_1 and D_2 lines in Li. By increasing the discharge current of the hollow cathode lamp, a spectral splitting can be seen clearly (especially in the D_2 line of curve C), which is due to the dc Stark effect of Li induced by a strong electric field in the hollow cathode [30, 59].

Doppler-free spectroscopy of atomic vapors has been carried out through atomic beam or nonlinear spectroscopy. High-sensitivity atomic beam spectroscopy is carried out, for example, on Cs or Rb. An example of sensitive experimental result for the Rb atomic beam is shown in Figure 6.26 [42]. It was obtained by using a 0.78

μm AlGaAs laser and the half-linewidth of the fluorescence spectral profiles caused by the transition from $F' = 1, 2$, and 3 levels of the excited state to the $F = 2$ level of the ground state and was as narrow as 70 MHz. This linewidth was determined by the residual doppler broadening due to a 5° divergence of the atomic beam [42]; however, it is narrow enough to clearly resolve each spectral component.

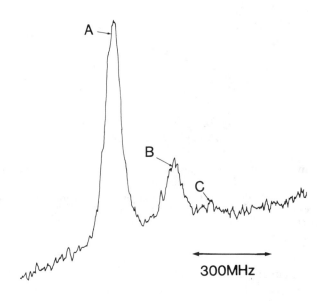

A

B

C

300MHz

Frequency

Figure 6.26 Fluorescence spectral profile of the Rb atomic beam: *A*, *B*, and *C* correspond to the transitions from $F' = 3, 2$, and 1 of the excited level to $F = 2$ of the ground level, respectively (from [42]).

As the first example of nonlinear spectroscopy, the saturated absorption technique has been employed, for example, on Cs [54] (see also Figure 4.4(b)), Rb [53, 60], and other materials. Figure 6.27(a) shows derivatives of the saturated absorption lineshapes in ^{87}Rb-D_2 obtained by using a 0.78 μm AlGaAs laser, in which 11 narrow spectral lines, including cross-resonance lines, are resolved [60]. They have linewidths as narrow as 40 MHz, which is limited by the lifetime of relevant energy levels. Their spectral strengths and positions on the abscissa agree well with those estimated by theoretical analyses, shown in Figure 6.27(b).

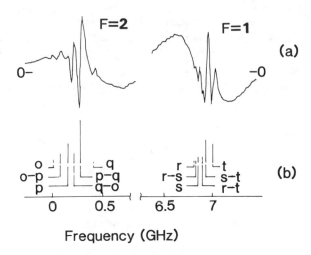

Figure 6.27 (a) Derivative of the saturated absorption lineshapes in ^{87}Rb-D_2 (from [60]). (b) Assigned spectral lines; for the symbols of transitions, refer to Figure 4.5(a); for the transition from the $F = 1$ level of the ground state, two saturated absorption lines (s and t) and three cross-resonance lines (r–s, r–t, and s–t) were observed; for the transition from $F = 2$ level, three saturated absorption lines (o, p, and q) and three cross-resonance lines (o–p, q–o, and p–q) were observed.

As the second example, optical-optical double-resonance has been carried out for the D_1 [61] and D_2 [62] lines in Rb by using 0.79 μm and 0.78 μm AlGaAs lasers, respectively. Figure 6.28 shows the double-resonance spectral shapes for the D_2 component of a ^{87}Rb atomic beam [63], which exhibit clear doppler-free spectral shapes. Because fixing the pump-laser frequency to the transition frequency between the $F = 2$ and $F' = 3$ levels resulted in saturation, the strength of the spectral component $F' = 3$ is weaker than the other two components. Figure 5.17(a) shows an experimental setup for a nonlinear pump-probe spectroscopy. Doppler-free spectral profiles due to pumping saturation from a 0.78 μm AlGaAs laser were probed using the second harmonic wave generated from a 1.56 μm InGaAsP laser active waveguide. Figure 5.18(b) shows the result of a first derivative of the doppler-free spectral shape. As described in Section 5.1.3, this spectral shape can be used as a frequency reference to stabilize the frequency of pump and probe lasers simultaneously, thus achieving a stabilized frequency link between the 0.78 μm AlGaAs and 1.56 μm InGaAsP lasers. Similar results can be expected for Li atoms by using 0.67 μm AlGaInP and 1.34 μm InGaAsP lasers.

The third example is the doppler-free two-photon spectroscopy for Li atomic vapor, carried out using a dye laser and an AlGaAs laser [64]. By using a thermoionic heat pipe diode as the sensitive detector for spectral measurements, clear spectral profiles have been obtained and the hyperfine components in ^{6}Li and ^{7}Li have been clearly resolved.

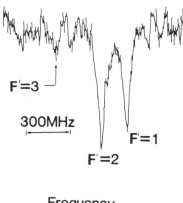

F'=3

300MHz

F'=1

F'=2

Frequency

Figure 6.28 Optical-optical double-resonance spectral shapes for the D_2 component of a ^{87}Rb atomic beam; the pump laser frequency was fixed to the transition frequency from $F = 2$ to $F' = 3$ (from [63]).

In another application of semiconductor lasers to alkali vapor spectroscopy, Rydberg states of alkali atoms can be produced by the stepwise excitation of Cs and Rb [65]. By this method, information on highly excited states can be obtained [66]. The Rydberg atoms prepared thus also have been used in an atom maser in the microwave region; that is, in one branch of the cavity QED.

The optical pumping (i.e., a technique of high-resolution spectroscopy) can be used in part of nuclear physics in which semiconductor lasers are used as coherent pumping sources. The optical pumping of atoms can be interpreted as the transfer of angular momenta of photons to the electrons in atoms. The angular momenta induced in the electrons then can be transferred to the nuclei of atoms by electron-nuclear magnetic interaction process. By such transfers, optical pumping can align the direction of nuclear spinning in atoms. This nuclear spin alignment can be observed by a laser spectrometer, which means that spectroscopy of the nuclei of atoms is possible.

An inert gas atom in its ground state has no magnetic coupling with the nucleus. Furthermore, as this atom is chemically inactive and isolated, the lifetime of its nuclear spin is very long. The nuclear resonance of this atom can realize a resonance spectral linewidth as narrow as 0.2 μHz. We can expect that the spectral shift as low as several nHz is measured for this narrow spectral line, for which very high-resolution laser spectroscopy is required. Even though direct optical pumping is not applied to the inert gas atoms, their nuclear spin alignment has been achieved by utilizing the spin-exchange collisions between the inert gas atoms and foreign atoms. For such indirect optical pumping, semiconductor lasers have been employed as pumping sources [67].

6.6.2 Test of Basic Principles of Physics

Four examples of the tests of basic principles of physics are reviewed in this section.

The Test of Quantum Electrodynamics

This test can be carried out by measuring the Lamb shift in muonic atoms [68]. A semiconductor laser is a promising candidate as the light source for accurate measurement of the Lamb shift. A frequency controlled 0.73 μm AlGaAs laser is used as the master laser for injection locking a high-power solid-state alexandrite laser to reduce its FM noise. The third harmonic radiation from the injection-locked alexandrite laser can be generated by using nonlinear optical crystals, such as KDP and ADP. This ultraviolet light can be used as a pumping source for muonic atoms.

The Test of Symmetry Violation with Regard to Time Reversal

This symmetry violation has been observed by carefully measuring the decay process of the K_0 meson [69, 70]. Although a lot of theoretical models have been proposed to explain the origin of the violation, no proof of the validity of the theoretical model has yet been provided due to lack of systematic experimental results. Preliminary experimental study began using, for example, neutrons, atoms, and molecules. Measurement of the *electric dipole moment* (EDM) d of an atom was tried recently because the nonzero value of d suggests that symmetry is violated with respect to time reversal. By using the experimental setup shown in Figure 6.29 [71], the value of d of an ^{129}Xe atom was measured as $d = (-0.5 \pm 1.8) \times 10^{-47}$ C · m by using a semiconductor laser. This result means that the d of ^{129}Xe is smaller than 1×10^{-47} C · m even if it exists. Because Xe is an inert gas atom, a spin-exchange collision with the optically pumped Rb atom was utilized to realize the nuclear spin alignment. A 3-mW AlGaAs laser, tuned to the D_1 line of Rb (794.9 nm wavelength) was used as the pumping source. Because the decay time of the precession of nuclear spin of the Xe atom was as long as 500 s, long-term continuous measurements were repeated to reduce measurement error. To improve the accuracy of this long-term measurement, highly coherent semiconductor lasers are indispensable. Further improvement in accuracy can be expected by using higher-power semiconductor lasers.

The Test of Parity Nonconservation

A weak interaction between elemental particles in atoms has been predicted by the standard electroweak theory developed by Glashow, Weinberg, and Salam [72] Experimental tests of this theory have been carried out in the field of high-energy

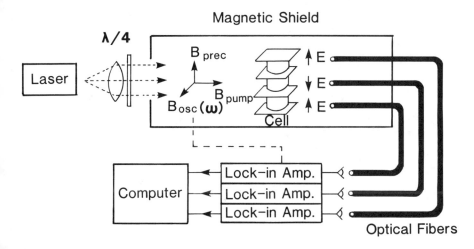

Figure 6.29 Experiment to measure the electric dipole moment of ^{129}Xe (from [71]).

physics using a huge accelerator. However, precision laser spectroscopy was found to be more convenient and less expensive in these tests [72, 73]. Because the parity conservation of the wave function of the atom could be violated by a weak interaction, the weak optical transition due to this violation can be detected by a carefully designed, sensitive laser spectrometer. Frequency controlled semiconductor lasers also have been used. Figure 6.30 shows an experiment to detect the change in polarization of the transmitted light through the Pb atomic vapor, in which a 1.3 μm InGaAsP laser was used as the coherent light source [74]. The optical transition caused by magnetic dipole interaction in Pb atoms was monitored by detecting the change in polarization induced by parity nonconservation. This spectrometer, employing polarization modulation and phase-sensitive detection, showed the sensitivity of polarization rotation measurement as high as 0.1 μ rad. Stark coefficients in Cs atoms also have been accurately measured by using a carefully frequency-controlled AlGaAs laser, by which several structural constants of Cs have been estimated to test the parity nonconservation [75].

The Test of Space Anisotropy

The special theory of relativity claims that absolute space does not exist; that is, it is impossible to measure any motion relative to the observer. A famous Michelson-Morley experiment tried to detect the motion relative to the ether [76]. As an improved experiment, the ratio between the precession frequencies of the optically pumped ^{201}Hg ($I = \frac{3}{2}$) atoms and ^{199}Hg ($I = \frac{1}{2}$) atoms were precisely measured, and the dependence of the ratio on the relative direction between the precession axes and

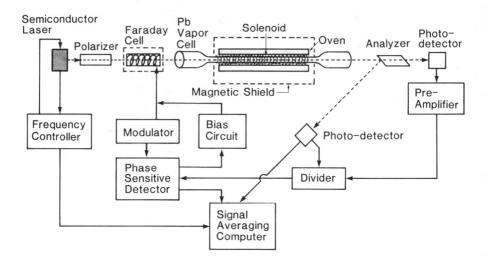

Figure 6.30 Experiment to test parity nonconservation of Pb atoms. Pb atomic vapor in an oven was irradiated by a 1.3 μm semiconductor laser whose wavelength is in resonance with the magnetic dipole of Pb atom, and the polarization of the transmitting laser beam was detected (from [74]).

the celestial sphere was checked [77]. Because this dependence means that the direction of observer's motion can be detected, it violates the invariance of Lorentz transformation. Furthermore, a theoretical model claiming that the gravitational field can couple not only with the particle mass but also with its spin also has been proposed [78, 79]. This model is related also to the "fifth force," which has been discussed recently [80]. In the experiment of Hg atoms described earlier, a frequency shift value as low as 1 μHz was derived from the experimental data obtained by continuous long-term measurement over 15 days. As this magnitude of the shift corresponds to a variation in the mass as low as 10^{-21} eV while the mass of nucleus is several GeV, this result shows very high precision measurement. Although this experiment found no significant deviation from isotropy of space, it gave the upper limit of the coupling constant in each theoretical model. If a nonzero value can be detected, as in the EDM experiment, the theory in basic physics should be modified drastically.

Although semiconductor lasers have not yet been used in the experiments on Hg atoms, they will be in the near future, because the efficiency of nonlinear wavelength conversion of semiconductor lasers has increased rapidly, as will be described in Section 7.2. Furthermore, semiconductor lasers will be employed to induce nuclear spin alignment in atoms. In particular, spin-aligned ^{3}He are essential to this field of study, as well as spin-aligned electrons and positrons. For aligning the spin on ^{3}He nuclei, a 300 mW output and 1.08 μm wavelength color center laser (pumped by a 0.89 μm wavelength dye laser) have been used, and alignment efficiency as high as 70% achieved [81]. However, because this laser system is very complicated and expensive, the dye and the color center lasers should be replaced by a high-power semiconductor laser and a semiconductor laser-pumped solid-state laser, such as a LNA laser, respectively. As another possibility, the color center laser could be replaced by a strained quantum well semiconductor laser. A variety of experiments using spin-aligned ^{3}He will become possible through using one of these simplified laser systems.

In the preceding examples, long-term and highly sensitive data acquisitions were required by using the techniques of an optical pumping and laser spectroscopy. For these purposes, the use of stable and highly coherent semiconductor lasers become more significant. Furthermore, improvement in the performance of the laser spectrometer can be expected if tunable low-noise solid-state lasers are employed by using semiconductor lasers as optical pumping sources.

6.6.3 Manipulations of Atoms and Ions

The contents of this section have been partly described in Section 3.1. That is, experimental studies on the deceleration of atomic motion in vacuum (laser cooling [82]) and confinement of atoms in a volume limited by laser beams have been recently developed owing to improvement in the laser frequency control technique. By radiating the laser beam on the atoms from direction opposite the trajectory of the atomic beam, photons with an energy lower than the energy difference between the two atomic energy levels are absorbed due to the first-order doppler effect. The photon energy emitted spontaneously after this absorption is equal to the energy difference and is larger than the absorbed photon energy. Therefore, by repeating these absorption and spontaneous emission processes, the atomic motion is decelerated by letting loose the thermal kinetic energy of atoms. As a result of this laser cooling technique, the relativistic phenomenon of the second-order doppler effect, and thus the shift in center frequency of the atomic spectral profile, can be reduced, which can be used advantageously as a high-quality frequency demodulator, as described in Section 3.1. The lowest equivalent temperature of the cooled atom is lower than the value determined by the doppler effect (<40 μK) [83, 84]. Furthermore, in a recent experiment, a temperature lower than 2 μK has been obtained, which corresponds to a thermal velocity of 3 cm/s [85]. This is even lower than the value determined by recoiling between an atom and photon. The technique of atomic badminton has been proposed [86], as an advanced method for manipulating atoms, and an atomic badminton experiment with cooled and slow atoms recently was performed using a gradient-light force mirror; that is, the gradient force of an evanescent wave from a Dove prism on which the cooled atom dropped [87].

A certain number of atoms (e.g., 1×10^7 atoms) with an atomic density as high as 1×10^{11}/cm^3 [88] can be confined to a limited volume in vacuum for more than several minutes. Such a high-density confined atomic mass exhibits specific characteristics that are similar to those of viscous fluids; as a result, this confined atomic mass has been called *optical molasses*. Figure 6.31 shows the optical molasses of Na atoms. For these experiments, dye lasers have been conventionally used. However, recent attention has focussed on the advantages of using the high efficiency of frequency modulation and controllability of semiconductor lasers. Figure 6.32 shows an experimental setup using $0.85~\mu\text{m}$ AlGaAs lasers for optical pumping, laser cooling, and producing optical molasses of Cs atoms [89]. Laser cooling of Rb atoms [90] and rare gases [91] also has been carried out using AlGaAs lasers. These experiments use expensive, complicated atomic beam apparatus; however, a simple experimental configuration using an inexpensive Cs vapor cell has also produced optical molasses [92].

The atomic fountain has been proposed as a method combining optical Ramsey resonance and laser cooling [93]. In it an atomic beam is spouted upward, as shown in Figure 6.33. Here, only a single laser beam (1) is required to generate optical Ramsey fringes, and the atomic beam is irradiated by this laser beam from a transverse direction. If the atomic beam is simultaneously irradiated by the cooling laser

Figure 6.31 Optical molasses of Na atoms. The elliptic image is the optical molasses, and the bright part on the right is the nozzle to form the Na atomic beam (by courtesy of S. Chu, AT&T Bell Laboratories, 1986).

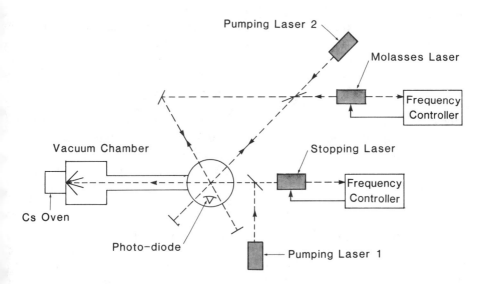

Figure 6.32 Experiment of laser cooling for Cs atoms. By using several semiconductor lasers, deceleration, cooling, and even production of optical molasses were performed for Cs atomic beam (from [89]).

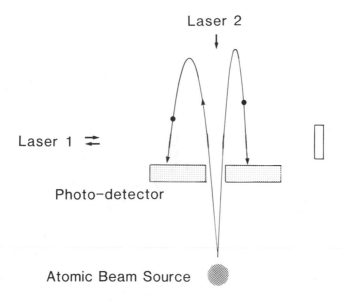

Figure 6.33 Schematic explanation of the atomic fountain: laser 1 is for producing the Ramsey fringe, and laser 2 is for laser cooling (from [93]).

(2) from a longitudinal direction, the atomic beam would be decelerated and then (1) the atoms would fall down. Thus, the atoms cross laser beam twice, by which a very narrow linewidth Ramsey spectral shape can be obtained. Based on this idea, a Ramsey fringe in the microwave frequency region was observed by using an Na atomic beam decelerated by laser cooling [94]. As in Figure 6.34, its spectral width was as narrow as 2 Hz. If these fringes are observed in the optical frequency region in the future, this narrow spectral shape could be used as a high-quality frequency demodulator, as described in Section 3.1. For example, because the transition spectral linewidth in Na is as narrow as 40 kHz when it is cooled down to several μK, the field spectral linewidth of the laser used for these cooling experiments should be narrower than 40 kHz. Furthermore, the laser frequency should be swept accurately over 1 GHz, for which the techniques described in Chapters 4 and 5 will be required.

The experimental study of ion trap (i.e., confining ions to the limited volume of an electromagnetic potential) has advanced remarkably by simultaneously making use of the laser cooling technique. Even in a cooled atomic beam, a shift in the center frequency of the atoms' resonant spectral shape could not be neglected due to collisions between cooled and confined atoms. To eliminate this shift, a single atom

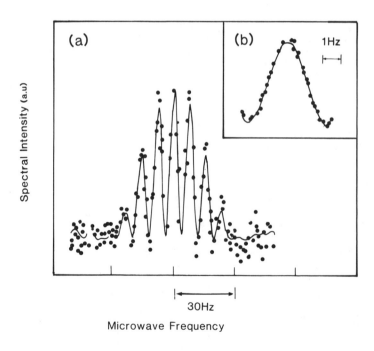

Figure 6.34 Microwave Ramsey fringe obtained with an atomic fountain: (a) the whole profile; (b) magnification of the center part of the profile (from [94]).

should be prepared in a vacuum. If this atom is stopped by the technique of laser cooling, the second-order doppler effect is eliminated, too. For this purpose, it is more advantageous to use ions than neutral atoms because a deep electromagnetic trap can be used for ions. A Penning trap composed of dc electric and magnetic fields or a Paul trap composed of a dc electric and RF magnetic fields has been employed. Figure 6.35(a) shows an experimental setup in which an ion is injected into a Paul trap by an electron gun and trapped at the minimum of the trap as a result of laser cooling [95]. Figure 6.35(b) shows a single Hg^+ ion at rest in the trap. Consequently, an ionic state, almost completely isolated from its surrounding circumstances, is achieved. This ionic state can be used as an ideal frequency demodulator in Section 3.1.

In quantum mechanics, the temporal variation of physical phenomenon is described by a transition process from one quantum state to another. This transition has been called a *quantum jump*. Because this jump is an inherently discrete stochastic phenomenon, it cannot be observed as long as macroscopic samples composed of a great number of atoms are employed for the experiments. However, the

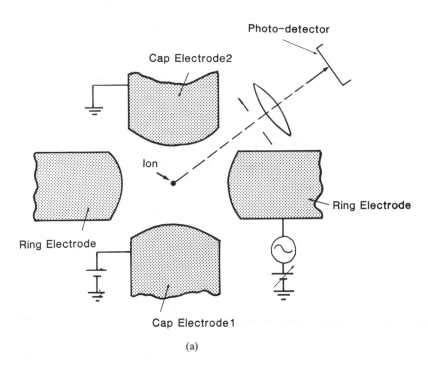

(a)

Figure 6.35 (a) Experiment combining the laser cooling and the ion trap for stopping ions (from [95]). (b) Hg^+ ion at rest (by courtesy of W. Itano, National Institute of Standard and Technology, 1990); arrow points to the fluorescence from one ion.

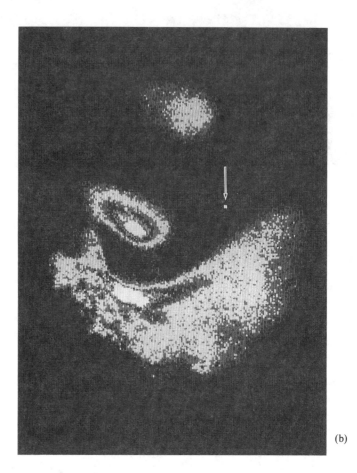

(b)

Figure 6.35 continued

techniques of the single ion trap have provided a way of observing the quantum jump in a cooled and confined single ion [96–100]. Although this phenomenon was first discussed by Bohr in 1913 [96], its experimental confirmation was not finalized until just recently. As shown in Figure 6.36(a), the on-off time-sequential signal demonstrates that the quantum jump can be clearly observed by counting the number of photons emitted from the Ba^+ [99]. Figure 6.36(b) diagrams the energy level relevant to this phenomenon.

As a result of further improvement in the performance of the trapping technique, squeezing (see Section 7.4) between uncertainties of the momentum and the position of the ion was observed [101]. Furthermore, because laser cooling can reduce the thermal kinetic energy below the Coulomb potential energy, several interesting phenomena can be seen:

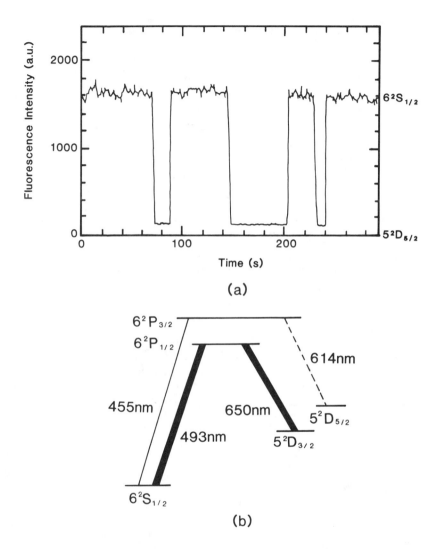

Figure 6.36 Result of the quantum jump experiment: (a) time sequence of the fluorescence emitted from the Ba$^+$, representing the quantum jump; (b) energy levels of Ba$^+$ (from [99]).

1. Formation of a strongly coupled plasma. One-component plasma is formed by trapped ions, which is equivalent to the group of charged particles fixed in the homogeneously oppositely charged background [102].
2. Formation of a body-centered cubic crystal. A macroscopic Wigner crystal can be formed when each cooled ion is fixed at the stable point of the potential [103].

3. The possibility of deterministic chaos. A crystal described in phenomenon (2) can be collapsed under certain values of trapping parameters, such as RF field strength and laser power. As a result, a sort of ionic cloud can be formed in which each ion revolves along a large diameter trajectory. It has been confirmed that the dynamic motion of this ionic cloud corresponded to the deterministic chaos which was induced by the nonlinearity of Coulomb interaction [104]. Furthermore, it was confirmed that the motion of two trapped ions exhibited deterministic chaos due solely to ion-ion collisions, it was confirmed [105]. By increasing the number of trapped ions, they can be used for simulation experiments on the dynamics of mesoscopic crystals, which are the microcrystals used for microelectronic or -optical devices in the future.
4. The possibility of a micromemory. Ions can be maintained in an upper energy level if the spontaneous emission from the upper level can be inhibited by the cavity QED method (see Section 6.6.4), which can realize the micro memory (i.e., one bit is stored in each ion).
5. Emission of nonclassical photons from the trapped single ion. The emitted photon follows the sub-Poissonian statistics [106]. We can expect this sort of nonclassical photon emission process to lead to novel light emitting devices in the future.

Using these trapped ions as high-quality frequency demodulators, as described in Section 3.1, also has been studied [107]. Figure 6.37(a) shows the energy levels of Hg^+ as used in the ion trap experiments. The transition used for laser cooling is $6^2S_{1/2} - 6^2P_{1/2}$, whose resonance wavelength is 194 nm. Because the $6^2D_{3/2}$ is a metastable level, the spectral linewidth of the transition $6^2S_{1/2} - 6^2D_{3/2}$ (282 nm resonance wavelength) is as narrow as 2 Hz [95], which can be used as a very high-quality opti-

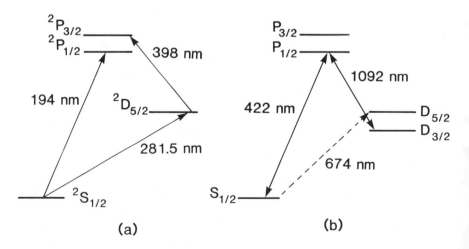

Figure 6.37 Energy levels of (a) Hg^+ and (b) Sr^+.

cal frequency demodulator. However, as these resonance wavelengths are in the visible-to-ultraviolet region, several expensive dye lasers and their second harmonic or sum-frequency radiations have to be used. Further, the efficiency of the wavelength conversion is rather low in these short wavelength regions. To overcome such difficulties, the use of easily controllable semiconductor lasers has been examined. Figures 6.36(b) and 6.37(b) show the energy levels of Ba^+ and Sr^+, respectively. Because the resonance wavelengths of the transitions in these ions are close to the emission wavelengths of semiconductor lasers, their second harmonics, and strained quantum well semiconductor lasers, we expect that expensive dye laser systems will be replaced by these novel lasers in the near future. These laser systems also can trap Ca^+.

6.6.4 Cavity Quantum Electrodynamics (Cavity QED)

As briefly described at the beginning of Chapter 3, the spontaneous emissions from atoms can be enhanced or inhibited by using a microcavity of about one-wavelength

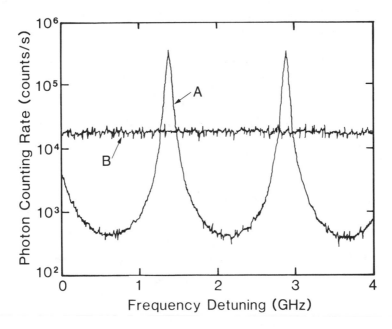

Figure 6.38 Experiment on the spontaneous emission control of Yb atoms in a Fabry-Perot cavity (from [109]). The laser frequency radiated to the Yb atoms coincides with the resonance frequency of Yb atoms. The vertical axis corresponds to the spontaneous emission intensity of Yb atoms in a confocal Fabry-Perot cavity, and the horizontal axis corresponds to the detuning between the resonance frequency of Yb atoms and that of the Fabry-Perot cavity: A is the result obtained using the Fabry-Perot cavity; B is the result without using the Fabry-Perot cavity (i.e., the spontaneous emission intensity in free space).

dimension. At the initial stage of the cavity QED study, experiments were carried out in the microwave frequency region [108]. In these experiments, several AlGaAs lasers were used as multistep optical pumping sources to excite the atoms to Rydberg states so that they would have a large transition dipole moment. A controlled rate of spontaneous emission and specific Rabi oscillation driven by vacuum fluctuations were observed by using a microcavity and single atom maser [108]. For example, to prepare the Cs atoms with a large transition dipole moment, AlGaAs lasers were used as pumping sources. Due to the technical difficulty of fabricating a microcavity in the optical frequency region, experiments on optical cavity QED were carried out by installing atoms in a high-finesse and mode-degenerated confocal Fabry-Perot cavity. As shown in Figure 6.38, the enhancement and inhibition of spontaneous emission from Yb atoms was observed at resonant and nonresonant frequencies of the confocal Fabry-Perot cavity, respectively [109].

Experiments on single-atom lasers also have progressed steadily. As shown in Figures 6.39(a) and (b), FM sidebands have been observed on the spontaneous emission spectral lines from Na atoms in the high-finesse Fabry-Perot cavity and attributed to vacuum Rabi oscillations [110] (refer also to Section 7.5). The cavity QED technique could become useful in developing new light-emitting semiconductor devices; for example, low-threshold semiconductor lasers. For this purpose, the Fabry-Perot microcavity with optical wavelength dimensions, as shown in Figure 6.40 [111], can be used. The enhancement and inhibition of spontaneous emission from a semiconductor quantum well have demonstrated using multilayer distrib-

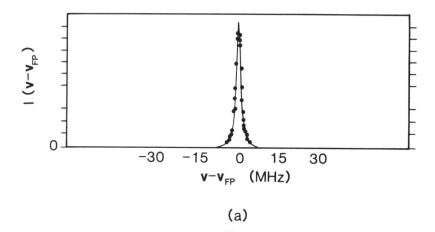

(a)

Figure 6.39 Experimental results of measuring the vacuum Rabi oscillation in Na atoms (from [110]): (a) the spectral profile of the empty Fabry-Perot cavity; (b) the spectral profile of the cavity with Na atoms. This profile has two peaks representing the FM sidebands due to the vacuum Rabi oscillation; ν_{FP} is the cavity resonance frequency.

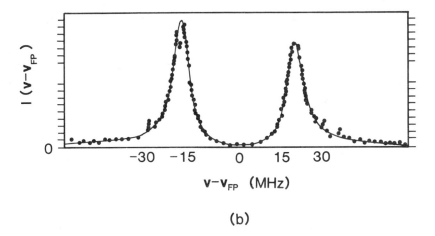

$v-v_{FP}$ (MHz)

(b)

Figure 6.39 continued

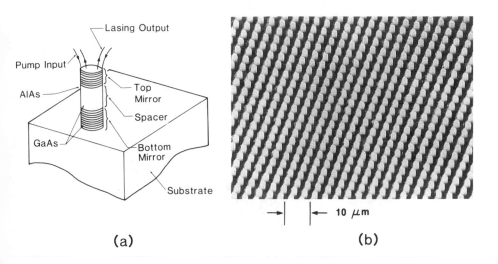

(a) (b)

Figure 6.40 A Fabry-Perot microcavity employing a semiconductor device fabrication technique. (a) Schematic of the device structure (from [111]). Its diameter and length are 1.5 μm and 4.0 μm, respectively. (b) Photograph of the two-dimensional array of the microcavities (by the courtesy of J. Jewell, AT&T Bell Laboratories, 1991).

uted Bragg reflectors as the microcavity [112]. Although the study of optical cavity QED is still in the early stages of development, we expect new and stable semiconductor lasers to be developed using the cavity QED technique. For example, because the enhancement of spontaneous emission may increase the quantum efficiency of a laser, lasers can be highly biased laser, that is, far above the oscillation threshold, thereby realizing a very low FM-noise laser.

REFERENCES

[1] Gordon, J.P., "Quantum Effects in Communication Systems," *Proc. IRE,* Vol. 50, No. 9, September 1982, pp. 1898–1908.
[2] Glance, B.S., and O. Scaramucci, "High-Performance Dense FDM Coherent Optical Network," *IEEE J. on Selected Areas in Communication,* Vol. 8, No. 6, August 1990, pp. 1043–1047.
[3] Ohtsu, M., M. Murata, and M. Kourogi, "FM Noise Reduction and Subkilohertz Linewidth of an AlGaAs Laser by Negative Electrical Feedback," *IEEE J. Quantum Electronics,* Vol. 26, No. 2, February 1990, pp. 231–241.
[4] Wang, Y., and W.R. Leeb, "Sensitivity Analysis and Performance Optimization of an Optical Costas Phase-Locked Loop," *J. Optical Communication,* Vol. 8, No. 1, March 1987, pp. 29–31.
[5] Wang, Y., and W.R. Leeb, "Costas Loop Self-Homodyne Experiment for a Diode Laser Receiver," *Electronics Letters,* Vol. 22, No. 13, June 1986, pp. 686–687.
[6] Hodgkinson, T.G., "Costas Loop Analysis for Coherent Optical Receivers," *Electronics Letters,* Vol. 22, No. 7, March 1986, pp. 394–396.
[7] Grant, M.A., W.C. Michie, M.J. Fletcher, "The Performance of Optical Phase-Locked Loops in the Presence of Nonnegligible Loop Propagation Delay," *IEEE J. Lightwave Technology,* Vol. LT-5, No. 4, April 1987, pp. 592–597.
[8] Kazovsky, L.G., "Decision-Driven Phase-Locked Loop for Optical Homodyne Receivers: Performance Analysis and Laser Linewidth Requirements," *J. Lightwave Technology,* Vol. LT-3, No. 6, December 1985, pp. 1238–1247.
[9] Cheng, Y.-H., T. Okoshi, and O. Ishida, "Performance Analysis and Experiment of a Homodyne Receiver Insensitive to Both Polarization and Phase Fluctuations," *J. Lightwave Technology,* Vol. 7, No. 2, February 1989, pp. 368–374.
[10] Marshalek, R.G., and G.A. Koepf, "Comparison of Optical Technologies for Intersatellite Links in a Global Telecommunications Network," *Optical Engineering,* Vol. 27, No. 8, August 1988, pp. 663–676.
[11] Ohtsu, M., and S. Araki, "Using a 1.5 μm DFB InGaAsP Laser in a Passive Ring Cavity-Type Fiber Gyroscope," *Applied Optics,* Vol. 26, No. 3, February 1987, pp. 464–470.
[12] Sagnac, G., "L'ether luminux demontre par l'effect du vent relatif d'ether dams un interferometre en rotation uniforme," *Compt. Rend.,* Vol. 157, October 1913, pp. 708–717.
[13] Carroll, R., C.D. Coccoli, D. Cardarelli, G.T. Coate, "The Passive Resonator Fiber Optic Gyro and Comparison to the Interferometer Fiber Gyro," *Proc. of Fiber Optic Gyros,* 10th Anniversary Conf. of SPIE, Cambridge, September 1986, Int. Society for Optical Engineers, Bellinghamm, WA, 1986, pp. 169–177.
[14] Imai, T., K. Nishide, H. Ochi, and M. Ohtsu, "The Passive Ring Resonator Fiber Optic Gyro Using Modulatable High Coherent Laser Diode Module," The Fiber Optics Gyros, SPIE OE/FIBERS '91, Boston, September 1991, paper number 1585-17.
[15] Lambeck, K., *The Earth's Variable Rotation: Geophysical Causes and Consequences,* Cambridge University Press, London, 1980, Chapter 8.

[16] Nishimura, T., "Micro-measurement Systems by Lasers," *Proc. of the Seminar on Optical Measurements,* May 1989, Tokyo, Society of Optical Measurement Instruments of Japan, Tokyo, 1989, pp. 1–10 [in Japanese].

[17] Binnig, G., and H. Rohrer, "Scanning Tunneling Microscopy," *Helvetia Physics Acta,* Vol. 55, No. 6, May 1982, pp. 726–735.

[18] Binnig, G., C.F. Quate, and C. Gerber, "Atomic Force Microscope," *Physics Review Letters,* Vol. 56, No. 9, March 1986, pp. 930–933.

[19] Pohl, D.W., W. Denk, and M. Lanz, "Optical Stethoscopy: Image Recording with Resolution $\lambda/20$," *Applied Physics Letters,* Vol. 44, No. 7, April 1984, pp. 651–653.

[20] Reddick, R.C., R.J. Warmack, and T.L. Ferrell, "New Form of Scanning Optical Microscopy," *Physics Review B,* Vol. 39, No. 1, January 1989, pp. 767–770.

[21] Ohtsu, M., K. Nakagawa, S. Jiang, and N. Tomita, "Super-Resolution Photon Scanning Tunneling Microscope," *Tech. Digest of the Third Optoelectronics Conf.,* July 1990, ed. Makuhari Messe, Institute of Electronics, Information and Communication Engineering, Tokyo, 1990, paper number 12D1-1.

[22] Jiang, S., N. Tomita, K. Nakagawa, and M. Ohtsu, "Superresolution Photon Scanning Tunneling Microscope Using Diode Lasers," Proc. Conf. on Lasers and Elecro-Optics, Baltimore, May 12–17, 1991, paper number CTh05

[23] Fukuda, M., I. Ogasawara, A. Nishimura, H. Suganuma, and S. Suzuki, "Characteristics of Crosstalk in Four-Core Graded-Index Multicore Fiber," *Tech. Digest of Optical Fiber Communication Conf.,* Sixth Int. Conf. on Integrated Optics and Optical Fiber Communication, OFC/IOOC '87, January 1987, Reno, Optics Society of America, and LEOS of IEEE, Washington, DC, 1987, paper number WI7.

[24] Takeuchi, N., "Development of Pseudo-Random Modulation CW Lidar and Its Application to Field Measurements," Research Rep. from the Nat. Institute for Environmental Studies, Japan, No. 122, 1989.

[25] Okano, S., M. Taguchi, and H. Fukunishi, "Development of a Laser Heterodyne Spectrometer Using a Tunable Diode Laser as a Local Oscillator (III)," *Proc. 13th Japanese Laser Sensing Symp.,* October 1989, Fukuoka [Laser Radar Society of Japan], Tokyo, 1989, paper number B7 [in Japanese].

[26] Yamanaka, C., chief ed., *Laser Handbook,* Ohmsha Publishing, Tokyo, 1978 [in Japanese].

[27] Streatere, A.D., J. Mooibroek, and J.P. Woerdman, "Enhanced Efficiency in Separation of Rb Isotopes by Light-Induced Drift with the Use of a Diode Laser with Relaxation Sidebands," *Applied Physics Letters,* Vol. 52, No. 8, February 1988, pp. 602–604.

[28] Lawrenz, J., A. Obrebski, and K. Niemax, "Measurement of Isotope Ratios by Doppler-Free Laser Spectroscopy, Applying Semiconductor Diode Lasers and Thermoionic Diode Detection," *Analytic Chemistry,* Vol. 59, No. 8, April 1987, pp. 1232–1236.

[29] Ohtsu, M., "Investigation on Applicability of Visible Semiconductor Lasers to Elementary Analysis," Proc. First Meeting on Lightwave Sensing Technology, June 1988, Tokyo, Lightwave Sensing and Technology Research Society Group, Japan Society of Applied Physics, Tokyo, paper number LST1-4 [in Japanese].

[30] Ohtsu, M., H. Suzuki, K. Nemoto, and Y. Teramachi, "Narrow-Linewidth Tunable Visible InGaAlP Laser, Application to Spectral Measurements of Lithium, and Power Amplification," *Japan J. Applied Physics,* Vol. 29, No. 8, August 1990, pp. L1463–L1465.

[31] Inoue, G., and M. Suzuki, "Laser-Induced Fluorescence of the SiH_2 Radical," *Chemical Physics Letters,* Vol. 105, No. 6, April 1984, pp. 641–644.

[32] Picque, J.L., "Hyperfine Optical Pumping of a Cesium Atomic Beam and Applications," *Metrologia,* Vol. 13, 1977, pp. 115–119.

[33] Ohshima, S., Y. Nakadan, and Y. Koga, "The Optically Pumped Cs Frequency Standard at the NRLM," *IEEE Trans. on Instruments and Measurements,* Vol. IM-37, No. 8, September 1988, pp. 409–413.

[34] Ramsey, N.F., *Molecular Beams,* Oxford University Press, Oxford, 1956.

[35] Nakadan, Y., S. Ohshima, T. Ikegami, and Y. Koga, "Characteristics of the Optically Pumped Cesium Beam Frequency Standard at NRLM (I)," *Extended Abstracts,* 49th Autumn Meeting, October 1988, Toyama, Japan Society of Applied Physics, Tokyo, 1988, paper number 4aZL1 [in Japanese].

[36] Sesko, D.W., and C.E. Wieman, "Observation of the Cesium Clock Transition in Laser-Cooled Atoms," *Optics Letters,* Vol. 14, No. 5, March 1989, pp. 269–271.

[37] Hashimoto, M., and M. Ohtsu, "Experiments on a Semiconductor Laser Pumped Rubidium Atomic Clock," *IEEE J. Quantum Electronics,* Vol. QE-23, No. 4, April 1987, pp. 446–451.

[38] Hashimoto, M., and M. Ohtsu, "Modulation Transfer and Optical Stark Effect in a Rubidium Atomic Clock Pumped by a Semiconductor Laser," *J. Optics Society of America, B,* Vol. 6, No. 10, October 1989, pp. 1777–1789.

[39] Ohtsu, M., M. Hashimoto, H. Furuta, and H. Suzuki, "Performance Evaluations of a Semiconductor Laser Pumped Rubidium Atomic Clock," *Second Workshop on the Precise Phase Locked Network,* June 1989, Tokyo, Institute of Electric Engineering of Japan, Tokyo, 1989, paper number 2-1 [in Japanese].

[40] Ohtsu, M., M. Hashimoto, and H. Suzuki, "Performance Evaluation of a Semiconductor Laser Pumped Rb Atomic Clock," *Extended Abstracts,* 50th Autumn Meeting, Japan Society of Applied Physics, Tokyo, 1989, paper number 29aX5 [in Japanese].

[41] Hashimoto, M., and M. Ohtsu, "A Novel Method to Compensate for the Effect of Light Shift in a Rubidium Atomic Clock Pumped by a Semiconductor Laser," *IEEE Trans. on Instruments and Measurement,* Vol. 39, No. 3, June 1990, pp. 458–462.

[42] Furuta, H., H. Suzuki, and M. Ohtsu, "Observation of Ramsey-Type Resonant Fringe Using a Cylindrical Microwave Cavity for a Diode Laser-Pumped Rb Beam Atomic Clock," *Japan J. Applied Physics,* Vol. 30, No. 3, March 1991, pp. 596–602.

[43] Furuta, H., "A Semiconductor Laser-Pumped Rubidium Beam Atomic Clock", Ph.D. Thesis, Tokyo Institute of Technology, 1991.

[44] Lenth, W., "Optical Heterodyne Spectroscopy with Frequency- and Amplitude-Modulation Semiconductor Lasers," *Optics Letters,* Vol. 8, No. 11, November 1983, pp. 575–577.

[45] Ohtsu, M., H. Kotani, and H. Tagawa, "Spectral Measurements of NH_3 and H_2O for Pollutant Gas Monitoring by 1.5 μm InGaAsP/InP Lasers," *Japan J. Applied Physics,* Vol. 22, No. 10, October, 1983, pp. 1553–1557.

[46] Fukuoka, K., M. Ohtsu, and T. Tako, "Accurate Wavelength Measurement of the Absorption Lines in H_2O Vapor by a 0.8 μm AlGaAs Laser," *Japan J. Applied Physics,* Vol. 23, No. 2, February 1984, pp. L117–L120.

[47] Darling, B.T., and D.M. Dennison, "The Water Vapor Molecule," *Physics Review,* Vol. 57, No. 15, January 1940, pp. 128–139.

[48] Kinugawa, S., H. Sasada, and K. Uehara, "Detection of C_2H_2 Absorption Lines with 1.5 μm DFB Lasers," Extended Abstracts, 49th Autumn Meeting, September 1988, Japan Society of Applied Physics, paper number 6pQ12 [in Japanese].

[49] Sasada, H., "1.5 μm DFB Semiconductor Laser Spectroscopy of HCN," *J. Chemical Physics,* Vol. 88, No. 2, January 1988, pp. 767–777.

[50] Nakagawa, K., "Localization of a Second Harmonic Vibration in a NH_3 Molecule," Ph.D. thesis, University of Tokyo, 1989.

[51] Bjorklund, G.C., "Frequency-Modulation Spectroscopy: A New Method for Measuring Weak Absorption and Dispersion," *Optics Letters,* Vol. 5, No. 1, January 1980, pp. 15–17.

[52] Wang, L.-G., H. Riris, C.B. Carlisle, and T.F. Gallangher, "Comparison of Approaches to Modulation Spectroscopy with GaAlAs Semiconductor Lasers: Application to Water Vapor," *Applied Optics,* Vol. 27, No. 10, May 1988, pp. 2071–2077.

[53] Tsuchida, H., M. Ohtsu, T. Tako, N. Kuramochi, and N. Oura, "Frequency Stabilization of AlGaAs Semiconductor Laser Based on the ^{85}Rb-D_2 line," *Japan J. Applied Physics,* Vol. 21, No. 9, September 1982, pp. L561–L563.

[54] Yabuzaki, T., A. Ibaraki, H. Hori, M. Kitano, and T. Ogawa, "Frequency-Locking of a GaAlAs Laser to a Doppler-Free Spectrum of the Cs-D_2 line," *Japan J. Applied Physics,* Vol. 20, No. 6, June 1981, pp. L451–L454.

[55] Yamaguchi, S., and M. Suzuki, "Frequency Stabilization of a Diode Laser by Use of the Optogalvanic Effect," *Applied Physics Letters,* Vol. 41, No. 7, October 1982, pp. 597–598.

[56] Chung, Y.C., "Frequency-Locking of a 1.3 μm DFB Laser Using a Miniature Argon Glow Lamp," *IEEE Photonics Technology Letters,* Vol. 1, No. 6, June 1989, pp. 135–136.

[57] Sakurai, K., and N. Yamada, "Second-Harmonic Radiation from an AlGaAs Laser and Its Application for Absorption Spectroscopy," *Optics Letters,* Vol. 14, No. 4, February 1989, pp. 233–235.

[58] Ohtsu, M., and E. Ikegami, "Frequency Stabilization of 1.5 μm DFB Laser Using Internal Second Harmonic Generation and Atomic ^{87}Rb Line," *Electronics Letters,* Vol. 25, No. 1, January 1989, pp. 22–23.

[59] Suzuki, H., I. Koshiishi, M. Ohtsu, and Y. Teramachi, "Frequency Control of Visible Semiconductor Laser," *Extended Abstracts,* 50th Autumn Meeting, September 1989, Japan Society of Applied Physics, Tokyo, 29pZL7 [in Japanese].

[60] Ohtsu, M., M. Hashimoto, and H. Ozawa, "A Highly Stabilized Semiconductor Laser and Its Application to Optically Pumped Rb Atomic Clock," *Proc. 39th Annual Symp. of Frequency Control,* Philadelphia, 1985, IEEE, Piscataway, NJ, 1985, pp. 43–53.

[61] Suzuki, M., and S. Yamaguchi, "Frequency Stabilization of a GaAs Semiconductor Laser by Use of the Optical-Optical Double Resonance Effect of the Doppler-Free Spectrum of the Rb-D_1 Line," *IEEE J. Quantum Electronics,* Vol. 24, No. 12, December 1988, pp. 2392–2399.

[62] Ikegami, E., H. Kusuzawa, H. Furuta, and M. Ohtsu, "Frequency Link Between InGaAsP and GaAs Lasers by Using the Doppler-Free Optical-Optical Double Resonance in Rb," *Extended Abstracts,* 37th Spring Meeting, March 1990, Japan Society of Applied Physics, Tokyo, 1990, paper number 31aG3 [in Japanese].

[63] Furuta, H., K. Nakagawa, and M. Ohtsu, "Diode Laser-Pumped Atomic Clock as a Novel Primary Frequency Standard," Proc. Conf. on Precision Electromagnetic Measurement, CPEM '90, June 1990, Ottawa, pp. 428–429.

[64] Vadla, C., A. Obrebski, and K. Niemax, "Isotope Shift of the $3s^2S_{1/2}$ and $3p^2S_J$ levels in ^{6,7}Li," *Optics Communications,* Vol. 63, No. 5, September 1987, pp. 288–292.

[65] Ohtsu, M., and T. Tako, "Coherence in Semiconductor Lasers," *Progress in Optics 25,* ed. E. Wolf, Elsevier, Amsterdam, 1988, pp. 191–278.

[66] Rinnenberg, H., "Ultrahigh n Rydberg Atoms," *Tech. Digest,* 14th Int. Conf. on Quantum Electronics, San Francisco, 1986, LEOS of IEEE, OSA, Washington, DC, 1986, paper number THKK1.

[67] Happer, W., "Optical Pumping," *Review of Modern Physics,* Vol. 44, No. 3, April 1972, pp. 169–249.

[68] Chu, S., AT&T Bell Laboratories, private communication, 1986.

[69] Fitch, V.L., "The Discovery of Charge-Conjugation Parity Asymmetry," *Review of Modern Physics,* Vol. 53, No. 3, July 1981, pp. 367–371.

[70] Cronin, J.W., "CP Symmetry Violation—The Search for Its Origin," *Review of Modern Physics,* Vol. 53, No. 3, July 1981, pp. 373–383.

[71] Vold, T.G., F.J. Raab, B. Heckel, and E.N. Fortson, "Search for a Permanent Electric Dipole Moment on the ^{129}Xe Atom," *Physics Review Letters,* Vol. 52, No. 25, June 1984, pp. 2229–2232.

[72] Gilbert, S.L., and C.E. Wieman, "Atomic-Beam Measurement of Parity Nonconservation in Cesium," *Physics Review A,* Vol. 34, No. 2, August 1986, pp. 792–803.

[73] Noecker, M.C., B.P. Masterson, and C.E. Wieman, "Precision Measurement of Parity Nonconservation in Atomic Cesium: A Low-Energy Test of the Electroweak Theory," *Physics Review Letters,* Vol. 61, No. 3, July 1988, pp. 310–313.

[74] Emmons, T.P., J.M. Reeves, and E.N. Fortson, "Parity-Nonconserving Optical Relation in Atomic Lead," *Physics Review Letters,* Vol. 51, No. 23, December 1983, pp. 2089–2092.

[75] Tanner, C.E., and C.E. Wieman, "Precision Measurement of the Stark Shift in the $6S_{1/2} \rightarrow 6P_{3/2}$ Cesium Transition Using a Frequency-Stabilized Laser Diode," *Physics Review A,* Vol. 38, No. 1, July 1988, pp. 162–165.

[76] Haugan, M.P., and C.M. Will, "Modern Tests of Special Relativity," *Physics Today,* May 1987, pp. 69–86.

[77] Lamoreaux, S.K., J.P. Jacobs, B.R. Heckel, F.J. Raab, and E.N. Fortson, "New Limits on Spatial Anisotropy from Optical Pumped ^{201}Hg and ^{199}Hg," *Physics Review Letters,* Vol. 57, No. 25, December 1986, pp. 3125–3128.

[78] Leitner, J., and S. Okubo, "Parity, Charge Conjugation, and Time Reversal in the Gravitational Interaction," *Physics Review,* Vol. 136, No. 5B, December 1964, pp. B1542–1546.

[79] Hari Dass, N.D., "Test for CP and T Nonconservation in Gravitation," *Physics Review Letters,* Vol. 36, No. 8, February 1976, pp. 393–395.

[80] Fischbach, E., S.H. Aronson, "Reanalysis of the Eotvos Experiment," *Physics Review Letters,* Vol. 56, No. 1, January 1986, pp. 3–6.

[81] Leduc, M., S.B. Crampton, P.J. Nacher, and F. Laloe, "Nuclear Polarization in Gaseous ^{3}He by Optical Pumping," *Nuclear Science Applications,* Vol. 2, 1984, pp. 1–20.

[82] Hänsch, T.W., and A.L. Schawlow, "Cooling of Gases by Laser Radiation," *Optics Communication,* Vol. 13, No. 1, January 1975, pp. 68–69.

[83] Lett, P.D., R.N. Watts, C.I. Westbrook, W.D. Phillips, P.L. Gould, and H.J. Metcalf, "Observation of Atoms Laser Cooled Below the Doppler Limit," *Physics Review Letters,* Vol. 61, No. 1, January 1988, pp. 169–172.

[84] Watts, R.N., P.D. Lett, C.I. Westbrook, S.L. Rolston, C.E. Tanner, and W.D. Phillips, "Laser Cooling Below the Doppler Limit," *Proc. Conf. on Quantum Electronics and Laser Science,* QELS '89, Baltimore, Optics Society of America, Washington, DC, 1989, paper number THLL1.

[85] Aspect, A., E. Arimond, R. Kaiser, N. Vansteenkiste, and C. Cohen-Tannoudji, "Laser Cooling Below the One-Photon Recoil Energy by Velocity-Selective Coherent Population Trapping," *Physics Review Letters,* Vol. 61, No. 7, August 1988, pp. 826–829.

[86] Shimoda, K., "Atoms in Precision Electromagnetic Measurements," *IEEE Trans. on Instruments and Measurement,* Vol. IM-38, No. 2, April 1989, pp. 150–155.

[87] Kasevich, M.A., D.S. Weiss, and S. Chu, "Normal-Incidence Reflection of Slow Atoms from an Optical Evanescent Wave," *Optics Letters,* Vol. 15, No. 11, June 1990, pp. 607–609.

[88] Raab, E.L., M.G. Prentiss, A.E. Cable, S. Chu, and D.E. Pritchard, "Trapping of Neutral Sodium Atoms with Radiation Pressure," *Physics Review Letters,* Vol. 59, No. 23, December 1987, pp. 2631–2634.

[89] Sesko, D., C.G. Fan, and C.E. Wieman, "Production of a Cold Atomic Vapor Using Diode-Laser Cooling," *J. Optics Society of America, B,* Vol. 5, No. 7, July 1988, pp. 1225–1227.

[90] Watts, R.N., D.H. Yang, B. Sheehy, and H. Metcaff, "Deceleration and Cooling of a Thermal Beam of Rubidium," *Proc. the 15th Int. Quantum Electronics Conf.* IQEC '87, Baltimore, Optics Society of America, Washington, DC, 1987, paper number TUGG37.

[91] Katori, H., T. Yamashita, and F. Shimizu, "Laser Cooling of Inert Gases by Semiconductor Lasers," *Proc. Annual Meeting of Japan Society of Physics,* Japan Society of Physics, Tokyo, 1989, paper number 5aZF11 [in Japanese].

[92] Monroe, C., H. Robinson, and C. Wieman, "Observation of the Cesium Clock Transition Using Laser-Cooled Atoms in a Vapor Cell," *Optics Letters,* Vol. 16, No. 1, January 1991, pp. 50–52.

[93] Beausoleil, R.G., and T.W. Hänsch, "Two-Photon Optical Ramsey Spectroscopy of Freely Falling Atoms," *Optics Letters,* Vol. 10, No. 11, November 1985, pp. 547–549.

[94] Kasevich, M.A., E. Riis, S. Chu, and R.G. DeVoe, "RF Spectroscopy in an Atomic Fountain," *Physics Review Letters,* Vol. 63, No. 6, August 1989, pp. 612–614.

[95] Itano, W.M., J.C. Bergquist, and D.J. Wineland, "Laser Spectroscopy of Trapped Atomic Ions," *Science,* Vol. 237, August 1987, pp. 612–617.

[96] Bohr, N., "On the Constitution of Atoms and Molecules," *Philosophy Magazine,* Vol. 26, September 1913, pp. 476–502.

[97] Schrodinger, E., "Are There Quantum Jumps? Part I," *British J. Philosophy and Science,* Vol. 3, No. 10, August 1952, pp. 109–123.

[98] Bergquist, J.C., R.G. Hulet, W.M. Itano, and D.J. Wineland, "Observation of Quantum Jump in a Single Atom," *Physics Review Letters,* Vol. 57, No. 14, October 1986, pp. 1699–1702.

[99] Nagourney, W., J. Sandberg, and H. Dehmelt, "Shelved Optical Electron Amplifier: Observation of Quantum Jumps," *Physics Review Letters,* Vol. 56, No. 26, June 1986, pp. 2797–2799.

[100] Sauter, T., W. Neuhauser, R. Blatt, and P.E. Toschek, "Observation of Quantum Jumps," *Physics Review Letters,* Vol. 57, No. 14, October 1986, pp. 1696–1698.

[101] Bergquist, J., National Institute of Standards and Technology, private communication, 1989.

[102] Bollinger, J.J., and D.J. Wineland, "Microplasmas," *Scientific American,* January 1990, pp. 124–130.

[103] Diedrich, F., E. Peik, J. Chen, W. Quint, and H. Walther, "Observation of a Phase Transition of Stored Laser-Cooled Ions," Vol. 59, No. 26, December 1987, pp. 2931–2934.

[104] Hoffnagle, J., R. G. DeVoe, L. Reyna, and R.G. Brewer, "Order-Chaos Transition of Two Trapped Ions," *Physics Review Letters,* Vol. 61, No. 3, July 1988, pp. 255–258.

[105] Brewer, R.G., J. Hoffnagle, R.G. DeVoe, L. Renya, and W. Henshaw, "Collision-Induced Two-Ion Chaos," *Nature,* Vol. 344, No. 22, March 1990, pp. 305–309.

[106] Diedrich, W.F., and H. Walther, "Nonclassical Radiation of a Single Stored Ion," *Physics Review Letters,* Vol. 58, No. 3, January 1987, pp. 203–206.

[107] Wineland, D.J., J.C. Bergquist, J.J. Bollinger, W.M. Itano, D.J. Heinzen, S.L. Gilbert, C.H. Manney, and M.G. Raizen, "Progress at NIST Toward Absolute Frequency Standards Using Stored Ions," *IEEE Trans. on Ultrasonics, Ferroelectrics, and Frequency Control,* Vol. 37, No. 6, November 1990, pp. 515–523.

[108] Meschede, D., H. Walther, and G. Muller, "One-Atom Maser," *Physics Review Letters,* Vol. 54, No. 6, February 1985, pp. 551–554.

[109] Heinzen, D.J., J.J. Childs, J.F. Thomas, and M.S. Feld, "Enhanced and Inhibited Visible Spontaneous Emission by Atoms in a Confocal Resonator," *Physics Review Letters,* Vol. 57, No. 11, September 1987, pp. 1320–1323.

[110] Raizen, M., R.J. Thompson, R.J. Brecha, H.J. Kimble, and H.J. Carmichael, "Normal-Mode Splitting and Linewidth Averaging for Two-State Atoms in an Optical Cavity," *Physics Review Letters,* Vol. 63, No. 3, July 1989, pp. 240–243.

[111] Jewell, J.L., S.L. McCall, Y.H. Lee, A. Scherer, A.C. Gossard, and J.H. English, "Lasing Characteristics of GaAs Microresonators," *Applied Physics Letters,* Vol. 54, No. 15, April 1989, pp. 1400–1402.

[112] Igeta, K., Y. Yamamoto, and S. Machida, "Control of Spontaneous Emission from a GaAs Quantum Well," *Extended Abstracts,* Autumn Meeting of Japan Society of Physics, Tokyo, 1989, paper number 4a-ZF-6 [in Japanese].

Chapter 7
TOWARD THE FUTURE

The preceding chapters discussed how to realize low FM-noise semiconductor lasers and how to use them in various applications. The lightwaves emitted from these lasers are similar to a classical sinusoidal wave. Advanced fabrication techniques that can be used to realize more stable lightwaves are reviewed in Sections 7.1 and 7.2. Because these devices may be available commercially within the next several years, these reviews can provide information on the design of advanced optical systems. Also, we can generate lightwaves with specific performances that are considerably different from those of the classical sinusoidal waves. Recent progress in this area and its application to quantum optics are reviewed and the problems remaining to be solved described in Sections 7.3 through 7.6.

7.1 IMPROVEMENT IN DEVICE STRUCTURE

7.1.1 Advanced Longitudinal-Mode Controlled Lasers

As pointed out in Section 2.5.2, a single longitudinal-mode semiconductor laser can only be approximated, due to the nonlinear mode coupling with side modes even in carefully fabricated *distributed feedback* (DFB) or *distributed Bragg reflector* (DBR) lasers. Because mode-partition noises are found even in these lasers, the side mode powers should be reduced sufficiently to secure a low bit error rate in the optical communication systems [1, 2]. For this reduction, advanced device fabrication techniques for the longitudinal-mode controlled lasers have been developed. These techniques help reduce the field spectral linewidth. Furthermore, they also reduce the magnitude of the chirping, which is the drastic increase of the field spectral linewidth of a directly modulated pulsed laser caused by the many and fast temporal variations in carrier density under the pulsed operation.

Here, we review these techniques for DFB lasers. As shown in Figure 2.12(a), a DFB layer and an active layer have been grown successively and independently in conventional DFB lasers, the structure of which has been called a *separate confine-*

ment heterostructure (SCH). Therefore, the distributed feedback mechanism of the lightwave in this device has been called *index coupling* because this feedback originates from the periodic variation of the refractive index. Figure 2.12(a) shows an example of such an index-coupling DFB laser. It was pointed out in Section 2.2 that it was advantageous to use a quarter-wavelength shifted (λ/4-shifted) DFB to avoid the simultaneous oscillation of two lowest-loss longitudinal modes. That is, as shown by Figure 7.1(a), two standing waves can exist in a conventional DFB laser whose wavelengths have been given by eq. (2.35). However, the λ/4-shifted DFB allows only one longitudinal mode, by which a single longitudinal-mode operation can be achieved [3]. This λ/4-shifted structure has been popular in InGaAsP lasers because of its simple fabrication processes [3–5]. However, even in this structure, parasitic longitudinal modes originating from the Fabry-Perot cavity configuration, formed by the two cavity facets, can oscillate when the reflectivity of these facets is not sufficiently reduced. This Fabry-Perot cavity mode therefore can disturb the stable operation of the DFB mode. An additional window structure has been employed to reduce this reflectivity [4, 6].

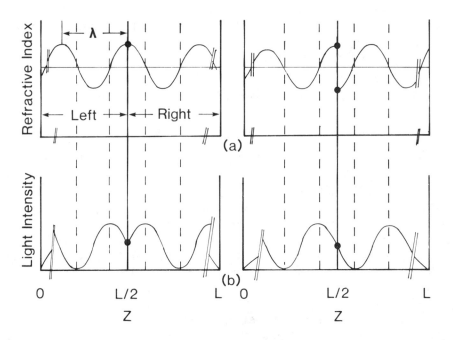

Figure 7.1 Comparison between conventional (left) and modified (right) DFB lasers: (a) variation of the refractive index along the cavity axis (z-axis); (b) variation of the light intensity along the cavity axis (z-axis); (c) resonance spectral lines of the DFB; A is the grating period; λ_B is the Bragg wavelength; L is the cavity length (from [3]).

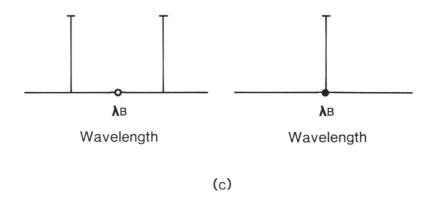

(c)

Figure 7.1 continued

Even in these advanced structures, transient lasing of side longitudinal modes can be observed, and through them the power drop-out of the main mode is induced, as has been demonstrated in Section 2.5.2. This is because the side modes still have some gains for lasing. A principal cause of these residual gains is attributed to the spatial hole burning along the optical axis (z-axis of Figure 2.7(a)). That is, even though the main mode lasing reduces the carrier density at antinodes of the longitudinal mode profile (corresponding to the spatial dependence of the self-saturation coefficient $\tilde{\alpha}_i^{(3)}$ (see eq. (2.38)) of the lasing gain, side modes still conserve their gains because the spatial distributions of these gains are different from that of the main mode due to differences in the mode profile. Although conventional dye lasers have employed a ring-cavity configuration to eliminate the spatial hole burning, it is more difficult to eliminate it in semiconductor lasers. In such lasers the light power is concentrated around the center of the cavity due to very high linear gain and cavity loss. To reduce the spatial hole burning, advanced techniques of the longitudinal-mode control have been tried, such as the following:

1. Modulation of the grating pitch. A grating with an inhomogeneous pitch of corrugation, called a *chirped grating* or *corrugation-pitch modulated-DFB* (CPM-DFB), is used [7]. By fabricating a CPM-DFB whose inhomogeneity along the cavity axis is symmetric to the center of the laser cavity, experiments have confirmed that the spatial hole burning reduction by this structure is superior to that by the $\lambda/4$-shifted DFB (see Figure 7.2(a)) [8].
2. Modulation of the stripe width. The stripe width of the DFB is modulated to modulate the effective refractive index of the active layer [9], as shown in Figure 7.2(b) [10]. In addition to the expected reduction in spatial hole burning, as high as those in technique 1, the lasing of the TM mode can be suppressed effectively because of the large difference in the cavity loss between the TE and TM modes [11].

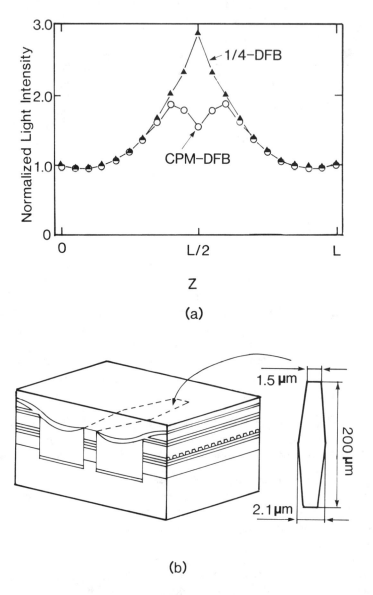

Figure 7.2 (a) Calculated results of light intensity profiles along the cavity axis (z-axis) (from [8]): L is the cavity length. (b) AlGaAs DFB laser with a modulated stripe width (from [10]).

The spatial hole burning can be reduced effectively by the two methods just listed because the inhomogeneity of the distribution of the light density along the cavity axis can be reduced due to gradual phase shift of the grating. Furthermore, contributions from the spatial hole burning to the chirping of a directly modulated pulsed laser can be reduced by appropriately modulating the stripe width [12, 13].

Note that the distributed feedback of the lightwave can also come through gain coupling. In this gain coupled DFB the two lowest-loss modes are not degenerated, which allows single longitudinal-mode oscillation [14]. Figure 7.3(a) shows a schematic of this structure [15]. Because the active layer has a corrugation, lasing gain varies periodically, by which the gain coupling is induced. Further, simultaneously induced refractive index coupling by the corrugation of the active layer is cancelled by the phase-inverted lossless grating. As an additional advantage of this structure, low-threshold oscillation is expected because the absorptive layers need not be used. Furthermore, the side mode suppression is not affected by the reflectivity of the cleaved facets [16]. Figure 7.3(b) shows the characteristics of the pulsed operation of a GaAlAs ridge-waveguide DFB laser with a gain coupling [15], from which high-quality single longitudinal-mode oscillation can be confirmed. By these advanced techniques of longitudinal-mode control, a side mode suppression ratio as high as 40–50 dB has been achieved, as shown in Figure 7.4 [17].

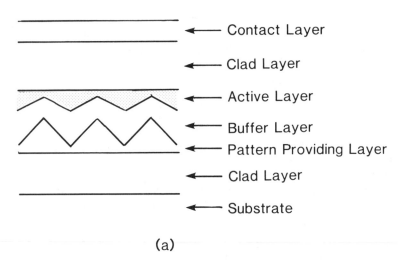

(a)

Figure 7.3 (a) Schematic of the structure of a gain-coupled DFB laser (from [15]); (b) characteristics of the pulsed operation of a AlGaAs ridge-waveguide DFB laser with a gain coupling (from 15]).

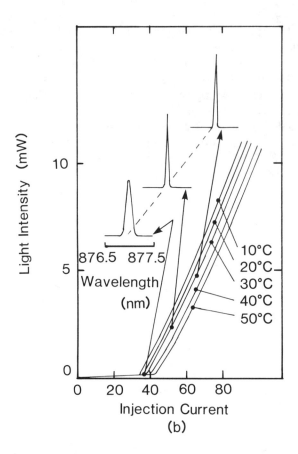

Figure 7.3 continued

7.1.2 Narrow-Linewidth Lasers

Longitudinal-mode controlled and narrow linewidth 1.5 μm InGaAsP lasers have been fabricated recently because they are indispensable to coherent optical communication systems. Three factors have been considered so far because they limited the linewidth reduction of laser devices:

1. Mode competition. Spatial hole burning has been reduced through the advanced techniques of longitudinal-mode control, as reviewed previously. Furthermore, it also has been reduced by controlling the values of current injected through the segmented electrodes of the DFB lasers [18]. Figure 7.5 shows the structure of such segmented-electrode lasers, in which a linewidth

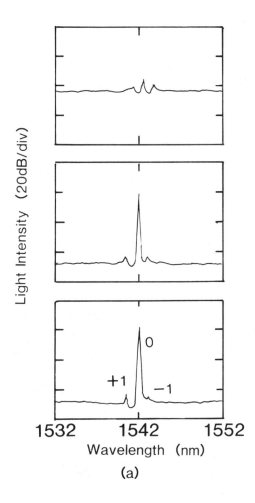

Figure 7.4 Characteristics of side longitudinal mode suppression in a λ/4-shifted InGaAsP DFB laser (from [17] © 1989 IEEE): (a) spectral profile of the longitudinal modes, injection current is $0.9I_{th}$ (upper), $1.7I_{th}$ (middle), and $3.9I_{th}$ (lower), where I_{th} is the threshold current; (b) side-mode suppression ratio as a function of the normalized injection current I/I_{th}: circles are the mode power ratio between the zeroth mode and +first mode in (a); triangles are that between the zeroth mode and −first mode.

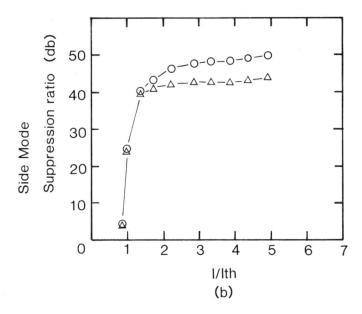

Figure 7.4 continued

narrower than 1 MHz has been achieved [19]. This segmented electrode laser has further advantages; homogeneous FM efficiency can be achieved over a wide modulation frequency range, as shown by Figure 3.21, because the DFB cavity loss is modulated by inhomogeneous carrier distribution by adjusting the ratio between the injection currents.

2. α-parameter. It is effective to reduce the value of α because the linewidth depends on α^2 (see eq. (2.58)). This can be achieved by introducing the *multiquantum well* (MQW) structure [19, 20]. Thus, a linewidth as narrow as 250 kHz could be obtained [20].

3. Cavity loss. Because the cavity loss is decreased by increasing the cavity length, a long cavity, on the order of 1 mm, has been employed even in devices whose fabrication is based on factors 1 and 2. The cavity length of the device in Figure 7.5 is 1.2 mm long.

A linewidth as narrow as 170 kHz has been achieved by considering all three factors simultaneously; that is, by the CPM-DFB laser with an MQW structure and the cavity as long as 1.2 mm [21]. Furthermore, a segmented electrode MQW-DBR laser has achieved a linewidth of 56 kHz [22]. A principal limiting factor of further reduction in linewidth is flicker noise ($1/f$ noise), as described in Section 2.4.2. Investigation of $1/f$ noise generation mechanisms and device design criteria for reducing

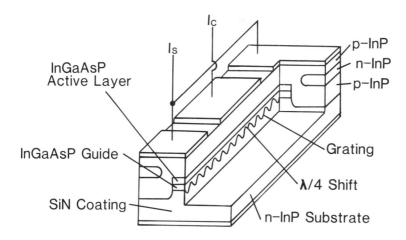

Figure 7.5 Structure of a segmented-electrode DFB laser (from [19]).

this noise remain for future research. However, recent research has demonstrated that $1/f$ noise can be effectively reduced by negative electrical feedback [23].

It should be pointed out that the direct FM efficiency of these narrow linewidth lasers is lower than those of the conventional wide linewidth lasers. This is easily understood by noting that the FM noise magnitude corresponds to the efficiency of the random FM induced by spontaneous emission fluctuations. This low FM efficiency requires higher gain amplifiers to reduce the laser linewidth by negative electrical feedback.

Linewidths in conventional lasers also have been reduced by integrating external feedback components with the laser devices. An external reflector has been integrated with a laser device; this corresponds to the optical feedback method [24]. Furthermore, to avoid deterministic instability induced by an external reflector, a phase modulator was integrated between the laser gain part and an external reflector (a DBR) to control the phase of the reflected light. The linewidth was reduced to several 100 kHz by these devices [25, 26]. Two DBRs and an optical waveguide have been integrated for optical feedback. The linewidth of a 1.3 μm InGaAsP laser was reduced to 7.1 kHz by this device [27]. Integration of these components with a laser could be a problem for future research. In negative electrical feedback, a principal factor limiting the feedback bandwidth could be the length of the feedback loop, which might be reduced by integrating the optical frequency demodulator, photodetectors, and amplifiers with the laser device. By such integration, further improvement in the performance of the negative electrical feedback system can be expected; that is, this system would be compatible with optoelectronic integrated circuits.

7.1.3 Wideband Frequency Sweep

The wideband sweep of laser frequency is an essential technique for a great number of applications, such as multichannel coherent optical communication systems and analytical spectroscopy. Techniques of accurate and fine frequency sweep were described in Section 5.2.1. A brief description of a wideband coarse sweep was given in Section 5.2.2. Here, we look at the future trends in wideband coarse sweep and, furthermore, the possibility of wideband and fine sweep.

The range of the frequency sweep can be defined as

$$S_w = 2(\nu_u - \nu_l)/(\nu_u + \nu_l) \tag{7.1}$$

where ν_u and ν_l represent the upper and lower limits of swept frequencies, respectively. A dye laser, conventionally used as a wavelength tunable laser, takes $S_w = 0.10$ if a single dye solution is used. For semiconductor lasers, the device of Figure 2.13 has obtained $S_w = 0.004$. By adjusting the values of the currents injected through the segmented electrodes, wideband frequency sweep can be realized, due to the change in the refractive index induced by the plasma effect of the carrier (see eq. (3.41)) [28, 29]. The DFB laser of Figure 7.5 is such a tunable laser. Figure 7.6(a) also shows this sort of tunable 1.5 μm InGaAsP laser [29], which is an integrated version of the optical feedback from the external grating. The injection current to the external DBR is varied for the frequency sweep. A coarse sweep range as wide as 380 GHz has been achieved, as shown in Figure 7.6(b), which corresponds to $S_w = 0.002$. For this sweep, the injection current of the phase-control region was controlled as well to avoid mode hopping. Furthermore, by introducing a quantum-well structure to the semiconductor laser device and using optical feedback from an external diffraction grating, a value of S_w as large as 0.12 has been achieved [30, 31]; this is comparable to that obtained by the dye laser. By a simple optical feedback structure, shown in Figure 5.23, a value of S_w as large as 0.08 has been achieved in a stable manner by carefully coating the *antireflection* (AR) film on a laser facet.

7.1.4 Realization of Novel Lasing Wavelengths

As shown in Figure 2.5, well-developed semiconductor laser devices have wavelengths of 1.3, 1.5 μm (InGaAsP lasers used for optical fiber communication systems), and 0.8 μm (AlGaAs lasers used for compact disc players). A 0.6 μm AlGaInP laser also is commercially available. Furthermore, novel wavelength lasers have been realized recently by introducing a strained quantum well structure. As is shown in Figure 7.7 [32], elastic strain energy can be stored in the crystal without inducing the misfit dislocation when the difference of the lattice constants between the crystal substrate and grown thin film is smaller than several percent and the film is sufficiently

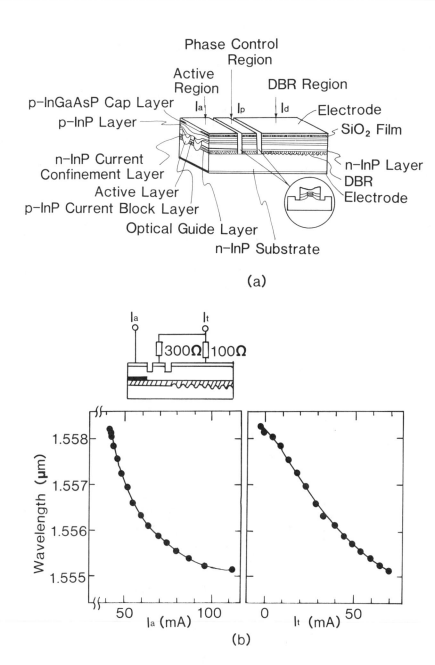

(a)

(b)

Figure 7.6 A tunable 1.5 μm InGaAsP laser (from [29]): (a) device structure; (b) characteristics of wavelength tuning by changing the injection current of the active region I_a (left) and the wavelength control region I_t (right).

thin, realized by quantum well fabrication techniques. In this case, pseudomorphic epitaxial layers can be formed, increasing our freedom in selecting materials for these strained quantum-well layers. After the studies of such structures began in 1982 [33], applications were found in laser devices, where they are used as pumping light sources of Er-doped optical fiber amplifiers. Because the pumping wavelengths needed for the highest gain in these amplifiers are 0.98 μm and 1.48 μm, 0.98 μm lasers have been developed by using the strained quantum well structure.

Compressive stress stored in the crystals can improve the performances of laser oscillation; for example, threshold current, Auger recombination current, and intra-valence band absorption are decreased. Decreases in the magnitudes of the α-parameter and chirping can be expected, too. The field spectral linewidth and chirping of a modulation-doped strained quantum well laser can be reduced to ⅙ times and ⅓ times those of a conventional double hetero-structure laser (⅓ times and ⅓ times those of a quantum well laser), respectively [34]. On the other hand, tensile stress can increase the lasing gain of the TM mode, which can lead to new functional laser devices, such as those switching between the TE and TM modes [35].

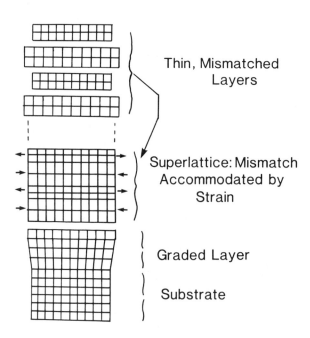

Figure 7.7 Schematic explanation of the strained layer (from [32] © 1986 IEEE).

Strained quantum well lasers with a wavelength range of 0.9–1.1 μm have been developed by using a GaAs substrate. However, progress has been made in the development of 1.5 μm wavelength laser devices using an InP substrate. Results of these developments can be summarized in the following:

1. 0.9–1.1 μm strained quantum well lasers. Threshold current as low as 0.9 mA (current density of 114 A/cm^2) has been developed [36]. A 0.98 μm ridge waveguide laser has been fabricated as a high-power laser for optical pumping in an optical-fiber amplifier, thus achieving an output power of 115 mW and a lifetime of over 2500 hours [37]. The maximum CW output power reported so far is 350 mW (180 mW in single transverse-mode operation) [38], 200 W quasi-CW output power in a two-dimensional array device, and so on [39].

2. 1.5 μm strained quantum well lasers. Studies on strained quantum well lasers using InP substrates began recently [40, 41]. A threshold current as low as 0.9 mA has been achieved by reducing the intervalence band absorption [42], which is the minimum value for the 1.5 μm laser reported so far.

Further improvement in the structure can make the strained quantum well popular as a basic structure of laser devices, and lasing wavelengths ranging from the visible to the infrared may be realized.

7.1.5 High-Power Laser Devices

A principal factor limiting increases in lasing power is *catastrophic optical damage* (COD) at laser facets; that is, the damage of cavity mirrors due to the high-density optical power. Three problems must be solved to avoid COD, and several solutions also are listed:

1. Control of facet reflectivity. Thin film should be coated to appropriately reduce the reflectivity of the output facet (AR coating).
2. Decrease in the optical absorption around the facets. A current noninjected region or window structure should be introduced around the facets.
3. Decrease in the optical power density around the facets. The light-emitting volume should be increased by decreasing the optical confinement factor. This can be done by decreasing the thickness of the active layer, introducing a *large optical cavity* (LOC) structure, or increasing the width of the active layer.

In addition to these solutions, the temperature increase can be suppressed by improving the thermal connection between the laser device and its heat sink.

Several trials have been carried out to attain a 3 W power in GaAlAs lasers, because 3 W of power is typically required in several application systems, such as surgery and cutting of biomembranes. Experimenters have tried for power higher than 3 W for optical disk systems and optical pumping of solid-state lasers. Power as high as 500 mW for a narrow stripe laser [43] (380 mW for single transverse-mode) and 3 W for a broad stripe laser [44] have been obtained. Using a laser array structure, a total output power as high as 76 W has been achieved under CW operation [45]. Noted that injection locking from a highly coherent laser is required to reduce the FM noise in these high-power lasers, because they oscillate in multilongitudinal and transverse modes. Experiments have found that low-temperature operation can increase the threshold light power of the COD. This is because the absorption around the laser facets can be reduced by increasing the band gap energy around the facets in low-temperature operation.

Increases in the output power of InGaAsP lasers, used mainly for optical communication systems, can limit performance of these systems due to increases in the magnitude of the scattered light in the optical fiber. Therefore, instead of high-power lasers, optical fiber amplifiers have been proposed to amplify the light for long-span optical fiber transmission. On the other hand, InP-based high-power lasers have been developed as optical pumping sources for these fiber amplifiers. Typical high-power lasers reported so far are the VIPS laser [46–49], the DC-PBH laser [50, 51], and the PPIBH laser [52, 53]. Figure 7.8 shows a high-power MQW laser in which five QW layers are grown to form a DC-PBH active layer [54]. A maximum output power of 250 mW has been achieved.

A strained QW structure has been used to fabricate a high-power laser as the pumping source of a fiber amplifier. Figure 7.9 shows a 0.98 μm laser so fabricated [55], the output of which power is 155 mW.

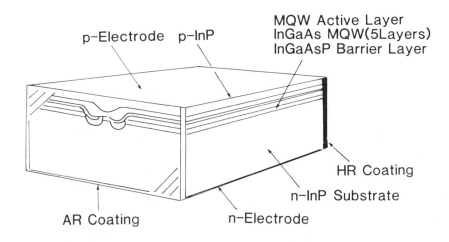

Figure 7.8 Structure of a high-power MQW InGaAsP laser (from [54]).

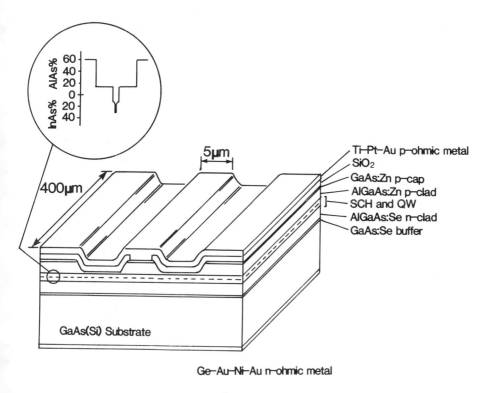

Figure 7.9 Structure of a 0.98 μm AlGaAs laser fabricated by using a strained single QW (from [55] © 1990 IEEE).

7.1.6 Reduction of Chirping

For the optical communication systems employing the *intensity modulation and direct detection* (IM-DD) method, pulsed semiconductor lasers with a pulse repetition rate of several GHz have been used as transmitter light sources. Under this pulsed operation, large magnitudes of phase and frequency shifts, called *chirping*, are induced by a fast and large magnitude variation of the refractive index. Because this variation is caused mainly by the carrier density variation, the magnitude of the chirping is proportional to the α-parameter. The chirping could give the time-averaged linewidth of a field spectral profile that is much larger than the Fourier transform-limited value. This linewidth thus could limit performance of the optical communication system due to the dispersion characteristics of the optical fibers. Several methods have been proposed to reduce the chirping: (1) use of an external phase modulator to compensate for the temporal phase variation of the laser; (2) design of a laser device to reduce the α-parameter (a gain-coupled DFB laser and a modulation-doped strained quantum-well laser are effective in reducing chirping. Under the 17 ps width pulsed operation of a gain-coupled AlGaAs laser, a time-averaged linewidth as narrow as 50 GHz has been achieved, which is close to the Fourier transform-limited linewidth (59 GHz) within the measurement accuracy [56]); and (3) use of injection locking.

In addition to these conventional methods, injection of a reflected light from a *phase conjugated mirror* (PCM) is another promising method. Figure 7.10 shows a schematic of this optical feedback scheme. Because the *phase conjugate wave* (PCW), that is, the reflected light from the PCM, is the time-reversed wave of the incident light, the phase shift of the reflected light has the opposite sign of that of the incident light. (Note that, from the quantum mechanical point of view, the incident light, that is, the probe beam, and the PCW correspond to a pair of photons whose amplitudes are equal and phases are opposite, as was in the annihilation and creation operators a and a^+ defined in Appendix I.) Thus, the chirping can be eliminated by superposing these two waves.

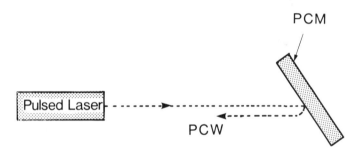

Figure 7.10 Schematic of chirping reduction by optical feedback of a phase conjugate wave (PCW); *PCM* is the nonlinear optical material for phase conjugate mirror.

As the PCM medium, a photorefractive material, such as a $BaTiO_3$ crystal, conventionally has been used; the material's refractive index is varied by irradiated lights [57]. To generate the PCW, two antiparallel high-power pump waves are irradiated to this medium. Interference between one pump light and the incident light (a probe beam, which is a light from the pulsed laser) causes spatial modulation of the refractive index inside the medium; that is, a light-induced diffraction grating is generated. The other pump beam is diffracted by this grating to produce the PCW. Thus, this process corresponds to real-time holography and is regarded as the four-wave mixing process. When the frequencies of the probe and pump lights are different (i.e., the non-degenerated case), the PCW power decreases with the increase in the frequency difference. This means that the PCM reflectivity depends on frequency detuning.

The bandwidth of this frequency dependence is determined by the inverse of the carrier lifetime in the PCM medium. Although the bandwidth of the PCM should be wider than the chirped time-averaged linewidth for chirping reduction, the bandwidth of conventional photorefractive materials are too narrow due to long carrier lifetimes.

Using a semiconductor laser as a PCM may be more advantageous in chirping reduction. High PCM reflectivity is expected because the value of the third-order nonlinear optical coefficient of semiconductor materials is large and the two oppositely running laser lights in the active layer can be used as the pump lights with high-power densities. Furthermore, a very wide bandwidth is expected because the interband relaxation time τ_s of the carriers is as short as a few ns. Four-wave mixing process and generation of the PCW from a broad-area semiconductor laser has been reported [58, 59], and a theoretical analysis given [60]. Figures 4.18(a) and (b) show the measured results of the bandwidths of the PCM reflectivity of a narrow-stripe 0.8 μm AlGaAs laser [61] and 0.67 μm AlGaInP laser [62], respectively. Resonant peaks on these curves are due to the relaxation oscillations of the laser. Bandwidths as wide as several GHz and PCM reflectivity as large as 1×10^2 can be confirmed from these curves. Figure 4.18(c) shows that even though the detuning is as large as 1 THz, the four-wave mixing can be observed if the probe beam is tuned to one longitudinal mode of the PCM laser (0.8 μm AlGaAs laser) [61]. This large bandwidth is due to the intraband relaxation time τ_{in} of the carrier, which is as short as 0.1 ps. Similar preliminary discussions have been given for an AlGaAs laser [63] and a 1.5 μm InGaAsP laser [64]. Based on these results, we can expect that a semiconductor laser works as a fast and efficient PCM for chirping reduction. Research has been proposed that this method of chirping reduction for visible AlGaInP lasers be used to generate narrow linewidth pulsed-light sources for isotope separation of ^{235}U [65]. As an additional application, the wide PCM bandwidth of a semiconductor laser can be utilized as a wideband optical frequency shifter [61].

7.2 EXPANSION OF THE LASING FREQUENCY RANGE

7.2.1 Short-Wavelength Lasers

The quality factor of a laser can be defined as the ratio between the half-linewidth $\Delta\nu$ and the center frqeuency ν_l of the field spectrum of a laser oscillation, given by

$$Q = \nu_l/\Delta\nu \tag{7.2}$$

Equation (2.58) shows that the linewidth $\Delta\nu$ is inversely proportional to the laser power P_0, where P_0 is proportional to the product of photon energy $h\nu_l$ and photon density N_p. Photon density N_p in stationary laser oscillation is given by eq. (AIV.5) as a solution of the rate equation. Furthermore, we can easily find that the value of g in eqs. (AIV.1) and (AIV.2), the linear gain $\tilde{\alpha}_i^{(1)}$ in eq. (2.38) (or in the other words, the Einstein's B-coefficient corresponding to the stimulated emission rate [66]) is independent of the optical frequency. Therefore, the value of Q is expressed by substituting eq. (2.58) into (7.2) as

$$Q \propto \nu_l \qquad (7.3)$$

This equation shows that the performance of the laser is higher for a higher frequency oscillation, from which we can conclude that the development of a short-wavelength laser is important.

However, it has been known popularly that the CW oscillation of a shorter wavelength is more difficult because the spontaneous emission rate (Einstein's A coefficient [66]) is proportional to ν_l^3. For fabrication of short-wavelength laser devices, a principal problem is reducing overflow of carriers beyond the hetero barrier. For these reasons, the shortest lasing wavelength achieved so far is 631 nm (CW operation at the room temperature) [67]. Figure 2.5 summarizes the possible lasing wavelength range emitted from several semiconductor materials. However, with progress in device fabrication, such as the *metal organic-chemical vapor deposition* (MOCVD) and *chemical beam epitaxy* (CBE), we expect wavelengths as short as 600 nm in the future.

Wavelength conversion techniques using nonlinear optical media have been tried as an alternative approach to short-wavelength emission. The principal problem for the nonlinear wavelength conversion of a semiconductor laser is the difficulty of achieving a high conversion efficiency due to the low laser power. To solve this problem, a nonlinear crystal such as $KNbO_3$ is installed in a high-finesse Fabry-Perot cavity to build up the power of the fundamental laser light [68]. By using a 12 mW semiconductor laser with an 865 nm wavelength, a second harmonic wave of 0.2 mW power is obtained, corresponding to a conversion efficiency as high as 1.7%. The reflected light from this built-up cavity is injected into the laser to reduce the laser linewidth, based on the principle of optical feedback in Figure 4.19. Figures 7.11(a) and (b) show the experimental setup [69]. By using a 100 mW semiconductor laser with an 862 nm wavelength, a second harmonic wave of 3.3 mW is obtained, corresponding to the conversion efficiency of 3.3%. Furthermore, by employing the negative electrical feedback technique to this optically fed-back laser, long-term stability of the second harmonic power is improved, as shown in Figure 7.11(c). The RF voltage is applied to the $KNbO_3$ crystal so that an IM efficiency of the second harmonic wave as high as 78% is obtained.

A $MgO:LiNbO_3$ crystal is polished, and high-reflection films are coated on the end surfaces of the crystal to form a monolithic ring cavity, as shown in Figure 7.12 [70]. A second harmonic wave of 30 mW is generated from this crystal by irradiating a semiconductor laser-pumped YAG laser of 53 mW power, and this yields wavelength conversion efficiency as high as 60% [70].

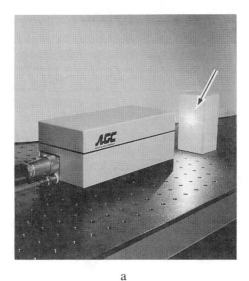

a

PZT   KNbO₃   Dichroic
Mirror

Second
Harmonic Wave

Laser   PD

PZT
Driver   ⊕   PI–
Controller   Lock–in
Amp.

b

Figure 7.11 Second harmonic generation of a 862 nm wavelength AlGaAs laser: (a) appearance of the system (bright spot on the brick represents a spot of the second harmonic beam); (b) experimental setup; (c) measured temporal variation of the second harmonic power (from [69]).

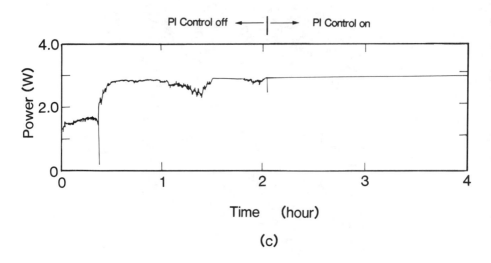

Figure 7.11 continued

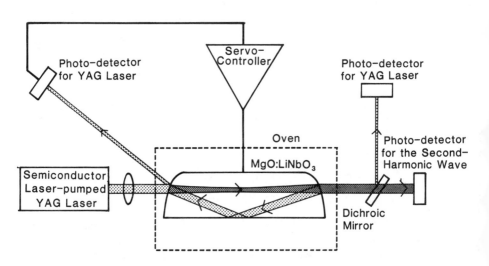

Figure 7.12 Experimental setup of a second harmonic generation from a semiconductor laser-pumped YAG laser; a monolithic ring cavity is used to build up the YAG laser power in the MgO:LiNbO$_3$ crystal (from [70] © 1988 IEEE).

Organic nonlinear optical crystals present an alternative to high efficiency wavelength conversion, examples of which are listed in Table 7.1 [71]. These crystals are very promising, especially for low-power semiconductor lasers, because of their fairly large nonlinear optical coefficients. The fabrication of nonlinear optical waveguides has been tried using these organic materials. It is advantageous to use these organic materials because a molecular design can reach the required performance. However, problems of reliability and length of life still remain in the fabrication of nonlinear optical devices, such as waveguides. If these problems could be solved, highly efficient wavelength conversions could be realized.

Table 7.1
Examples of Organic Nonlinear Optical Materials for High-Efficiency Wavelength Conversion
(from [71])

Name	Structure	Second Harmonic Intensity in the Case of Powder (Normalized to the Value of Carbon)	Molecular Polarization of the Second order ($\times 10^{-30}$ esu)
Urea	H_2NCONH_2	1.0	0.45
P–NA	O_2N–◯–NH_2	0.0	35
m–NA	H_2N ◯–NO_2	–	6
M–NA	CH_3 H_2N–◯–NO_2	22	42
MAP	O_2N ◯–NO_2 NH＊$COOCH_3$	10	220
POM	H_3C O_2N–◯ N–O	13	5
DAN	O_2N–◯–$N(CH_3)_2$ $NHCOCH_3$	80	–
DANS	O_2N–◯～◯–$N(CH_3)_2$	0	450
Merocyanine	CH_3–N◯～◯=O	0	1000

7.2.2 Stable, Wideband Optical Sweep Generators

Several frequency tunable laser devices were reviewed in Section 7.1.3. However, a wideband frequency sweep and high-frequency stability cannot always be realized

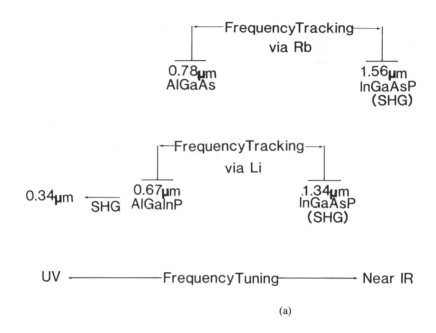

(a)

Figure 7.13 (a) Schematic of the system of a Peta-Hz class optical sweep generator (from [72, 73]); (b) pictures of a MNA single crystal film with the size of 25 mm × 50 mm × 1 μm (upper) and of a diffraction grating fabricated on a glass plate (lower), which are used for an optical parametric oscillator (from [72]).

simultaneously by these devices, even though this is essential to realizing a high-quality optical sweep generator. Figure 7.13(a) shows a schematic of the system proposed to meet these needs [72, 73]. Four kinds of lasers (with the wavelengths of 1.56 μm, 1.34 μm, 0.78 μm and 0.67 μm) are available as primary light sources. FM noise reduction and frequency tracking are carried out by techniques described in Chapters 4 and 5. For a frequency link between two different wavelength lasers, a second harmonic wave generation is employed by using organic nonlinear optical waveguides. By using the pump-probe spectroscopy technique for Rb and Li atomic vapors, these laser frequencies are locked to the common center frequency of the spectral lines (see Figures 5.17–5.19), to ensure the optical frequency link. Coarse frequency tuning is accomplished by sum- or difference-frequency generation and frequency conversions by the parametric oscillation, where organic nonlinear optical waveguides are used. Figure 7.13(b) shows large-area thin film of the organic nonlinear single crystal (a material named MNA) and diffraction grating fabricated on a glass plate to realize a two-dimensional DFB cavity for the optical parametric oscillator [72]. The techniques described in Section 5.2.1 are used for fine sweeping. By combining these techniques, a frequency sweep from the infrared (1.56 μm wavelength) to the ultraviolet (0.34 μm) is estimated, with a value of S_w (see eq. (7.1)) as

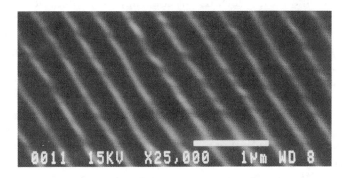

(b)

Figure 7.13 continued

large as 1.28. Although an accurate optical sweep generator with a value of S_w larger than unity has not been developed so far, Figure 7.13(a) demonstrates the possibility of a very high-quality system for a peta-Hz (1×10^{15} Hz) class optical sweep generator using the controllability of semiconductor lasers and the techniques of negative electrical feedback, nonlinear spectroscopy, and nonlinear optical waveguides.

7.3 ULTRAFAST DETECTION OF LIGHTWAVES, WAVEFORM CONVERSION, AND OPTICAL-FREQUENCY COUNTING SYSTEMS

It sometimes is complicated to use lightwaves because the optical frequency is higher than 100 THz. Although a fast optical frequency counter has not yet been invented, an optical frequency-counting scheme has been employed using the techniques of the frequency division and heterodyne detection, as well as frequency comparison with a stable microwave oscillator (e.g., a Cs atomic clock described in Section 6.5.1). The optical frequency of a 576 nm wavelength laser (520 THz) has been measured within an error of 1.6×10^{-10} by using a *metal-insulator-metal* (MIM) point-contact diode composed of a tungsten wire and nickel plate as a harmonic mixer and by using a nonlinear optical crystal as a second harmonic generator [74]. Although the response frequency of the MIM diode is as large as 200 THz (1.5 μm wavelength), the sensitivity is rather low (minimum detectable laser power is about 200 mW) and its life is short. On the other hand, the response frequency of a Josephson device made by a *superconductor-insulator-superconductor* (SIS) junction is low (4 THz) although its sensitivity is quite high (its minimum detectable power is less than 1 mW) [75].

To overcome these difficulties in conventional photodetectors, three candidates may be involved in future devices: (1) the Josephson junction of an oxide superconductor film [76]; (2) the fast response of virtual polarization of the carriers in a quantum-well semiconductor [77]; (3) the large nonlinear characteristics of an organic thin film [78].

Although a high sensitivity can be expected from (1), due to the large optical absorption coefficient of the oxide superconductor film, the problems remain in the fabrication of a thin and homogeneous Josephson junction and the development of a detailed theoretical model to analyze the dynamic response to the lightwave. Preliminary studies have used a thin film of oxide superconductor as a fast photodetector by irradiating the intensity modulated laser light [79, 80]. Figure 7.14 shows such an experiment [80]. Nonbolometric signals have appeared at a temperature slightly below the Curie point T_c of a 1 μm thick TlBaCaO film grown on MgO substrate, which could be interpreted by a photoenhanced flux creep model [81]. A very fast response, as fast as several 10 GHz, can be expected, which can be used as a very fast and sensitive photodetector. For (2), the problems center around the precise structure of multidimensional quantum confinement for the carrier and improvement in the sensitivity of the dynamic response to the lightwave. For (3), the problems are the single crystal growth of an optimally designed organic material, the device fabrication, and lengthening the device's life. However, we can expect an ultrahigh-speed optical detector to be developed in the future by improving the theoretical background of oxide superconductors, submicron fine-device fabrication techniques, and reliability in organic materials. The full utilization of a high-quality lightwave can be expected by using these ultrafast detectors.

A new scheme has been proposed for precise optical-frequency measurements [82, 83]. This scheme can be realized by using several semiconductor lasers and nonlinear optical crystals. Although the scheme requires no ultrafast photodetectors, a number of frequency-controlled semiconductor lasers and efficient nonlinear optical crystals are indispensable to it. Figure 7.15(a) shows a block diagram of the novel

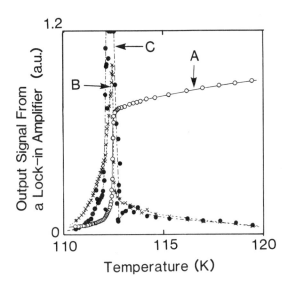

Figure 7.14 Temperature dependence of the characteristics of a TlBaCaO superconductor film: *A* is the temperature dependence of the resistance; *B* is the derivative of curve *A*; *C* is the voltage drop of the thin film driven by a constant current, which was measured by a lock-in detection method under the irradiation of the intensity-modulated laser light (from [80]).

optical frequency measurement system with an accuracy of 1×10^{-9} [83]. This system was proposed for the frequency measurement of 1.5 μm wavelength InGaAsP laser for *frequency-division-multiplex* (FDM) coherent optical communication systems. As shown in Figure 7.16, an optical fiber has been known to have minimal loss at the wavelength 1.55 μm. Around this wavelength, a window, at which the fiber loss is low, has the width of about 20 THz, in which channels of the FDM coherent optical communication system are distributed with a channel separation of about 10 GHz. Therefore, as many as 2000 channels can be expected, leading to very large capacity optical communication. However, note that accurate measurement of each channel frequency is required to assure reliable switching between channels, for which an accurate optical frequency measurement system is indispensable. In the system of Figure 7.15(a), this high accuracy is secured by using two He-Ne lasers whose frequencies are stabilized to saturated-absorption spectral lines in I_2 (0.63 μm wavelength) and CH_4 (3.39 μm wavelength). Their frequencies ν_1 and ν_2 already have been calibrated within an accuracy of 1×10^{-9} [84]. The frequency ν_r of a 1.5 μm semiconductor laser (LD_r), whose FM noise has been reduced by the methods of Chapter 4, can be fixed to $(\nu_1 - \nu_2)/2$, as long as the two *optical phase-locked loops* (OPLLs) in this figure are closed by utilizing two nonlinear optical frequency converters: a *sum-frequency generator* (SFG) and a *difference-frequency generator*

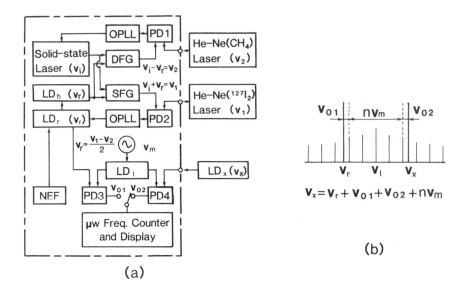

Figure 7.15 (a) Block diagram of an optical frequency measurement system at the 1.55 μm wavelength region (from [83]): LD_r is a low FM-noise semiconductor laser; LD_h is a high-power semiconductor laser; LD_l is a frequency modulated semiconductor laser used as a local oscillator; LD_x is the semiconductor laser under test; *OPLL* is an optical phase-locked loop, *NEF* is the negative electrical feedback system; *SFG* is a sum-frequency generator; *DFG* is a difference-frequency generator. (b) Relation between the frequencies of LD_r, LD_x, and LD_l; v_m and n are the modulation frequency of LD_l and number of FM sidebands of the LD_l that fall in the frequency range between v_r and v_x, respectively.

(DFG). A solid-state laser, such as a semiconductor laser-pumped YAG laser or a Ti:Al$_2$O$_3$ laser, and an injection-locked high-power semiconductor laser (LD_h) can be used as local oscillators for highly efficient nonlinear optical frequency conversion. A similar preliminary proposal for optical frequency conversion uses a shorter wavelength region [85]. Finally, the frequency v_x of the laser under test (LD_x) is measured by heterodyning with the frequency-calibrated LD_r. Another local oscillator (LD_l) is used if the heterodyne frequency is too high to detect by the photodetectors PD1–PD4. In this case, the heterodyne frequencies v_{01} and v_{02} between LD_r and LD_l, and between LD_l and LD_x, are measured by an RF frequency counter; thereby, v_x is given by $v_r + v_{01} + v_{02} + nv_m$ (see Figure 7.15(b)), where n is the number of sidebands of LD_l located between v_r and v_x. For such heterodyning, the LD_l is used as a wideband frequency comb generator, as is schematically explained in Figure 7.15(b). A wideband frequency comb can be realized by sidebands of a Fabry-Perot electro-optic modulator [86] or an ultra-short-pulse generation technique. Furthermore, in the future we will be able to replace a fragile 0.63 μm He-Ne laser and 3.39 μm He-Ne laser by an AlGaInP laser and a 1.7 μm wavelength semiconductor laser (fabricated by the techniques of, say, strained quantum well) with its degenerated optical parametric oscillator, respectively. We expect that a compact, all-solid-state optical frequency counter with very high accuracy will be realized in the near future by this system, for which techniques are described in Chapters 4 and 5 and Sections 7.1 and 7.2.

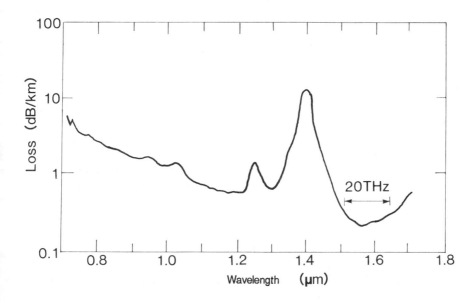

Figure 7.16 Wavelength dependence of the loss of a single-mode fiber.

7.4 GENERATION AND APPLICATION OF NONCLASSICAL PHOTONS

The characteristics of coherent and hyper coherent states of light have been described and their application systems have been demonstrated in the previous chapters. These lightwaves show quite low FM noises, as low as the quantum noise limit of each system, and are close to classical waves. In contrast to these, it is also possible to generate novel lightwaves (non-classical photons) and to apply them to advanced application systems. They are described in this section.

7.4.1 Photon Antibunching and the Properties of the Squeezed State of Light

When a constant intensity light beam is received by a photodetector, the frequency of the photon arriving at the detector (i.e., the statistical property of the time series of this arrival process) depends on the quantum state of light. As shown in Figure

7.17 [87], the property of the coherent state of light is expressed as the Poisson process because photons arrive in a completely random manner. That of the incoherent thermal radiation is expressed as a Boltzmann distribution; that is, photons arrive in a bunched manner. This phenomenon, called *photon bunching,* is a specific characteristic of classical light, represented as a statistical superposition of the coherent state of light. On the other hand, the phenomenon in which photons do not bunch is called *photon antibunching.* This is the statistical property of light whose photon number uncertainty is smaller than that in the coherent state of light. The photon-number state $|N_p\rangle$ and the squeezed state described later have this property; they can be called *nonclassical photons,* in which the photon-number distribution takes a sub-Poisson distribution whose variance is lower than that of a Poisson distribution [87].

The properties of the squeezed state, which are different from those of the coherent state, are described here. Coherent and hypercoherent states of light correspond to classical sinusoidal waves whose fluctuation magnitudes have been limited by the quantum noise; that is, spontaneous emission fluctuations and the shot noise of the feedback loop, respectively. However, nonclassical photons can exceed this quantum noise limit in the following way. The product of the uncertainty of measurement $\Delta X_1 \cdot \Delta X_2$ of two Hermite-conjugate physical quantities, X_1 and X_2, cannot exceed the limit imposed by the uncertainty principle, which has been described in eq. (2.14). In the coherent state, the minimum uncertainty condition, the equality of eq. (2.14), holds and, furthermore, $\Delta X_1 = \Delta X_2$, where $X_1 = a + a^+$ and $X_2 = a - a^+$, respectively. However, the state in which $\Delta X_1 < \Delta X_2$ or $\Delta X_1 > \Delta X_2$ can be realized too as long as this minimum uncertainty is maintained. Realizing one of these situations is called *squeezing.* The state of physical quantity obtained by this procedure is called a *squeezed state.* For example, if a variation in the optical phase is utilized for some optical systems, the uncertainty of the optical power need not be low. In this case, the condition $\Delta\phi < 1/\sqrt{2}$ and $\Delta N_p > 1/\sqrt{2}$ in eq. (2.20) should be useful for this system. This condition corresponds to a squeezed state in which phase fluctuation is low. If such phase squeezing is realized for the frequency control in Chapters 4 and 5, a very low FM-noise laser beyond the quantum noise limit can be developed. Furthermore, the measurement accuracy of the gravitational wave detector, described in Section 7.6, can be improved if phase-squeezed light is employed. It is also possible to realize the photon number squeezed state (i.e., $\Delta\phi > 1/\sqrt{2}$ and $\Delta N_p < 1/\sqrt{2}$) by which the performance of a long-distance optical communication system using power modulation or photon counting could be improved. However, a careful treatment of squeezed light should be required as the uncertainty ΔX_2 of the counterpart physical quantity increases if that of the relevant physical quantity ΔX_1 decreases. Therefore, the characteristics of the squeezed state are different from those of coherent or hypercoherent states.

Although the squeezed state can be realized in all physical systems, as long as they are described by a harmonic oscillator model, recent research activities have concentrated on light. To obtain a squeezed state, the values of ΔX_1 and ΔX_2 should

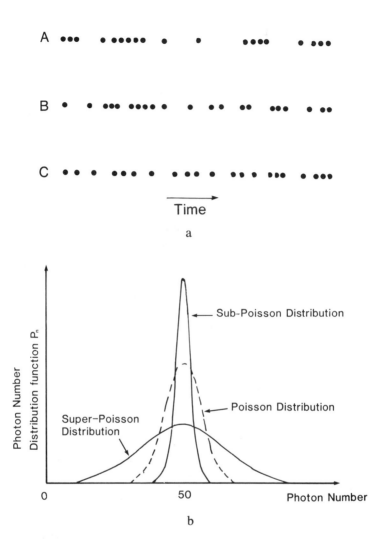

Figure 7.17 Relation between photon number distribution and the temporal variation of photon counting (from [87]): (a) temporal variation of photon counting representing the state of photon
ensemble (the temporal variation of photoelectrons generated from the photon-counting
detector are shown by the dots: *A* is the bunching state, *B* is the random state, *C* is the anti-
bunching state); (b) distribution functions of photon numbers.

be controlled by utilizing a pair of photons that are correlated quantum mechani-
cally to each other. Thus, to obtain a squeezed light, two mutually correlated photons
have to be generated. This means that the concept of squeezing is close to that of the
photon pair in the phase-conjugated wave generation described in Section 7.1.6. For

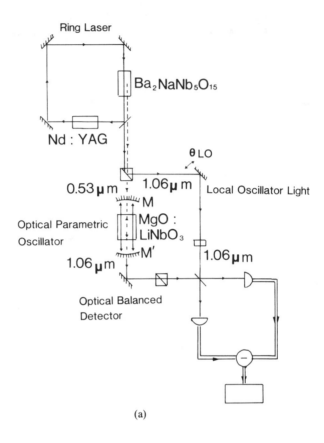

(a)

Figure 7.18 Generation of a squeezed light by the optical parametric process (from [89]): (a) setup of a degenerated parametric amplifier and a balanced detector composed of a ring-cavity YAG laser and a nonlinear optical crystal; (b) measured noise magnitude (the dashed line represents the magnitude of quantum limit corresponding to the vacuum fluctuation).

example, a squeezed state can be realized if the Hamiltonian representing the photon generation process has the following form:

$$\mathcal{H} = h(V_s aa + V_s^* a^+ a^+) \tag{7.4}$$

where V_s is a proportional constant. Because most optical processes having this kind of Hamiltonian are nonlinear, we use a parametric amplification due to the nonlinear susceptibility of the second-order, four-wave mixing, due to the nonlinear susceptibility of the third-order, *et cetera*. For the generation and detection of squeezed light, several problems should be solved: (1) use of an optical process that exhibits a large nonlinearity; (2) removal of additional optical processes such as absorption and

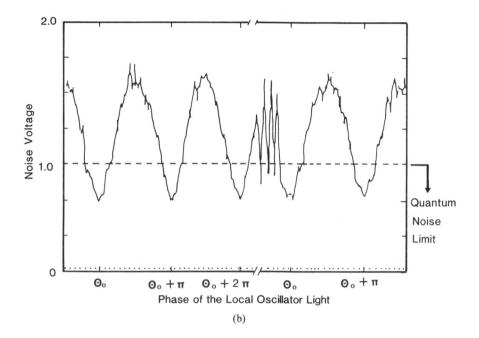

Figure 7.18 continued

spontaneous emission, as they can easily destroy squeezed light; and (3) removal of additional noises, as a very low magnitude of fluctuation below the quantum noise is measured for squeezed state detection. It is effective to observe the beat signal between the relevant phase component of the measured light and the reference local light by the homodyne or heterodyne techniques to directly measure the fluctuations of the conjugate quantities ΔX_1 and ΔX_2.

Because of the complicated experimental requirements just presented, it is not easy to obtain squeezed light. However, after the successful experiments were reported in 1985 [88], others succeeded in performing these experiments. The first experiments employed a four-wave mixing process by using the Na atomic beam as a nonlinear medium and dye lasers as light sources [88]. The largest value of noise suppression reported so far was realized by using a parametric process [89]. As shown in Figure 7.18(a), the second harmonic wave from a Nd:YAG laser was used as a pumping wave (frequency ν_p) to obtain parametric oscillation by a MgO:LiNbO$_3$ crystal in the cavity. By using this experimental setup, squeezed light of a frequency $\nu_p/2$ generated by the degenerated parametric oscillation was detected [89]. To reduce additional noise, several techniques were employed: A parametric oscillator was operated below the threshold level, and the pumping wave was used as local light in the balanced homodyne detection using an optical balanced detector. Figure

7.18(b) shows the result. The noise level was reduced to 2/3 that of the quantum noise limit by adjusting the phase of the local light. This figure easily confirms that a squeezed state was really generated. By carefully reducing additional noise in a semiconductor laser, squeezing of 10 dB in the light amplitude fluctuations recently has been realized [90]. The future problem remaining to be solved might be to find how to use this squeezed light in an optical system.

7.4.2 Quantum Nondemolition Measurements

When a physical quantity is measured, the measurement process itself can perturb the condition of the physical quantity. For example, if the position of the free particle is measured with an error of Δq, this measurement induces a measurement error Δp in the momentum, which is given by eq. (2.15); that is, $\Delta p > (\hbar/2\Delta q)$. Therefore, velocity fluctuations in the particle are induced by this measurement. The fluctuations are as large as $\Delta v = \Delta p/M$, where M is the mass of the particle. As a result of these velocity fluctuations, the error of the position measured at time t after the initial measurement is $\Delta q \geq \sqrt{\hbar t/2M}$. The magnitude of this additional error is nonnegligibly large; for example, especially in the case of the mirror position measurement of the interferometer for the gravitational wave detection described in Section 7.6. To solve this problem, a gravitational wave detection method, called *quantum nondemolition* (QND) measurement, has been proposed [91]. As shown in Figure 7.19, this measurement does not induce any change in the measured physical quantity. In contrast to the previously mentioned measurement procedures, the measurement of momentum is discussed. If momentum is measured with an error of Δp, the minimum measurement error of the position Δq is given by eq. (2.15). However, this error Δq does not affect the measurement error of the succeeding measurement of the momentum because no change in particle velocity has been induced by Δq. This procedure is the QND measurement for the momentum. The physical quantity for which the QND measurement is possible is called the *QND variable*. The reason why the momentum p is the QND variable is that the Hamiltonian $\mathcal{H} (= p^2/2M)$ of the free particle commutes with the momentum operator p. Because the Hamiltonian of the light field given in Section 2.1 has the same form as that of a harmonic oscillator, the QND variables are the photon number N_p. Furthermore, $a + a^+$ and $a - a^+$ can be QND variables corresponding to the sine and cosine components of the classical electrical field amplitude, respectively. Therefore, we say that this method is basically possible.

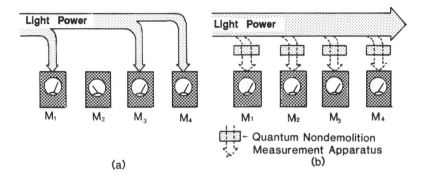

Figure 7.19 Measurement of informations transmitted by light: (a) common measurement (when the information is indicated by the meters M_1–M_4, a part of power must be dissipated for the measurements and lead the loss of the transmitted light power); (b) quantum nondemolition measurement (information can be measured without a power dissipation, and therefore, no power is lost after the measurement).

Studies on QND measurements have been carried out in connection with those on the squeezed state because the generation of a quantum mechanical correlation using nonlinear optical processes is common to both types of research. Because research on the squeezed state focused on generating a quantum mechanical correlation, some magnitudes of losses in nonlinear optical media are allowable. As shown in Figure 7.18, squeezed light actually has been observed. However, QND measurement is more difficult than the generation of a squeezed state because it is essential to avoid destroying the state of light by losses in nonlinear optical media. However, if QND measurements are realized, the measurement sensitivity of the gravitational wave detection can be improved. As another application, detection by tapping and demodulating the transmitted signal becomes possible without losing its power in optical communication systems, which can dramatically increase the communication capacity.

7.5 CONTROL AND MANIPULATION OF ATOMS AND PHOTONS

Resonance frequencies in low-pressure atomic vapor could be shifted slightly from an intrinsic Bohr frequency due to atomic collision, a second-order doppler effect, thermal motion, and so forth. To eliminate this shift, the preparation of new atomic states has tried to control atomic motion to bring atoms up to an ultrahigh-precision frequency standard for use in ultrahigh-resolution laser spectroscopy and basic studies on quantum optics. These new states are reached by the laser cooling and ion trapping described in Section 6.6.3.

On the other hand, the techniques of controlling and manipulating photons could correspond to those using the cavity QED described in the introduction of Chapter 3 and Section 6.6.4. As an application of the cavity QED, the interaction between one atom and a high-Q single mode cavity is described [92, 93]. The situation of this interaction implies that only one mode of the vacuum interacts with the atom. In the case, when a single mode light field of a frequency v_q interacts with one atom, the Hamiltonian of this system can be expressed as

$$\mathcal{H} = h v_q \, S^z + h v_q a^+ a + h g (S^+ \cdot a + S^- \cdot a^+) \tag{7.5}$$

where S^z, S^+, and S^- are spin-operators for the atom, g is a coupling constant of the interaction between an atom and the vacuum field. If only the two cases (i.e., when the atom is in the upper state $|a\rangle$ and no photon $|0\rangle$ or when the atom is in the lower state $|b\rangle$ and one photon $|1\rangle$) are considered, the state of this system can be expressed as

$$|\psi\rangle = c_a |a,0\rangle + c_b |b,1\rangle \tag{7.6}$$

By using the Hamiltonian of (7.5), the coefficients c_a and c_b of this expression can be given by

$$c_a = -i \cdot \sin(2\pi g t) \tag{7.7}$$
$$c_b = \cos(2\pi g t)$$

The coupling coefficient g is expressed as [93]

$$g = \frac{p}{h} \sqrt{\frac{h v_q}{\epsilon_0 V}} \tag{7.8}$$

where p is the transition dipole moment and V is the cavity volume. We see from (7.7) that the atom can move back and forth between the upper and lower states with a constant time period of T ($= \frac{1}{2}\pi g$), and consequently, the photon number also changes between 0 and 1 with this period. Note that the g always takes a nonzero value in the present system; that is, an interaction can take place between the atom and field without any external optical fields incident to the atom. Therefore, phenomenon given by (7.7) is called the *Rabi oscillation induced by vacuum fluctuation*. By utilizing this phenomenon, we can realize a very low threshold laser. Although it is not straightforward to demonstrate experimentally this phenomenon in the optical frequency region, it has been already demonstrated in the microwave frequency region by using a Rydberg atom and a superconductor cavity [94]. A small number of sodium (Na) atoms and a high-Q Fabry-Perot interferometer have been used to demonstrate this phenomenon in the optical frequency region. As has been shown by Figure 6.39, spectral splitting of spontaneous emission has been observed, due to the Rabi oscillation in vacuum [93].

Although theoretical studies of this novel phenomenon, controlling or manipulating atoms and photons, and its application have been carried out for a long time, most experimental progress is recent and builds on progress in the experimental techniques of laser control, described in Chapters 4 and 5, and material and device fabrication. Furthermore, the interaction of a single atom and photon can be a powerful tool to test the basic theories of physics [95] and the applicability of thermodynamics [96]. On the other hand the results of these studies can be applied back to the techniques of laser control and fabrication of new materials and devices. Studies of the control and manipulation of a single atom or photon are continuing. As the next step in the interaction between the single atom and single photon, the photon-photon scattering of the intense laser radiation in vacuum has been predicted [97]. Furthermore, this prediction proposes that a second-harmonic generation also is possible in a dc magnetized vacuum, due to the broken symmetry of the interaction [98]. These studies of quantum optics under an ultimate condition could establish a new basis of physics and open the way to progress in highly coherent semiconductor lasers.

7.6 HIGH-POWER LASERS AND OPTICAL ENERGY STORAGE

High-quality lightwaves can be generated by a laser, and its modulation, transmission, and detection also is possible by using electro-optical materials, optical fibers, and photodiodes, respectively. Optical communication and optical computing systems have been developed by using these techniques. However, efficient utilization of optical energy is limited because no method of optical power storage has been found, as photon energy $h\nu$ is low and spatial photon localization is not straightforward. However, optical power storage is essential for highly coherent semiconductor lasers because an efficient optical power confinement in the laser cavity can reduce the FM noise of the laser oscillation, as shown by eq. (2.53). The laser fusion system is an example of optical energy utilization. High-power lasers have been used in progressing toward break-even, a situation in which the output energy due to the laser fusion is equal to the input energy. Break-even could expand the applications of optical energy systems; for example, interplanetary rocket propulsion by laser fusion [99]. In practical and commercial laser fusion systems constructed after break-even, high-power semiconductor lasers could be used as light sources because of their high quantum efficiency and small size.

Figure 7.20 shows a highly coherent, high-power laser used in a gravitational wave detection system. Gravitational wave detection is an effective tool to test the general theory of relativity. A heavy metal rod (called a *Weber bar*) hung by metal wires is used as the detection sensor [100]. However, its detection bandwidth is narrow because the Weber bar works as a band-pass filter whose resonant frequency is determined by its size and weight. Use of a laser interferometer has been proposed to expand the bandwidth, as shown by this figure. A long-baseline interferometer is constructed by using a low FM-noise laser as a light source. The gravitational wave is generated from a neutron star or by the phenomena of gravitation collapse in the galaxy and propagates to the earth. If the gravitational wave hits one of the interferometer mirrors hung by a wire, the difference in optical path length between the two interferometer arms changes slightly. As a result, the output light power of the interferometer changes, by which the gravitational wave can be detected. Frequent measurements can be carried out if the amplitude of a gravitational wave d as low as 1×10^{-21} is measured because such a gravitational wave is generated about once a month by the gravity collapse in the Virgin galaxy. The relationship between the amplitude d and the displacement of the interferometer mirror δ_l is given by

$$d = 2\delta l/l \tag{7.9}$$

where l is the length of the interferometer. This equation shows that the value of l should be 100 km because the values of d and the minimum displacement measured by the low FM-noise laser are 1×10^{-21} and 1×10^{-14} cm, respectively. Because it is technically difficult to construct such a long interferometer, an interferometer with a folded optical path or a high finesse Fabry-Perot interferometer has been proposed. Furthermore, a very long-baseline interferometer, as long as 10,000 km, has also been proposed to be constructed in space by using satellites [101]. Another indis-

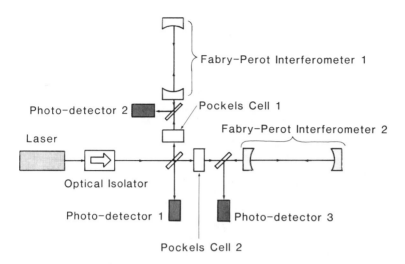

Figure 7.20 Gravitational wave detection system using a highly coherent, high-power laser and very long Fabry-Perot interferometers.

pensable consideration is a laser with a frequency stability higher than 1×10^{-15}. Furthermore, based on eq. (2.23), power higher than 100 W is required, as the inaccuracy of phase measurement is inversely proportional to the light power. A semiconductor laser-pumped Nd:YAG laser is considered to be a promising light source satisfying these requirements. By using a low-power, frequency-controlled Nd:YAG laser as the master laser, the high-power slave laser can track frequency by using the technique described in Section 5.1 or injection locking. Based on these ideas, a large experimental system for the gravitational wave detection has been under construction recently, and success of the detection is expected at the beginning of the twenty-first century. A preliminary experimental setup, using a 10 m Michelson interferometer and an Ar+ laser, is shown in Figure 7.21. We expect that a highly coherent laser can be realized in the future by using the techniques of Chapters 4 and 5. However, achieving very high power presents problems, because it is not straightforward to realize such high CW power from a low FM-noise single YAG laser, and also also optical damage of cavity mirrors and YAG crystals must be considered. To overcome this difficulty, a technique of coherent addition has been proposed [102]. Figure 7.22 shows a schematic explanation of this technique, where a number of low-to-medium power slave lasers are injection locked to a stable master laser. Under this condition, the optical path lengths are servo controlled so that the phases of all the

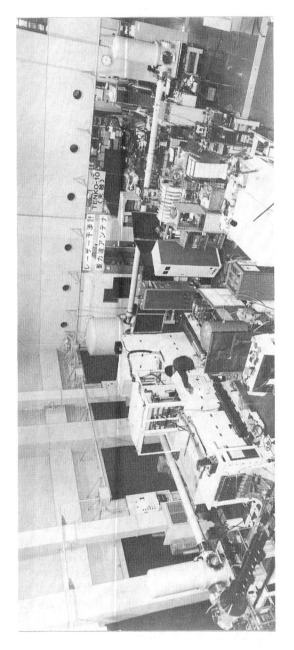

Figure 7.21 Preliminary experimental setup of the gravitational wave detection system (by courtesy of N. Kawashima, the Institute of Space and Astronomical Science, 1989).

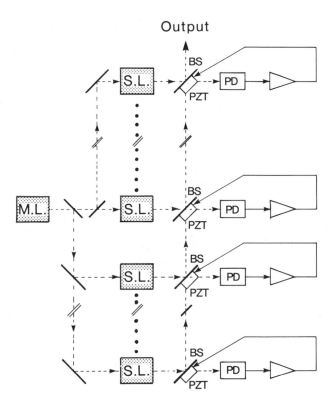

Figure 7.22 Experiment for coherent addition: *M.L.* is a master laser; *S.L.* is a slave laser.

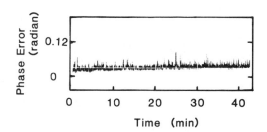

Figure 7.23 Residual phase error of the coherent addition between the two phase-locked 1.5 μm InGaAsP lasers (from [103]).

slave lasers coincide with each other at the output beam splitter. Thus, a very high total power, superposed coherently, can be realized. Figure 7.23 shows the results of coherent addition between the two phase-locked semiconductor lasers [103]. Residual phase difference has been reduced to lower than 0.05 radian by the servo control of the optical path length. This sort of experiment could be essential because future practical gravitational wave detection systems could be operated by highly coherent, high-power semiconductor lasers. For further improvement in phase detection sensitivity in gravitational wave detection systems, the use of the squeezed light and the quantum nondemolition measurement, as described in the Section 7.4, have been studied.

Storage of the optical energy from high-power lasers in an optical container, can open the way to a wide variety of applications: motive power, heating, dynamo, actuators [104], digital logic devices, microrobots, and micromanipulators. Although the technique of cavity QED of Section 7.5 can provide an example of optical energy storage, stored energy still is low. To realize practical optical power storage, a power container, such as a capacitor in the electric circuit, is required. A super-high-finesse Fabry-Perot cavity corresponds to such a container. Although the supercavity with the finesse as high as 1×10^6 has been developed, its storage time (i.e., the photon lifetime) is still less than several seconds. On the other hand, a low-loss superconductor cavity has been already developed in the microwave frequency region [105]. Such a high-quality cavity should be developed in the optical frequency region. To realize this kind of optical energy storage, the basic technologies given by Section 7.5 and material or device fabrication techniques will play essential roles. If the light can be used for transmission of not only information but also energy, highly coherent semiconductor lasers will play essential roles in a variety of advanced optical systems.

REFERENCES

[1] Linke, R.A., B.L. Kasper, C.A. Burrus, Jr., I.P. Kaminov, J.S. Ko, and T.P. Lee, "Mode Power Partition Events in Nearly Single-Frequency Lasers," *J. Lightwave Technology,* Vol. LT-3, No. 4, June 1985, pp. 706–712.

[2] Ohtsu, M., Y. Teramachi, and T. Miyazaki, "Mode Stability Analysis of Nearly Single-Longitudinal-Mode Semiconductor Lasers," *IEEE J. Quantum Electronics,* Vol. 24, No. 5, May 1988, pp. 716–723.

[3] Sekartedjo, K., N. Eda, K. Furuya, Y. Suematsu, F. Koyama, and T. Tanbun-ek, "1.5 μm Phase-Shifted DFB Lasers for Single-Mode Operation," *Electronics Letters,* Vol. 20, No. 2, January 1984, pp. 80–81.

[4] Utaka, K., S. Akiba, K. Sakai, and Y. Matsushima, "λ/4-Shifted InGaAsP/InP DFB Lasers by Simultaneous Holographic Exposure of Positive and Negative Photoresists," *Electronics Letters,* Vol. 20, No. 24, November 1984, pp. 1008–1010.

[5] Soda, H., K. Wakao, H. Sudo, T. Tanahashi, and H. Imai, "GaInAsP/InP Phase-Adjusted Distributed Feedback Lasers with a Step-like Nonuniform Stripe Width Structure," *Electronics Letters,* Vol. 20, No. 24, November 1984, pp. 1016–1018.

[6] Hirata, S., K. Tamamura, and C. Kojima, "λ/4 Shifted AlGaAs/GaAs Lasers with Double Window Structures," *Electronics Letters,* Vol. 23, No. 12, June 1987, pp. 627–628.

[7] Suzuki, A., and K. Tada, "Fabrication of Chirped Gratings on GaAs Optical Waveguides," *Thin Solid Films,* Vol. 72, No. 3, October 1980, pp. 419–426.

[8] Okai, M., N. Chinone, H. Taira, and T. Harada, "Corrugation-Pitch-Modulated Phase-Shifted DFB Laser," *Tech. Digest of 7th Int. Conf. Integrated Optics and Optical Fiber Communication,* Kobe, Japan, July 18–21, 1989, pp. 102–103.

[9] Suzuki, A., and K. Tada, "Analysis of Distributed Feedback Lasers with Axial Variation in Effective Refractive-Index," Tech. Rep. IECEC, Japan, January 1978, paper no. QOE77-88.

[10] Nakano, Y. and K. Tada. "Complete Single Longitudinal Mode Oscillation in a GaAlAs/GaAs Distributed Feedback Laser with a Modulated Stripe-Width Structure Fabricated using Reactive Ion Etching," *Applied Physics Letters,* Vol. 51, No. 6, August 1987, pp. 387–389.

[11] Kinoshita, J., "Analysis of TE/TM Mode Selectivity in DFB Lasers with a Phase-Shift Region," *IEEE Photonics Technology Letters,* Vol. 1, No. 1, January 1989, pp. 4–5.

[12] Nakano, Y., O. Kamatani, and K. Tada, "Effects of Longitudinal Spatial Hole Burning on the Characteristics of Phase-Shifted DFB Lasers—Calculation Considering Longitudinal Gain Distribution," *Technical Digest,* 11th IEEE Int. Semiconductor Laser Conf., Boston, August 29–September 1, 1988, pp. 102–103.

[13] Nakano, Y., O. Kamatani, and K. Tada, "Stable Oscillation at High Injection Level in Modulated Stripe-Width Distributed Feedback Laser," *Technical Digest,* 2nd Optoelectronics Conf., Tokyo, October 1988, pp. 222–223.

[14] Kogelnik, H., and C.V. Shank, "Coupled-Wave Theory of Distributed Feedback Lasers," *J. Applied Physics,* Vol. 43, No. 5, May 1972, pp. 2327–2335.

[15] Luo, Y., Y. Nakano, and K. Tada, "Purely Gain-Coupled Distributed Feedback Semiconductor Lasers," *Applied Physics Letters,* Vol. 56, No. 17, April 1990, pp. 1620–1622.

[16] Luo, Y., Y. Nakano, and K. Tada, "Purely Gain-Coupled Distributed Feedback Semiconductor Lasers," *Applied Physics Letters,* Vol. 56, No. 17, April 1990, pp. 1620–1622.

[17] Okai, M., S. Tsuji, and N. Chinone, "Stability of the Longitudinal Mode in λ/4-Shifted InGaAsP/ InP DFB Lasers," *IEEE J. Quantum Electronics,* Vol. 25, No. 6, June 1989, pp. 1314–1319.

[18] Ikegami, T., M. Fukuda, and H. Yasaka, "Current Tailoring for Lowering Linewidth Floor," Proc. 11th IEEE Int. Semiconductor Laser Conf., Boston, August 29–September 1, 1988, pp. 100–101.

[19] Kotaki, Y., S. Ogita, and H. Ishikawa, "Wavelength Tunable Semiconductor Lasers," *Trans. Institute of Electronic, Information, and Communication Engineering* Vol. J73-C-1, No. 5, May 1990, pp. 253–260 [in Japanese].

[20] Yamazaki, H., T. Sasaki, N. Kida, M. Kitamura, and I. Mito, "Narrow Linewidth 1.5 μm MQW-DFB-LD," Proc. 7th Semiconductor Laser Symp., February 17, 1990, p. 25.

[21] Okai, M., T. Tsuchiya, K. Uomi, N. Chinone, and T. Harada, "Corrugation-Pitch-Modulated MQW-DFB Laser with Narrow Spectral Linewidth (170 kHz)," *IEEE Photonics Technology Letters,* Vol. 2, No. 8, August 1990, pp. 529–530.

[22] Okai, M., T. Tsuchiya, and N. Chinone, "Ultra-Narrow Spectral Linewidth (56 kHz) Corrugation-Pitch-Modulated Multi-Quantum-Well Distributed Feedback Lasers," *Technical Digest of Conferences on Lasers and Electro-Optics* (CLEO'91), Baltimore, 1991, paper number CPDP40.

[23] Ohtsu, M., M. Murata, and H. Kourogim, "FM Noise Reduction and Subkilohertz Linewidth of an AlGaAs Laser by Negative Electrical Feedback," *IEEE J. Quantum Electronics,* Vol. 26, No. 2, February 1990, pp. 231–241.

[24] Fujita, T., J. Ohya, K. Matsuda, M. Ishino, H. Sato, and H. Serizawa, "Narrow Spectral Linewidth Characteristic of Monolithic Integrated-Passive-Cavity InGaAsP/InP Semiconductor Lasers," *Electronics Letters,* Vol. 21, No. 9, April 1985, pp. 374–376.

[25] Mito, I., and K. Kitamura, "GaInAs/GaInAsP Multiquantum Well DFB Lasers," Proc. Conf. Lasers and Electro-Optics, Baltimore, April 24–28, 1989, paper number TUD5.

[26] Imai, H., "Optical Device for High Speed Transmission Including Widely Tunable DFB/DBR Lasers," Proc. Conf. Lasers and Electroc-Optics, Baltimore, April 24–28, 1989, paper number FB4.

[27] Ackerman, D.A., M.I. Danbura, Y. Shani, C.H. Henry, R.C. Kisler, R.Y. Kazarinov, and C.Y. Kuo, "Compact Hybrid Resonant Optical Reflector Lasers with Very Narrow Linewidths," *Applied Physics Letters,* Vol. 58, No. 5, February 1991, pp. 449–451.

[28] Tohmori, Y., Y. Suematsu, H. Tsushima, and S. Arai, "Wavelength Tuning of GaInAsP/InP Integrated Laser with Butt-Jointed Built-In Distributed Bragg Reflector," *Electronics Letters,* Vol. 19, No. 17, August 1983, pp. 656–657.

[29] Mito, I., "Wavelength Tunable Semiconductor Lasers and Their Application to Optical Coherent Communication Systems," Oyo Buturi, Vol. 59, No. 9, September 1990, pp. 1136–1153 [in Japanese].

[30] Mehuys, D., M. Mittelstein, and A. Yariv, "(GaAl)As Quantum Well Semiconductor Lasers Tunable over 105 nm with an External Grating," Proc. Conf. Lasers and Electro-Optics, Baltimore, April 24–28, 1989, paper number FL4.

[31] Tabuchi, H., and H. Ishikawa, "External Grating Tunable MQW Laser with Wide Tuning Range of 240 nm." *Tech. Digest,* 3rd Optoelectronics Conference, Makuhari, Japan, July 11–13, 1990, pp. 30–31.

[32] Osbourn, G.C., "Strained-Layer Superlattices: A Brief Review," *IEEE J. Quantum Electronics,* Vol. QE-22, No. 9, September 1986, pp. 1677–1681.

[33] Osbourn, G.C., R.M. Biefield, and P.L. Gourley, "A $GaAs_xP_{1-x}$/GaP Strained-Layer Superlattice," *Applied Physics Letters,* Vol. 41, No. 2, July 1982, pp. 172–174.

[34] Ohtoshi, T., "Strained Quantum Well Lasers," *Oyo Buturi* [*J. of Applied Physics Society of Japan*] Vol. 59, No. 9, September 1990, pp. 1193–1197 [in Japanese].

[35] Chong, T.C., and C.G. Fonstad, "Theoretical Gain of Strained-Layer Semiconductor Lasers in the Large Strain Regime," *IEEE J. Quantum Electronics,* Vol. QE-25, No. 2, February 1989, pp. 171–174.

[36] Eng., L.E., T.R. Chen, S. Sanders, Y.H. Zhuang, B. Zhao, and A. Yariv, "Submilliampere Threshold Current Pseudomorphic InGaAs/AlGaAs Buried-Heterostructure Quantum Well Lasers Grown by Molecular Beam Epitaxy," *Applied Physics Letters,* Vol. 55, No. 14, October 1988, pp. 1378–1379.

[37] Okayasu, Y., M. Fukuda, T. Takeshita, O. Kogure, T. Hirano, and S. Uehara, "Stable, High Power 0.98-μm InGaAs/GaAs Strained Quantum Well Ridge Waveguide Lasers for Pumping Fiber Amplifier," *Tech. Digest,* Conf. Optics and Communication, San Francisco, January 22–26, 1990, paper number PD29.

[38] Welch, D.F., M. Cardinal, W. Streifer, and D. Scifres, "High Power Single Mode InGaAs/AlGaAs Laser Diodes at $910nm$," *Electronics Letters,* Vol. 26, No. 4, February 1990, pp. 233–234.

[39] Bour, D.P., P. Stabile, A. Rosen, W. Janton, L. Elbaum, and D.J. Holms, "Two-Dimensional Array of High-Power Strained Quantum Well Lasers with $\lambda = 0.95$ μm," *Applied Physics Letters,* Vol. 54, No. 26, June 1989, pp. 2637–2638.

[40] Tothill, J.N., L. Westbrook, C.B. Hatch, and J. H. Wilkie, "Novel Strained Quantum Well Laser Grown by MOVPE," *Electronics Letters,* Vol. 25, No. 9, April 1989, pp. 578–580.

[41] Thijs, P.J.A., and T.V. Dongen, "High Quantum Efficiency, High Power, Modulation Doped GaInAs Strained-Layer Quantum Well Laser Diodes Emitting at 1.5μm," *Electronics Letters,* Vol. 25, No. 25, December 1989, pp. 1735–1737.

[42] Zah, C.E., F.J. Favire, R. Bhat, S.G. Menocal, N.C. Andreadakis, D.M. Hwang, M. Koza, and T.P. Lee, "Submilliampere Threshold 1.5 μm Strained-Layer Multiple Quantum Well Lasers," *Conf. Digest,* 12th IEEE Int. Semiconductor Laser Conf., Davos, Switzerland, September 9–14, 1990, pp. 42–43.

[43] Jaeckel, H., G.L. Bona, P. Buchmann, H. Meier, P. Vettiger, W.J. Kozlovsky and W. Lenth, "Very High Power (500 mW) AlGaAs SQW Grinsch Ridge Laser with Frequency Doubled Output (40 mW at 428 nM)," *Conf. Digest,* 12th IEEE Int. Semiconductor Laser Conf., Davos, Switzerland, September 9–14, 1990, pp. 270–271.

[44] Shigihara, K., A. Shima, Y. Nagai, A. Takami, S. Karakida, Y. Kokubo, H. Matsubara, and S. Kakimoto, "High Power Operation of GaAs and AlGaAs Single Quantum Well Broad-Area Laser Diodes for Nd:YAG Laser Pumping," *Conf. Digest,* 12th IEEE Int. Semiconductor Laser Conf., Devos, Switzerland, September 9–14, 1990, pp. 274–275.

[45] Sakamoto, M., D.F. Welch, J.G. Endriz, D.R. Scifres, and W. Streifer, "76 W CW Monolithic Laser Diode Arrays," *Applied Physics Letters,* Vol. 54, No. 23, June 1989, pp. 2299–2300.

[46] Imanaka, K., H. Horikawa, A. Matoba, Y. Kawai, and M. Sakuta, "High Power Output Low Threshold Inner-Stripe GaInAsP Laser Diode on *p*-Type InP Substrate," *Conf. Digest,* 9th IEEE Int. Semiconductor Laser Conf., Rio de Janeiro, August 7–10, 1984, pp. 40–41.

[47] Imakaka, K., H. Horikawa, A. Matoba, Y. Kawai, and M. Sakuta, "High Power Output, Low Threshold, Inner Stripe GaInAsP Laser Diode on a *p*-type," *Applied Physics Letters,* Vol. 45, No. 3, August 1984, pp. 282–283.

[48] Horikawa, H., S. Oshiba, A. Matoba, and Y. Kawai, "*V*-Grooved Inner-Stripe Laser Diodes on a *p*-Type Substrate Operating over 100 mW at 1.5 μm Wavelength," *Applied Physics Letters,* Vol. 50, No. 7, February 1987, pp. 374–376.

[49] Oshiba, S., H. Horikawa, A. Matoba, M. Kawahara, and Y. Kawai, "High-Power Output over 200 mW of GaInAsP/InP VIPS-LD," *Conf. Digest,* 10th IEEE Int. Semiconductor Laser Conf., Kanazawa, October 14–17, 1986, pp. 148–149.

[50] Mito, I., K. Kuroiwa, H. Lang, K. Kobayashi, M. Kitamura, S. Murata, M. Seki, M. Sugimoti, and K. Kobayashi, "InGaAsP Double Channel Planar Buried Heterostructure Laser Diode," Tech. Report, Institute of Electronics and Communication Engineers of Japan, January 1982, pp. 21–28, paper number OQE82-98 [in Japanese].

[51] Mito, I., H. Yamazaki, H. Yamada, T. Sasaki, S. Takano, Y. Aoki, and M. Kitamura, "170mW High Power CW Operation in 1.48–1.15 μm InGaAs MQW-DC-PBH LD," *Tech. Digest,* 7th International Conference on Integrated Optics and Optical Fiber Communication, Kobe, Japan, July 18–21, 1989, paper number 20PDB-12.

[52] Imanaka, K., H. Horikawa, A. Matoba, Y. Kawai, and M. Sakuta, "High Power Output Low Threshold Inner-Stripe GaInAsP Laser Diode on *p*-type InP Substrate," *Conf. Digest,* 9th IEEE Int. Semiconductor Laser Conf., Rio de Janeiro, August 7–10, 1984, pp. 40–41.

[53] Takemoto, A., Y. Sakakibara, H. Higiti, Y. Nakajima, Y. Yamamoto, K. Goto, M. Fujiwara, S. Kakimoto, K. Takahashi, M. Namizaki, and W. Susaki, "High Power and High Efficiency Operation of 1.2–1.55 μm InGaAsP *p*-Substrate Buried Crescent Laser Diodes," *Conf. Digest,* 10th IEEE Int. Semiconductor Laser Conf., October 14–17, 1986, Kanazawa, Japan, paper number K-2, pp. 150–151.

[54] Asano, H., S. Takano, M. Kawaradani, M. Kitamura, and I. Mito, "1.48 μm High Power InGaAs/InGaAsP MQW-LDs for Er-Doped Fiber Amplifiers," *Tech. Digest,* 3rd Optoelectronics Conf., Makuhari, Japan, July 11–13, 1990, pp. 56–57.

[55] Bour, D.P., N.A. Dinkel, D.B. Gilbert, K.B. Fabian, and M.G. Harvey, "980 nm Diode Laser for Pumping Er^{3+}-Doped Fiber Amplifiers," *IEEE Photonics Technology Letters,* Vol. 2, No. 3, March 1990, pp. 153–155.

[56] Lou, Y., R. Takahashi, Y. Nakano, K. Tada, T. Kamiya, H. Hosomatsu, and H. Iwaoka, "Low-Chirp Optical Short Pulse Generation from a Gain Coupled DFB Laser," Proc. 8th Semiconductor Laser Symp., Natatsuta, Japan, March 1, 1991, p. 18.

[57] Feinberg, J., "Photorefractive Nonlinear Optics," *Physics Today,* October 1988, pp. 46–52.

[58] Nakajima, H., and R. Frey, "Intracavity Nearly Degenerate Four-Wave Mixing in a (GaAl)As Semiconductor Laser," *Applied Physics Letters,* Vol. 47, No. 8, October 1985, pp. 769–771.

[59] Ohtsu, M., I. Koshiishi, and Y. Teramachi, "A Semiconductor Laser as a Stable Phase Conjugate Mirror for Linewidth Reduction of Another Semiconductor Laser," *Japan J. Applied Physics,* Vol. 29, No. 11, November 1990, pp. L2060–L2062.

[60] Agrawal, G.P., "Population Pulsations and Nondegenerate Four-Wave Mixing in Semiconductor Lasers and Amplifiers," *J. Optics Society of America, B,* Vol. 5, No. 1, January 1987, pp. 147–159.

[61] Suzuki, H., "Four-Wave Mixing in Semiconductor Lasers," Masters thesis, Tokyo Institute of Technology, February 1991.

[62] Awaji, A., "Phase Conjugate Mirrors by Visible Semiconductor Lasers," Bachelors thesis, Tokoyo Institute of Technology, Feburary 1991.

[63] Provost, J.G., and R. Frey, "Cavity-Enhanced Highly Nondegenerate Four-Wave Mixing in GaAlAs Semiconductor Lasers," *Applied Physics Letters,* Vol. 55, No. 6, August 1989, pp. 519–521.

[64] Murata, S., A. Tomita, J. Shimizu, M. Kitamura, and A. Suzuki, "Observations of Highly Non-degenerate Four-Wave Mixing (> 1 THz) in an InGaAsP Multiple Quantum Well Laser," *Applied Physics Letters,* April 1991.

[65] Ohtsu, M., "Investigation of Applicability of Visible Semiconductor Lasers to Elementary Analysis," Proc. 1st Meeting on Lightwave Sensitivity and Technology, Tokyo, June 23–24, 1988, pp. 17–23.

[66] Loudon, R., *The Quantum Theory of Light,* Clarendon Press, Oxford, 1973.

[67] Hamada, H., M. Shono, S. Honda, R. Hiroyama, K. Yodoshi, and T. Yamaguchi, "AlGaInP Visible Laser Diodes Grown on Misoriented Substrates," Proc. 12th IEEE Int. Semiconductor Laser Conf., Davos, Switzerland, September 9–14, 1990, pp. 174–175.

[68] Dixon, G.J., C.E. Tanner, and C.E. Wieman, "432-nm Source Based on Efficient Second-Harmonic Generation of GaAlAs Diode-Laser Radiation in a Self-Locking External Resonant Cavity," *Optics Letters,* Vol. 14, No. 14, July 1989, pp. 731–733.

[69] Senoh, T., Y. Fujino, Y. Tanabe, M. Ohtsu, and K. Nakagawa, "Direct Modulation of Stable Blue Radiation from Frequency Doubled GaAlAs Laser Diode by Using EO Effect in $KNbO_3$ Nonlinear Crystal," Proc. Conf. on Lasers and Electro-Optics, Baltimore, May 12–17, 1991, paper number CWA6.

[70] Kozlovsky, W.J., C.D. Nabors, and R.L. Byer, "Efficient Second Harmonic Generation of a Diode-Laser-Pumped CW Nd:YAG Laser Using Monolithic $MgO:LiNbO_2$ External Resonant Cavities," *IEEE J. Quantum Electronics,* Vol. 24, No. 6, June 1988, pp. 913–919.

[71] Kajikawa, K., and H. Takezoe, "Nonlinear Optics and Material Technology," *Optical and Electro-Optical Engineering Contact,* Vol. 27, No. 7, July 1989, pp. 405–415 [in Japanese].

[72] Ohtsu, M., "Progress Toward Highly Coherent Semiconductor Lasers," Proc. 7th Int. Conf. Integrated Optics and Optical Fiber Communication, Kobe, Japan, July 18–21, 1989, pp. 14–15, paper number 19A3-1.

[73] Suzuki, H., I. Koshiishi, K. Nakagawa, and M. Ohtsu, "Frequency Control of Visible Semiconductor Laser," *Extended Abstracts,* 50th Annual Meeting, Japan Society of Applied Physics, September 27–30, 1989, paper number 29pZL7 [in Japanese].

[74] Pollock, C.R., D.A. Jennings, F.R. Petersen, J.S. Wells, R.E. Drullinger, E.C. Beaty and K.M. Evenson, "Direct Frequency Measurements of Transitions at 520 THz (576 nm) in Iodine and 260 THz (1.15 μm) in Neon," *Optics Letters,* Vol. 8, No. 3, March 1983, pp. 133–135.

[75] Evenson, K.M., J.S. Wells, F.R. Petersen, B.L. Danielson, and G.W. Day, "Accurate Frequencies of Molecular Transitions Used in Laser Stabilization; the 3.39 μm Transition in CH_4 and the 9.33- and 10.18-μm Transitions in CO_2," *Applied Physics Letters,* Vol. 22, February 1973, pp. 192–195.

[76] Enomoto, Y., and T. Murakami, "Optical Detector Using Oxide Superconductor," *Extended Abstracts,* 36th Spring Meeting, Japan Society of Applied Physics, Tokyo, 1989, paper number 2pZD4 [in Japanese].

[77] Yamanishi, M., "Ultrafast Optical Processes Through Virtual Charge Polarization in Quantum Well Structures," *Oyo Buturi,* Vol. 58, No. 12, September 1989, pp. 1696–1707 [in Japanese].

[78] Yabe, A., Y. Taniguchi, H. Masuhara, and H. Matsuda, *Introduction to Organic Ultra-Thin Films,* Baifukan Publishing, Tokyo, 1989 [in Japanese].

[79] Tanabe, K., Y. Enomoto, M. Suzuki, T. Iwata, and A. Yamaji, "Nonbolometric Infrared Detection in $La_{2-x}Sr_xCuO_4$ and $YBa_2Cu_3O_y$ Epitaxial Thin Films," *Japan J. Applied Physics,* Vol. 29, No. 3, March 1990, pp. L466–L469.

[80] Kawate, E., Y. Miki, Y. Higashino, M. Ohtsu, A. Onae, and M. Okaji, "Optical Response of Tl-Ba-Ca-Cu-O Thin Films," *Extended Abstracts,* 51st Autumn Meeting, September 26–29, 1990, Japan Society of Applied Physics, Iwate, paper number 26aZB5 [in Japanese].

[81] Zeldov, E., N.M. Amer, G. Koren, and A. Gupta, "Nonbolometric Optical Response of YBa$_2$Cu$_3$O$_{7-x}$ Epitaxial Films," *Physics Review, B,* Vol. 39, No. 12, May 1989, pp. 9712–9714.

[82] Telle, H.R., D. Meschede, and T.W. Hansch, "Realization of a New Concept for Visible Frequency Division: Phase Locking of Harmonic and Sum Frequencies," *Optics Letters,* Vol. 15, No. 10, May 1990, pp. 532–534.

[83] Kourogi, M., K. Nakagawa, C.-H. Shin, M. Teshima, and M. Ohtsu, "Proposal of an Accurate Frequency Measurement System for 1.5 μm Wavelength Laser Diodes," Proc. Conf. Lasers and Electro-Optics, Baltimore, May 12–17, 1991, paper number CThR57.

[84] Jennings, D.A., K.M. Evenson, and J.J.E. Knight, "Optical Frequency Measurements," *Proc. IEEE,* Vol. 74, No. 1, January 1986, pp. 168–179.

[85] McIntyre, D.H., and T.W. Hänsch, "Novel Optical Frequency Divider and Synthesizer," Proc. Annual Meeting, Optics Society of America, October 30–November 4, 1988, Santa Clara, CA, paper number ThG3, p. 131.

[86] Kobayashi, T., T. Sueta, Y. Cho, and Y. Matsuo, "High-Repetition-Rate Optical Pulse Generator Using a Fabry-Perot Electro-Optic Modulator," *Applied Physics Letters,* Vol. 21, No. 8, October 1972, pp. 341–343.

[87] Yajima, T., "Quantum Effects of Light," *Quantum Electronics and New Technology,* ed. Japan Society of Physics, Baifukan Publishing, Tokyo, 1987 [in Japanese].

[88] Slusher, R.E., L.W. Hollberg, B. Yurke, J.C. Mertz, and J.F. Valley, "Observation of Squeezed States Generated by Four-Wave Mixing in an Optical Cavity," *Physics Review Letters,* Vol. 55, No. 22, November 1985, pp. 2409–2412.

[89] Wu, L.A., H.J. Kimble, J.L. Hall, and H. Wu, "Generation of Squeezed States by Parametric Down Conversion," *Physics Review Letters,* Vol. 57, No. 20, November 1986, pp. 2520–2523.

[90] Richardson, W.H., S. Machida, and Y. Yamamoto, "Observation of 10 db Squeezing in the Amplitude Fluctuations of Light from a Diode Laser," Proc. 27th Int. Quantum Electronics Conf., Anaheim, CA, May 21–25, 1990, paper number QPDP28.

[91] Braginsky, V.B., Y.I. Vorontsov, and K.S. Thorne, "Quantum Nondemolition Measurements," *Science,* Vol. 209, No. 1, November 1980, pp. 547–557.

[92] Agrawal, G.S., "Vacuum-Field Rabi Splittings in Microwave Absorption by Rydberg Atoms in a Cavity," *Physics Review Letters,* Vol. 53, No. 18, October 1984, pp. 1732–1734.

[93] Raizen, M.G., R.J. Thompson, R.J. Brecha, H.J. Kimble, and H.J. Carmichael, "Normal-Mode Splitting, Linewidth Averaging for Two-State Atoms in an Optical Cavity," *Physics Review Letters,* Vol. 63, No. 3, July 1989, pp. 240–243.

[94] Meschede, D., H. Walther, and G. Muller, "One-Atom Maser," *Physics Review Letters,* Vol. 54, No. 6, February 1985, pp. 551–554.

[95] Diedrich, F., J. Krause, G. Rempe, M.O. Scully, and H. Walther, "Laser Experiments with Single Atoms as a Test of Basic Physics," *IEEE J. Quantum Electronics,* Vol. 24, No. 7, July 1988, pp. 1314–1319.

[96] Feshbach, H., "Small Systems: When Does Thermodynamics Apply?" *IEEE J. Quantum Electronics,* Vol. 24, No. 7, July 1988, pp. 1320–1321.

[97] Heisenberg, W., and H. Euler, "Folgerungen aus der Diracschen Theorie des Positrons," *Z. Physics,* Vol. 98, December 1936, pp. 714–732.

[98] Ding, Y.J., and A.E. Kaplan, "Nonlinear Magneto-Optics of Vacuum: Second-Harmonics Generation," *Physics Review Letters,* Vol. 63, No. 25, December 1989, pp. 2725–2728.

[99] Nakajima, H., "Is a Laser Fusion Rocket Possible?" *Parity,* Vol. 4, No. 7, 1989, pp. 69–71 [in Japanese], and references cited there; for example, R. Hyde, L. Wood, J. Nuckolls, "Prospects for Rocket Propulsion with Laser-Induced Fusion Microexplosions," AIAA Paper No. 72-1063, 1972.

[100] Weber, J., "Evidence for Discovery of Gravitational Radiation," *Physics Review Letters,* Vol. 22, No. 24, June 1969, pp. 1320–1324.

[101] Stebbins, R.T., "The LAGOS Optical System and Pointing Requirements," Proc. Workshop on

Technologies for Laser Gravitational Wave Observatory in Space, Annapolis, MD, April 19–20, 1991.

[102] Kerr, G.A., and J. Hough, "Coherent Addition of Laser Oscillators for Use in Gravitational Wave Antennas," *Applied Physics, B,* Vol 49, No. 5, November 1989, pp. 491–495.

[103] Nakagawa, K., M. Teshima, and M. Ohtsu, "Highly Coherent and High Power Diode Laser at 1.5 μm Wavelength by Injection-Locking," *Optics Letters,* accepted for publication.

[104] Morikawa, T., "Expectations for Optical Acutators," Proc. 1st Meeting on Lightwave Sensing Technology, Tokyo, June 1988, paper number LST1-5 [in Japanese].

[105] Stein, S.R., and J.P. Tuneaure, "Superconducting-Cavity Stabilized Oscillators with Improved Frequency Stability," *Proc. IEEE,* Vol. 63, No. 2, August 1975, pp. 1249–1250.

Chapter 8
CONCLUSION

Recent semiconductor laser devices have the lasing wavelengths covering the spectrum from visible to infrared. Furthermore, their linewidths, powers, and modulation bandwidths could reach to several mHz, several 10 W, and several GHz, respectively. Based on these high performances, they will be used for almost all the advanced optical systems, from basic physics to commercial industrial systems. Because these applications require advanced light sources, new semiconductor laser devices, and furthermore, new light sources will be fabricated in the future.

For the conventional design of highly coherent light sources, atomic motions have been controlled. New light sources can be expected in the future by controlling and manipulating a single atom or photon and utilizing nonclassical photons. Today looks like a transition period toward a new era in quantum optics and technology.

Appendix I

QUANTIZATION OF THE LIGHT FIELD

When quantizing the light field, note that the light can be formulated by the Maxwell's equations given by [1–5]

$$\nabla \times \mathbf{H} = \partial \mathbf{D}/\partial t \qquad (\text{AI.1})$$

$$\nabla \times \mathbf{E} = -\partial \mathbf{B}/\partial t \qquad (\text{AI.2})$$

$$\nabla \cdot \mathbf{B} = 0 \qquad (\text{AI.3})$$

$$\nabla \cdot \mathbf{D} = 0 \qquad (\text{AI.4})$$

$$\mathbf{B} = \mu_0 \mathbf{H} \qquad (\text{AI.5})$$

$$\mathbf{D} = \epsilon_0 \mathbf{H} \qquad (\text{AI.6})$$

where $\mathbf{H}$, $\mathbf{E}$, $\mathbf{B}$, $\mathbf{D}$, μ_0, and ϵ_0 represent the magnetic field vector, electric field vector, magnetic induction vector, dielectric displacement vector, permeability of vacuum, and dielectric constant of vacuum, respectively. To discuss the light field inside the laser cavity, we assume that the light is confined to the cavity shown by Figure AI.1, and that the wave vector $\mathbf{k}$ is parallel to the z-axis, where the Cartesian coordinates are used. Under this configuration, we easily find that an electric field vector $\mathbf{E}$ of a plane wave, linearly polarized along the x-axis, and with the frequency of ω is a solution to the Maxwell's equations of eqs. (AI.1)–(AI.6). The x-component of this vector $\mathbf{E}$ can be expressed as

$$E_x(z,t) = q(t) \cdot \sqrt{\frac{8\pi^2 \omega M}{\epsilon_0 V}} \cdot \sin kz \qquad (\text{AI.7})$$

where V is a cavity volume, M is a quantity with the dimension of mass, and $q(t)$ is a quantity with the dimension of length. By using (2.1), (AI.6), and (AI.7), a nonzero component of the magnetic field vector $\mathbf{H}$ is given by

---

$$H_y(z,t) = \frac{dq}{dt} \cdot \frac{\epsilon_0}{k} \sqrt{\frac{8\pi^2 \omega M}{\epsilon_0 V}} \cdot \cos kz \tag{AI.8}$$

The Hamiltonian of this light is given by

$$\mathcal{H} = \frac{1}{2} \int_V (\epsilon_0 E_x^2 + \mu_0 H_y^2) \, dv \tag{AI.9}$$

The integration is carried out for the whole cavity volume. By substituting (AI.7) and (AI.8) into this equation, we obtain

$$\mathcal{H} = \frac{1}{2}\left(4\pi^2 \omega^2 M q^2 + \frac{p^2}{M} \right) \tag{AI.10}$$

where the quantity p is defined as

$$p \equiv M \frac{dq}{dt} \tag{AI.11}$$

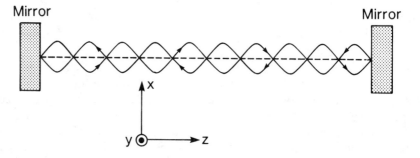

Mirror   Mirror

Figure AI.1 Spatial distribution of the electric field in a cavity with two reflecting mirrors. This figure shows a standing wave composed of the two running waves along the $+z$- and $-z$-axes.

We easily find from (AI.10) and (AI.11) that $\mathcal{H}$ has the same form as the Hamiltonian of a harmonic oscillator with the mass of M, frequency of ω, position of $q(t)$, and the momentum of $p(t)$. Therefore, the quantization of the light can also be carried out by following the same procedure as that for the harmonic oscillators, which follows the commutation relation given by

$$[q,p] \equiv qp - pq = \hbar \tag{AI.12}$$

where [ ] is the commutator and $\hbar$ is the Planck's constant divided by 2π ($\hbar = h/2\pi$). Two alternative operators are defined by

$$a \equiv \frac{1}{\sqrt{2Mh\omega}}(2\pi\omega Mq + ip) \qquad (AI.13)$$

$$a^+ = \frac{1}{\sqrt{2Mh\omega}}(2\pi\omega Mq - ip) \qquad (AI.14)$$

Note from these definitions that a and a^+ are not Hermitian operators. However, the Hamiltonian of (AI.10) is a Hermitian operator, which can be expressed by a and a^+ as

$$\mathcal{H} = h\omega(a^+a + \tfrac{1}{2}) \qquad (AI.15)$$

The commutation relation of (AI.12) is given by

$$[a,a^+] = 1 \qquad (AI.16)$$

and, furthermore,

$$[a,a] = [a^+,a^+] = 0 \qquad (AI.17)$$

The E_x of (AI.7) is then expressed as

$$E_x(z,t) = E_{x0}(a + a^+)\sin kz \qquad (AI.18)$$

where

$$E_{x0} = \sqrt{\frac{h\omega}{\epsilon_0 V}} \qquad (AI.19)$$

The operator E_x given by (AI.18) is also a Hermitian operator. Furthermore,

$$[\mathcal{H},a] = -h\omega a, \qquad [\mathcal{H},a^+] = h\omega a^+ \qquad (AI.20)$$

The Heisenberg equation of motion for operator a is

$$\frac{d}{dt}a(t) = \frac{i}{\hbar}[\mathcal{H},a] = -2\pi i\omega a \qquad (AI.21)$$

which has a solution expressed as

$$a(t) = a(0) \cdot \exp(-2\pi i\omega t) \tag{AI.22}$$

A similar procedure gives the expression for a^+, which is

$$a^+(t) = a(0)^+ \exp(2\pi i\omega t) \tag{AI.23}$$

By substituting (AI.22) and (AI.23) into (AI.18), and by noting that $\sin kz = [\exp(ikz) - \exp(-ikz)]/2i$, we can find that the $E_x(z,t)$ of (AI.18) is composed of $\exp[i(2\pi\omega t - kz)]$, $\exp[i(2\pi\omega t + kz)]$, and their complex conjugates. From the classical viewpoint, this means that these exponential terms correspond to the running wave propagating along the $+z$- and $-z$-axes in Figure AI.1, respectively, and the standing wave in the cavity is formed by the superposition of these two running waves. Furthermore, we find that the quantity ω corresponds to the frequency of the light whose Hamiltonian is given by (AI.15).

For the discussions that follow, the equation for the eigenvalue of the energy W_N and eigenstate $|N_P\rangle$

$$\mathcal{H} |N_P\rangle = W_N \cdot |N_P\rangle \tag{AI.24}$$

is solved here. The term $|N_P\rangle$ represents the key vector, which is a vector representation of the wave function appearing in the time-independent Schrödinger equation. By using (AI.20), we can find that

$$\mathcal{H}a|N_p\rangle = (a\mathcal{H} - \mathcal{H}a)|N_P\rangle = (W_N - h\omega)a|N_P\rangle \tag{AI.25}$$

This equation means that the vector $a|N_P\rangle$ represents the energy eigenstate with the eigenvalue $W_N - h\omega$. Therefore, we find that operator a decreases the energy by $h\omega$, for which operator a is called an *annihilation operator*. On the other hand, a^+ is called a *creation operator* because it increases the energy by $h\omega$.

We can find that the minimum of W_N takes a positive value. To prove this, note that the expectation value of the Hamiltonian operator for the arbitrary state $|\phi\rangle$ can be expressed as

$$\langle\phi|\mathcal{H}|\phi\rangle = h\omega\langle\phi'|\phi'\rangle + \tfrac{1}{2} h\omega \tag{AI.26}$$

where $\langle\phi|$ is a bra vector, and $|\phi'\rangle = a |\phi\rangle$. If the eigenstate corresponding to the minimum eigenvalue W_0 is represented by $|0\rangle$, we have

$$a|0\rangle = 0 \tag{AI.27}$$

Therefore, from (AI.26),

$$\langle 0|\mathcal{H}|0\rangle = 0 + \tfrac{1}{2} h\omega \tag{AI.28}$$

This equation represents the result of the proof; that is, it gives the positive minimum eigenvalue $W_0 = (\tfrac{1}{2})h\omega$.

From the second equation of (AI.20), we have

$$\begin{aligned}\mathcal{H}a^+|0\rangle &= (a^+\mathcal{H} + h\omega a^+)|0\rangle \\ &= h\omega(1 + \tfrac{1}{2})a^+|0\rangle\end{aligned} \tag{AI.29}$$

Furthermore, by repeating the procedure for (AI.29),

$$\mathcal{H}(a^+)^{Np}|0\rangle = h\omega(N_p + \tfrac{1}{2})(a^+)^{Np}|0\rangle \tag{AI.30}$$

Therefore, $(a^+)^{Np}|0\rangle$ corresponds to the energy eigenstate $|N_p\rangle$, and the corresponding eigenvalue is

$$W_N = h\omega \cdot (N_p + \tfrac{1}{2}) \tag{AI.31}$$

We find from (AI.15), (AI.24), and (AI.31) that a^+a and $|N_p\rangle$ are a photon number operator and photon number eigenstate, respectively; and

$$a^+a|N_p\rangle = N_p|N_p\rangle \tag{AI.32}$$

By noting that $a|N_p\rangle$ is expressed by using a scalar s_N as

$$a|N_p\rangle = s_N|N_p - 1\rangle \tag{AI.33}$$

the eigenstate $|N_p\rangle$ given by (AI.24) can be normalized. That is,

$$\begin{aligned}|s_N|^2\langle N_p - 1|N_p - 1\rangle &= \langle N_p|a^+a|N_p\rangle \\ &= N_p\langle N_p|N_p\rangle\end{aligned} \tag{AI.34}$$

from which $s_N = \sqrt{N_p}$ for the normalization, and

$$a|N_p\rangle = \sqrt{N_p}\,|N_p - 1\rangle \tag{AI.35}$$

By a similar procedure, we have

$$a^+|N_p\rangle = \sqrt{N_p + 1}\,|N_p + 1\rangle \tag{AI.36}$$

Therefore, by using (AI.30), the normalized eigenstate is expressed as

$$|N_p\rangle = \frac{1}{\sqrt{N_p!}} (a^+)^{N_p} |0\rangle \tag{AI.37}$$

As the last step of the discussion on the photon number state $|N_p\rangle$, we consider the coordinate representation of $|N_p\rangle$; that is,

$$\phi_N(q) \equiv \langle q | N_p \rangle \tag{AI.38}$$

Because, using (AI.13) and (AI.27), we find that

$$(2\pi\omega Mq + ip) \cdot \phi_0(q) = 0 \tag{AI.39}$$

we easily derive, using the momentum operator $p = -i\hbar\, d/dq$ that

$$\frac{d}{dq} \phi_0(q) = -\frac{2\pi\omega M}{\hbar} q \cdot \phi_0(q) \tag{AI.40}$$

A solution of this differential equation is expressed as

$$\phi_0(q) = \left(\frac{2M\omega}{\hbar}\right)^{1/4} \cdot \exp\left[-\frac{1}{2}\left(\frac{2\pi\omega M}{\hbar}\right) q^2\right] \tag{AI.41}$$

where this function has been already normalized so that the integration value of $|\phi_0(q)|^2$ for $-\infty < q < \infty$ is equal to unity. The expression for $\phi_N(q)$ can be derived by using (AI.14), (AI.37), and (AI.41):

$$
\begin{aligned}
\phi_N(q) &= \frac{1}{\sqrt{N_p!}} (a^+)^{N_p} \phi_0(q) \\[2mm]
&= \frac{1}{\sqrt{N_p!(2Mh\omega N_p!)^{N_p}}} \left(2\pi\omega Mq - \hbar\frac{d}{dq}\right)^{N_p} \phi_0(q) \\[2mm]
&= \frac{1}{\sqrt{2^{N_p}N_p!}} \cdot H_N\left(\sqrt{\frac{2\pi\omega M}{\hbar}}\, q\right) \cdot \phi_0(q)
\end{aligned} \tag{AI.42}
$$

where H_N represents the Hermite polynomial of the N_p-th order.

When the light stays in this state $|N_p\rangle$, the expectation value of the electric field operators E_x of (AI.18) is

$$\langle E_x \rangle \equiv \langle N_p | E_x | N_p \rangle$$
$$= E_{x0} \cdot \sin kz \, \langle N_p | a | N_p \rangle + \text{c.c.} \tag{AI.43}$$
$$= 0$$

where c.c. represents the complex conjugate. Furthermore, the expectation value of operator E_x^2 is

$$\langle E_x^2 \rangle = \langle N_p | E_x^2 | N_p \rangle \tag{AI.44}$$
$$= 2E_{x0}^2(N_p + \tfrac{1}{2}) \sin^2 kz$$

Equations (AI.43) and (AI.44) mean that the electric field fluctuates around the zero ensemble average. That is, when the magnitudes of electric field are measured for many systems in which the field stays in the state $| N_p \rangle$, the quantum mechanical average of the field amplitude is zero, whereas its standard deviation

$$\Delta E_x \equiv \sqrt{\langle E_x^2 \rangle - \langle E_x \rangle^2} \tag{AI.45}$$
$$= \sqrt{2(N_p + \tfrac{1}{2})} \cdot E_{x0} \cdot \sin kz$$

is not zero. We can interpret from this result that it is rather difficult to find the wave properties of light through the measurements when the light is in the state $| N_p \rangle$. It should be more reasonable to interpret that there are N_p pieces of photon of energy $h\omega$, from which we understand that the eigenstate $| N_p \rangle$ is called a *photon number state*. Although the photon is a quantum taking a discrete energy value digitized by the unit $h\omega$, note that the photon is not localized spatially and temporally but is spread homogeneously in the whole volume of the cavity.

If only the photons are contained in the cavity, it is not compatible with the energy conservation principle to decrease or increase the optical energy by a or a^+, which means that annihilation or creation of photons cannot take place. To be compatible with the energy conservation principle, we implicitly assumed in the preceding discussion that the cavity also contains a low-density atomic vapor. Figure AI.2 shows two energy levels of the atom relevant to this discussion. The eigenvalue and eigenstate for these energy levels are represented by W_a, W_b ($W_a > W_b$), $|a\rangle$, and $|b\rangle$, respectively. We assume here that one of the Bohr's postulates

$$W_a - W_b = h\omega \tag{AI.46}$$

holds for the total system composed of these photons and atoms; that is, the light is exactly resonant to the atoms. If the initial state of the atom and photon is $|b\rangle$ (lower energy) and $|N_p\rangle$, respectively, transition of photon to the state $|N_p - 1\rangle$ by operator

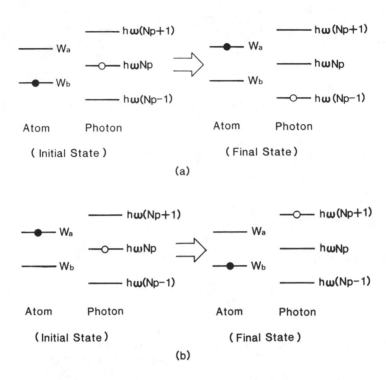

Figure AI.2 Schematic explanation of (a) the (stimulated) absorption process and (b) the stimulated emission that takes place in a system composed of atoms and photons. The closed and open circles represent the atoms and photons, respectively.

a (see eq. (AI.35)), resulting in a decrease of photon energy by $\hbar\omega$, means that the atomic energy increases by $\hbar\omega$ (see eq. (AI.46)) due to a simultaneous transition of the atom to the upper energy state $|a\rangle$ because of the atom's stimulation by the photon. By this simultaneous decrease and increase in energy, energy is conserved in a total system composed of atoms and photons. These transitions correspond to the (stimulated) absorption of a photon by an atom. On the other hand, the transition of photon to the state $|N_p + 1\rangle$ by operator a^+, inducing the increase of the photon energy by $\hbar\omega$, means that the atom is deexcited from the upper energy state $|a\rangle$ to the lower energy state $|b\rangle$ and decreases the atomic energy by $\hbar\omega$ due to being stimulated by the photon. This process corresponds to the stimulated emission of photons by the atom, which is opposite to the absorption process described earlier.

The value $(\tfrac{1}{2})\hbar\omega$ in (AI.28) and (AI.31) is called the *zero-point energy,* which is interpreted as the fluctuation energy of a vacuum field; that is, it corresponds to the process of spontaneously emitting the photon from the upper state atom $|a\rangle$ which is stimulated by the light field fluctuations of (AI.44). This process is called *sponta-*

neous emission; the spontaneous emission corresponds to the stimulated emission induced by the vacuum field.

Because the light is not always in the state $|N_p\rangle$, a general state can be expressed as

$$|\psi\rangle = \sum_{N_p} c_{Np}|N_p\rangle \tag{AI.47}$$

where c_{Np} is the expansion coefficient.

REFERENCES

[1] Shimoda, K., T. Yajima, Y. Ueda, T. Shimizu, and T. Kasuya, *Quantum Electronics,* Shokabo Publishing, Tokyo, 1972 [in Japanese].

[2] Sargent, M., III, M.O. Scully, and W.E. Lamb, Jr., *Laser Physics.* Addison-Wesley, Reading, MA, 1974.

[3] Haken, H., *Light,* Vol. 1, *Waves, Photons, Atoms,* North-Holland Press, Amsterdam, 1981.

[4] Loudon, R., *The Quantum Theory of Light,* Clarendon Press, Oxford, 1973.

[5] Shimoda, K., *Introduction to Laser Physics,* 2nd Ed., Springer Verlag, Berlin, 1986.

Appendix II
DEFINITIONS OF THE MEASURES FOR EVALUATING THE FM NOISE MAGNITUDE

In this book, definitions of frequency stability, reproducibility, and accuracy of the laser (i.e., the quantum oscillator) follow those presented by [1, 2], summarized as follows:

1. Stability. A sequence of N readings of a particular oscillator frequency in a particular adjustment, against a reference oscillator assumed temporally constant, will fluctuate. The standard deviation of these fluctuations is called the *stability* [1].
2. Reproducibility. A sequence of comparisons for the independent adjustment of a particular oscillator frequency, against an available and temporally constant reference oscillator frequency, will yield a standard deviation. The standard deviation of such observations may be called the *reproducibility*. In this sense, reproducibility indicates the degree to which the frequency can be reset [1].
3. Accuracy. *Accuracy* means the fractional uncertainty in determining an atomic transition frequency of a free atom and is expressed by 3σ limits for statistically determined frequencies [2].

The FM noise characteristics of lasers can be represented by these three quantities. In the following sections, several measures for representing the FM noise magnitude of oscillators are defined; these are compatible with the definitions just given.

AII.1   MEASURES OF FREQUENCY STABILITY

The electric field of an oscillator output signal can be expressed as

$$E(t) = \sqrt{2P_0} \sin[2\pi\nu_0 t + \phi(t)] \qquad (AII.1)$$

where P_0 is the detected average power of the oscillator, ν_0 is the nominal frequency of the oscillator, and $\phi(t)$ is the instantaneous phase of the signal. In this equation, we assume that the time variations of the amplitude is negligibly small. The instantaneous frequency then is written as

$$\nu(t) = \nu_0 + \frac{d\phi(t)}{2\pi dt} \tag{AII.2}$$

and the fractional frequency deviation $y(t)$, normalized to ν_0, is defined as

$$y(t) \equiv \frac{d\phi(t)}{2\pi\nu_0 \, dt} \tag{AII.3}$$

The autocorrelation of $y(t)$ is defined by

$$R_y(\tau) = \langle y(t') \cdot y(t' + \tau) \rangle \equiv \lim_{T \to \infty} \frac{1}{T} \int_{-T/2}^{T/2} y(t')y(t' + \tau) \, dt' \tag{AII.4}$$

and its Fourier transform $S_y(f)$ Hz^{-1} is the power spectral density of the fractional frequency deviation, given by

$$S_y(f) = 4 \int_0^\infty R_y(\tau) \cos(2\pi f \tau) \, d\tau \tag{AII.5}$$

which is the measure of the frequency stability in the Fourier frequency domain. Note that (AII.5) represents the one-sided power spectral density defined in the range of $0 \leq f < \infty$. The relation between $S_y(f)$ and the power spectral densities of the FM and phase noises ($S_{FM}(f)$ Hz^2/Hz and $S_{PH}(f)$ rad^2/Hz, respectively), are given by

$$S_y(f) = \frac{S_{FM}(f)}{\nu_0^2} = S_{PH}(f) \left(\frac{f^2}{\nu_0^2} \right) \tag{AII.6}$$

These power spectral densities have been used as measures of frequency stability [3].

The Allan variance $\sigma_y^2(\tau)$ [4] is an alternative measure of the frequency stability defined in the time domain. It is given by

$$\sigma_y^2(\tau) = \left\langle \frac{(\bar{y}_{k+1} - \bar{y}_k)^2}{2} \right\rangle \tag{AII.7}$$

where $\langle\ \rangle$ denotes the infinite time average, and $\bar{y}_{k+1}$ and $\bar{y}_k$ are the $(k + 1)$th and kth time-averaged fractional frequency fluctuation during the measurement with duration τ, called the *integration time*. However, of course, actual measurement of the Allan variance is carried out using finite samples of data.

The conversion from $S_y(f)$ to $\sigma_y^2(\tau)$ is possible by using the following formula [3, 5, 6]:

$$\sigma_y^2(\tau) = 2 \int_0^\infty S_y(f) \frac{\sin^4(\pi f \tau)}{(\pi f \tau)^2} \, df \tag{AII.8}$$

Examples of this conversion are discussed and tabulated in [3, 5, 7]. Those for semiconductor lasers have been studied in detail [6].

The field spectral profile $I(\nu)$ of the laser can be calculated by using the measured power spectral density of FM noise. It is given by

$$I(\nu) = 4 \cdot \mathrm{Re} \left[\int_0^\infty \exp\left\{ 2\pi i(\nu_0 - \nu)\tau \right.\right.$$
$$\left.\left. - 2(\pi\tau)^2 \int_0^\infty S_{\mathrm{FM}}(f) \frac{\sin^2(\pi f \tau)}{(\pi f \tau)^2} \, df \right\} \, d\tau \right] \tag{AII.9}$$

where Re[ ] represents taking the real part of the complex inside the brackets [6, 8]. The field spectral linewidth of the laser $\Delta\nu$ (full-width at a half maximum) is defined by

$$I(\nu = \nu_0 \pm \Delta\nu/2) = \tfrac{1}{2}I(\nu = \nu_0) \tag{AII.10}$$

AII.2   POWER CONCENTRATION RATIOS OF FREQUENCY STABILIZED AND PHASE-LOCKED LASERS

The power concentration ratio of a laser within a certain bandwidth, B, may be a useful measure. For example, if a laser is assumed to have the Lorentzian spectral profile, this profile is expressed as

$$I(\nu) = \frac{\Delta\nu}{2\pi} \frac{1}{(\nu - \nu_0)^2 + (\Delta\nu/2)^2} \tag{AII.11}$$

where $\Delta\nu$ and ν_0 are the field spectral linewidth and the center frequency of the profile, respectively. The term $I(\nu)$ has been normalized to satisfy

$$\int_{-\infty}^{\infty} I(\nu)\, d\nu = 1 \tag{AII.12}$$

Then the power concentration ratio R_{pc} within $\nu_0 - B \leq \nu \leq \nu_0 + B$ can be defined by [9, 10]

$$R_{pc} = \int_{\nu_0-B}^{\nu_0+B} I(\nu)\, d\nu \tag{AII.13}$$

For the Lorentzian spectral profile, the substitution of (AII.11) in (AII.13) gives the exact expression of R_{pc}, given by

$$R_{pc} = \frac{2}{\pi} \tan^{-1}\left(\frac{2}{\Delta\nu} B\right) \tag{AII.14}$$

This result is shown in the curve A in Figure AII.1.

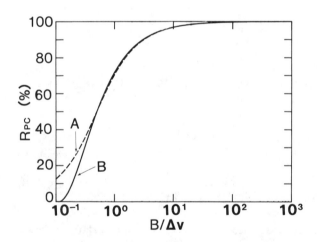

Figure AII.1 Power concentration ratio R_{pc} of the laser with the Lorentzian spectral lineshape for the considered bandwidth B normalized to the field spectral linewidth $\Delta\nu$ of the laser (from [10]): curves A and B show the result obtained by an exact calculation, eq. (AII.14), and an approximated calculation, eq. (AII.15), respectively.

Because the signal with the Lorentzian spectral profile can be regarded as the superposition of a zero-linewidth signal and modulated side-frequency components by phase noise, the approximated expression for R_{pc} can be derived by calculating the value of R_{pc} of the phase modulated signal without any noise, simply expressed as

$$R_{pc} = |J_0(\beta)|^2 \qquad (AII.15)$$

where β and $J_0(\beta)$ are the phase modulation index and Bessel function of the zeroth order, respectively. The value of β can be given by

$$\beta = \sum_{k=B}^{\infty} \beta_k \qquad (AII.16)$$

where

$$\beta_k = \sqrt{2S_{PH}(k)} \qquad (AII.17)$$

is the zero-to-peak value of the phase fluctuation component at the Fourier frequency k. To confirm the validity of this approximation, the curve B of Figure AII.1 represents the value of the signal's R_{pc} with the Lorentzian spectral profile calculated by using this approximated formula. Comparing the solid and dashed lines, we confirm that the expression given by (AII.15) can be an acceptable approximation under the condition $B/\Delta\nu > 0.5$; that is, $\beta < 1.13$.

The term β alternatively can be expressed by the square root of the phase error variance σ_ϕ^2:

$$\beta = \sqrt{2} \cdot \sigma_\phi |_B^{\infty} \qquad (AII.18)$$

$$\sigma_\phi^2 |_B^{\infty} = \int_B^{\infty} S_{PH}(f)\, df, \qquad \text{rad}^2 \qquad (AII.19)$$

where $S_{PH}(f)$ is the power spectral density of phase noise. For the signal with a Lorentzian spectral profile, (AII.18) can be expressed simply as

$$\sigma_\phi^2 |_B^{\infty} = \frac{\Delta\nu}{\pi B} \qquad \text{rad}^2 \qquad (AII.20)$$

By following these discussions, the phase-locked power concentration ratio R_{pl} of the slave laser also can be approximated as

$$R_{pl} \cong |J_0(\sqrt{2}\,\sigma_\phi)|^2 \qquad (AII.21)$$

for $\sigma_\phi^2 < 0.6$ rad^2. Curve A of Figure AII.2 shows the calculated result obtained by using this equation. From this figure, we find that further approximation can be obtained as

$$R_{pl} \cong 1 - \sigma_\phi^2 \tag{AII.22}$$

for $\sigma_\phi^2 > 0.1$ rad^2. These simple relations between the phase-locked power concentration ratio and the phase error variance are important for applications such as noise reduction of the slave laser by phase locking it to a highly stable master laser. Furthermore, the phase-locked power concentration ratio of the slave laser can be considered a comprehensive measure representing the degree of temporal coherence transfer from the master laser to the slave laser; that is, the frequency stabilization by optical phase locking.

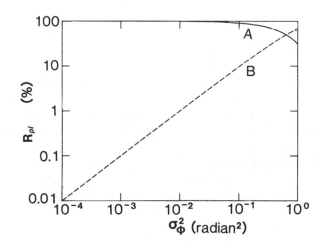

Figure AII.2 Phase-locked power concentration ratio R_{pl} of the slave laser as a function of the phase-error variance of the phase-locked loop σ_ϕ^2 (from [10]): curves A and B are for the total phase-locked and unlocked powers, respectively.

REFERENCES

[1] Beehler, R.E., R.C. Mocker, and J.M. Richardson, "Cesium Beam Atomic Time and Frequency Standards," *Metrologia,* Vol. 1, No. 3, July 1965, pp. 114–131.

[2] Beehler, R.E., and D.J. Glaze, "The Performance and Capability of Cesium Beam Frequency Standards at the National Bureau of Standards," *IEEE Trans. on Instruments and Measurement,* Vol. IM-15, Nos. 1, 2, February 1966, pp. 48–55.

[3] Barnes, J.W., A.R. Chi, L.S. Cutler, D.J. Healey, D.B. Leeson, T.E. McGunigal, J.A. Mullen, Jr., W.L. Smith, R.L. Sydnor, R.F.C. Vessot, and G.M.R. Winkler, "Characterization of Frequency Stability," *IEEE Trans. on Instruments and Measurement,* Vol. IM-20, No. 2, May 1971, pp. 105–120.

[4] Allan, D.W., "Statistics of Atomic Frequency Standards," *Proc. IEEE,* Vol. 54, No. 2, February 1966, pp. 221–230.

[5]   Cutler, L.S., C.L. Searle, "Some Aspects of the Theory and Measurement of Frequency Fluctuations in Frequency Standards," *Proc. IEEE,* Vol. 54, No. 2, February 1966, pp. 136–154.

[6]   Ohtsu, M., H. Fukada, T. Tako, and H. Thuchida, "Estimation of the Ultimate Frequency Stability of Semiconductor Lasers," *Japan J. Applied Physics,* Vol. 22, No. 7, July 1983, pp. 1157–1166.

[7]   Walls, F.L., and D.W. Allan, "Measurements of Frequency Stability," *Proc. IEEE,* Vol. 74, No. 1, January 1986, pp. 162–168.

[8]   Ohtsu, M., Murata, and M. Kourogi, "FM Noise Reduction and Subkilohertz Linewidth of an AlGaAs Laser by Negative Electrical Feedback," *IEEE J. Quantum Electronics,* Vol. 26, No. 2, February 1990, pp. 231–241.

[9]   Shin, C.-H., and M. Ohtsu, "Stable Semiconductor Laser with a 7-Hz Linewidth by an Optical-Electrical Double-Feedback Technique," *Optics Letters,* Vol. 15, No. 24, December 1990, pp. 1455–1457.

[10] Shin, C.-H., "Optical Phase-Locking of Semiconductor Lasers," PhD thesis, Tokyo Institute of Technology, 1991.

Appendix III
METHODS FOR MEASURING FM NOISE AND THE ALLAN VARIANCE REAL-TIME PROCESSING SYSTEM

There are several methods of measuring the FM noise magnitude of lasers; and they differ considerably from those for the microwave oscillators because of very high optical frequency. Specific methods are reviewed and one of the measurement instruments is introduced in this appendix.

AIII.1 METHODS OF MEASURING THE FM NOISE OF A LASER

Because practical detectors do not respond to the optical frequency on the order of 100 THz, specific methods have been employed to evaluate the FM noise magnitude of the laser. The principles of these measurements are explained schematically by Figure AIII.1.

Figure AIII.1(a) shows the heterodyne method employed when a stable reference laser, with FM noise much lower than that of the laser under test, can be prepared. In this case, the two laser frequencies should be tuned so that the heterodyne frequency between the two lasers is lower than the bandwidth of the square-law photodetector (i.e., the magnitude of the output photocurrent from this detector is proportional to the square of the incident electric field of the lightwaves), such as *pin* photodiodes and avalanche photodiodes. The following measurements are possible by using the setup in Figure AIII.1(a):

1. The power spectral density of the FM noise of the laser under test can be measured by applying the output signal from the photodetector to a microwave spectrum analyzer after passing through a frequency-voltage converter.
2. The Allan variance can be measured by applying the output signal from the photodetector to the microwave frequency counter and by processing the counted frequency values using (AII.7). However, in this case, the gate of

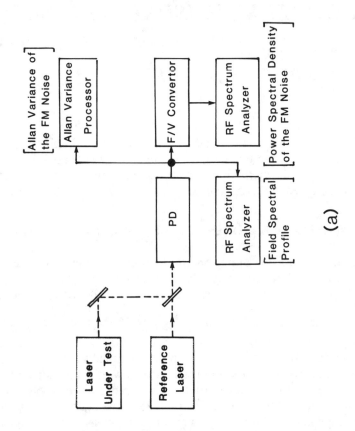

(a)

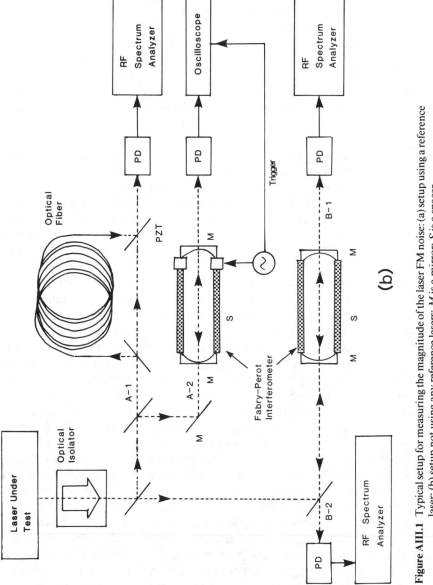

Figure AIII.1 Typical setup for measuring the magnitude of the laser FM noise: (a) setup using a reference laser; (b) setup not using any reference lasers; *M* is a mirror; *S* is a spacer.

the frequency counter should have a dead time sufficiently shorter than the integration time to realize accurate measurements. A highly precise measurement instrument, named *ARPS,* has been developed for this purpose; it will be introduced in the next section.

3. The field spectral profile of the laser under test can be measured by applying the output signal from the photodetector to the microwave spectrum analyzer.

Even if a reference laser is not available, the heterodyne method is still valid when an additional laser, oscillating independently to the laser under test, can be prepared. In this case, the three measurements provide the sum of the FM noise magnitude of the two lasers.

Figure AIII.1(b) shows the setup used when an additional laser is not available. Parts A-1 and A-2 in this figure show the setups for measuring the field spectral profile. Part A-1 represents the system called a *delayed-self homodyne method* [1]. The laser beam is split into two parts and mixed again after one beam has been propagated through an optical fiber that is used as a delay line so that the stochastic properties of the mixed beams can be considered uncorrelated with each other. The resolution of this method is limited by the validity of such uncorrelation. Therefore, it is given by $c/2n_fL_f$ [1], where c is the speed of light in a vacuum, n_f and L_f are the refractive index and length of the optical fiber, respectively. This is called a *delayed self-heterodyne method,* if the optical frequency of one split beam is shifted by, say, an acousto-optic modulator. Note that the low Fourier frequency components of the FM noise cannot be measured by these systems because these measurement systems are equivalent to low-cut filters. Part A-2 shows the method in which a scanning Fabry-Perot interferometer is used as an optical spectrum analyzer. The resolution is limited by the linewidth of the resonance spectral profile of the interferometer.

Part B shows a more general system of measuring the FM noise characteristics of the laser. In this case, an optical frequency demodulator should be used in front of the photodetector to measure the power spectral density of the FM noise. Characteristics of the optical frequency demodulators have been described in Section 3.1. A sufficiently stable optical frequency demodulator should be used because this detection scheme does not correspond to the measurement of the absolute magnitude of the frequency fluctuations but to the measurement of the deviation of the laser frequency from the reference frequency of the optical frequency demodulator. The power spectral density of the FM noise can be measured by applying the output signal from the photodetector to a microwave spectrum analyzer. The Allan variance and field spectral profile can be calculated by substituting the value of this power spectral density to (AII.8) and (AII.9), respectively. If a voltage-to-frequency converter is used at the next stage of the photodetector, the Allan variance can be measured by applying the output signal from the voltage-to-frequency converter to the ARPS.

AIII.2 THE ALLAN VARIANCE REAL-TIME PROCESSING SYSTEM

To measure the Allan variances of the laser frequency fluctuations or the heterodyne signal between two lasers, the version 6 of the Allan variance real-time processing system, (ARPS 6) has been proposed [2] and developed after several modifications of the first version [3].

Figure AIII.2 shows a block diagram of the ARPS 6 system, which uses the direct frequency counting method for a signal with a frequency lower than 90 MHz [2]. The Allan variance is calculated by using the following approximated equation:

$$\sigma_y^2(\tau) = \left(\frac{1}{\nu_0\tau}\right)^2 \left[\frac{1}{N-1} \sum_{k=1}^{N-1} \frac{(C_{k+1} - C_k)^2}{2}\right] \tag{AIII.1}$$

where ν_0 is the nominal optical frequency, C_k is the counted value of the digital counter for the kth sampling period, and N is the number of measured samples (usually 100 or more). The measurement limit of the ARPS 6 is determined by ± 1 count ambiguity in a sampling period, which is expressed as [2]

$$\sigma_{y,\min}^2(\tau) = \left(\frac{1}{\tau\nu_0}\right)^2 \tag{AIII.2}$$

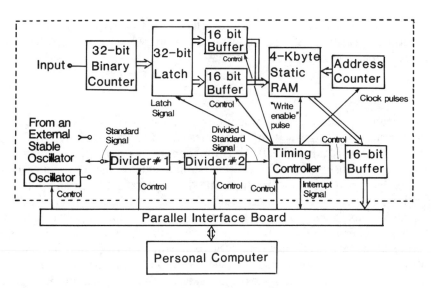

Figure AIII.2 Schematic diagram of version 6 of the Allan variance real-time processing system (ARPS 6) (from [2] © 1990 IEEE).

This value is sufficiently small to measure accurately the frequency stability of a semiconductor laser [2].

However, when the heterodyne signal between two semiconductor lasers is phase locked to a highly stable microwave oscillator, the frequency stability of the heterodyne signal approaches that of the microwave oscillator, which cannot be measured by the ARPS 6. Such high stability can be evaluated by the time interval analysis method. A modified system, named ARPS 8, was developed employing this method [4]; its block diagram is shown in Figure AIII.3 [5]. The Allan variance can be calculated by substituting the collected data into the equation given by

$$\sigma_y^2(\tau) = \left(\frac{\nu_B}{\nu_0}\right)^2 \left(\frac{1}{\tau\nu_{\text{TB}}}\right)^2 \left[\frac{1}{N-1} \sum_{k=1}^{N-1} \frac{(C_{k+1} - C_k)^2}{2}\right] \tag{AIII.3}$$

where ν_{TB} is the frequency of the time-base signal of the ARPS 8, ν_B is the frequency difference between the input signal frequency and ν_{TB}; that is, the down-converted frequency for time interval analysis. The measurement limit is determined by ± 1 count ambiguity of the time-base signal during a sampling period, given by

$$\sigma_{y,\text{min}}^2(\tau) = \left(\frac{\nu_B}{\nu_0}\right)^2 \left(\frac{1}{\tau\nu_{\text{TB}}}\right)^2 \tag{AIII.4}$$

The frequency under test ν_0 is down-converted to a lower frequency so that the final beat frequency ν_B can satisfy the following condition by heterodyning with oscillators 1 (the reference oscillator) and 2 (time base):

$$\nu_B \ll \nu_{\text{TB}} \tag{AIII.5}$$

A commercial crystal oscillator was used as the time-base oscillator (oscillator 2). Then, the sinusoidal signals with frequencies ν_B and ν_{TB} are converted to TTL level by *zero-crossing detectors* (ZCD). The number of pulses generated by the time-base signal is continuously counted by a 32-bit counter, which consisted of four 8-bit TTL counters. Each digital signal corresponding to ν_B generates two timing pulses at the same time; that is, one is the interrupt signal to the personal computer and the other is the latch-enable signal to the 32-bit data latch. By these timing signals, the 32-bit data latch latches onto the value of the 32-bit nonstop counter, and the computer reads the latched value through two 16-bit data buffers and a parallel interface board on receiving the interrupt signal. By this operation, the computer can collect the number of pulses corresponding to the frequency of the time-base during each period of $1/\nu_B$ with no dead time for measurement. The integration time τ can be determined by

$$\tau = m/\nu_B \tag{AIII.6}$$

where m is an integer selected by the software program. The minimum measurable integration time τ_{min} therefore is given by

$$\tau_{min} = \frac{1}{\nu_B} \tag{AIII.7}$$

The maximum distinguishable counting value is 2^{32}, because the value of the counter is cleared when the number reaches to 2^{32}. The condition of

$$\left(\frac{2^{32}}{\tau\nu_B}\right) > 1 \tag{AIII.8}$$

therefore is required so that the computer can correctly calculate the number of the time-base signals in a sampling period. Timing and gating circuits, the counter, the data latch, and the data buffer are constructed by commercial TTL-ICs. The maxi-

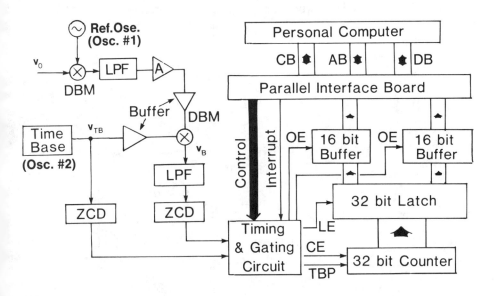

Figure AIII.3 Schematic diagram of version 8 of the Allan variance real-time processing system (ARPS 8) (from [4]): *DBM* is a double-balanced mixer; *LPF* is a low-pass filter; *ZCD* is a zero-crossing detector; *TBP* is the pulse generated by the time-base signal; *CE* is count enable; *LE* is latch enable; *OE* is output enable; *CB* is the control bus; *AB* is the address bus; *DB* is the data bus.

mum operating frequency of the system was about 30 MHz. The total required sample number N for each τ can be selected by a software program, and the Allan variance $\sigma_y^2(\tau)$ can be calculated by substituting the values of the collected data into (AIII.3).

The frequency stabilities of oscillators 1 and 2, used for the frequency down-conversion of ν_0 and the time base, respectively, have to be higher than that of the oscillator under test. Under this condition, the measurement limit is determined by 1 count ambiguity of the time-base signal during a sampling period and given by (AIII.4). Compared with the measurement limit of ARPS 6 given by (AIII.2), the measurement limit of ARPS 8 is improved by the factor of $(\nu_{TB}/\nu_B)^2$.

To test the performance of the ARPS 8, precise frequency tracking between two lasers was carried out by a heterodyne OPLL for which two 0.83 μm CFP-lasers were used [6] (see Section 5.1.1). In this experiment, ν_{TB} and ν_B were 5 MHz and 1 kHz, respectively. The optical-frequency tracking error of the heterodyne OPLL was measured by ARPS 8. The measured result is shown by the closed circles in Figure AIII.4. Lines A and B in this figure are the measurement limits for the ARPS 6, eq. (AIII.2), and ARPS 8, eq. (AIII.3), respectively. Comparison between the closed circles and lines A and B confirms that a very small magnitude of the frequency fluctuations can be measured by the ARPS 8, which have not been measured by the ARPS 6.

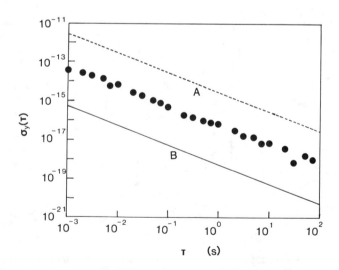

Figure AIII.4 The square root of the Allan variance $\sigma_y^2(\tau)$, where τ is the integration time (from [4]): closed circles are an example of the measured results of a phase-locked laser heterodyne signal, where $\nu_B = 1$ kHz and $\nu_{TB} = 5$ MHz; A is the measurement limit of the ARPS 6; B is the measurement limit of the ARPS 8.

REFERENCES

[1]   Okoshi, T., K. Kikuchi, and A. Nakayama, "Novel Method for High Resolution Measurement of Laser Output Spectrum," *Electronics Letters,* Vol. 16, No. 16, July 1980, pp. 630–631.

[2]   Kuboki, K., and M. Ohtsu, "An Allan Variance Real-Time Processing System for Frequency Stability Measurement of Semiconductor Lasers," *IEEE Trans. on Instruments and Measurement,* Vol. 39, No. 4, August 1990, pp. 637–641.

[3]   Siio, I., M. Ohtsu, and T. Tako, "Real-Time Processing System of the Measurement of Laser Frequency Stability," *Trans. IECE,* Vol. J64-C, No. 3, March 1981, pp. 204–208 [in Japanese].

[4]   Shin, C.-H., and M. Ohtsu, "Improved Allan Variance Real-Time Processing System to Measure Frequency Tracking Error of Heterodyne Optical Phase-Locked Loops," *Electronics Letters,* Vol. 26, No. 19, September 1990, pp. 1571–1572.

[5]   Shin, C.-H., "Optical Phase-Locking of Semiconductor Lasers," PhD thesis, Tokyo Institute of Technology, January 1991.

[6]   Shin, C-.H., and M. Ohtsu, "Heterodyne Optical Phase-Locked Loop by Confocal Fabry-Perot Cavity Coupled AlGaAs Lasers," *IEEE Photonics Technology Letters,* Vol. 2, No. 4, April 1990, pp. 297–300.

Appendix IV
RATE EQUATION AND RELAXATION OSCILLATION

To study the dynamic behavior of a single longitudinal-mode semiconductor laser, the rate equations given by eqs. (2.36) and (2.37) are used. However, the suffix i and the spontaneous emission coefficient C are omitted, because the single-mode operation and the deterministic dynamic behavior are studied here. These equations then are reduced to

$$\frac{dN_p}{dt} = -\frac{N_p}{\tau_p} + g(N_c - N_G)N_p \tag{AIV.1}$$

$$\frac{dN_c}{dt} = \frac{I}{eV_a} - g(N_c - N_G)N_p - \frac{N_c}{\tau_s} \tag{AIV.2}$$

As a first step, the characteristics of a steady state are discussed. Because $N_p = 0$ below the threshold, the steady-state value of N_c^s is derived from (AIV.2) by fixing $d/dt = 0$, expressed as

$$N_c^s = \frac{\tau_p}{eV_a} I \tag{AIV.3}$$

Above the threshold, (AIV.1) and (AIV.2) give the steady-state values of

$$N_c^s = N_G + \frac{1}{g\tau_p} \; (\equiv N_{c,th}^s) \tag{AIV.4}$$

$$N_p^s = \frac{\tau_p}{\tau_s} \cdot \left(N_G + \frac{1}{g\tau_p} \right)\left(\frac{I}{I_{th}} - 1 \right) \tag{AIV.5}$$

As shown by Figure AIV.1, these expressions mean that the carrier density is increased by increasing the dc injection current I and is clipped to a threshold value $N_{c,th}^s$ at $I = I_{th}$. The photon density N_p^s can increase linearly with the increase of I, as is given by (AIV.5). These characteristics correspond to those given by Figure 2.8.

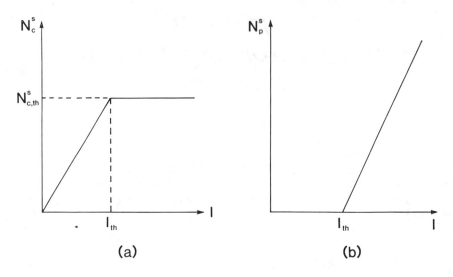

(a)　　　　　　　　　　　(b)

Figure AIV.1 Relations between the dc injection current I and (a) steady-state carrier density N_c^s and (b) photon density N_p^s: I_{th} and $N_{c,th}^s$ are the threshold values of the injection current and carrier density, respectively.

As a second step, the discussion focuses on a carrier whose density shows a slight temporal variation induced by adding a small amplitude modulation current $i(t)$ to I. Equations (AIV.1) and (AV.2) are linearized by adding the small fractions $n_p(t)$ and $n_c(t)$ to the steady-state values of (AIV.4) and (AIV.5). They are expressed as

$$\frac{dn_p}{dt} = -\frac{n_p}{\tau_p} + g(N_c^s n_p + N_p^s n_c) \qquad \text{(AIV.7)}$$

$$\frac{dn_c}{dt} = \frac{i(t)}{eV_a} - g(N_c^s n_p + N_p^s n_c) - \frac{n_c}{\tau_s} \qquad \text{(AIV.8)}$$

By combining these equations, we can readily obtain a linear differential equation for $n_p(t)$, which is given by

$$\frac{d^2 n_p}{dt^2} + \frac{1}{T}\frac{dn_p}{dt} + \Omega^2 n_p = gN_p^s \frac{i(t)}{eV_a} \qquad \text{(AIV.9)}$$

where

$$T \equiv \tau_s/(I/I_{th}) \qquad \text{(AIV.10)}$$

$$\Omega = \sqrt{\frac{I/I_{th} - 1}{\tau_p \tau_s}} \qquad \text{(AIV.11)}$$

We easily find that the solution of this differential equation can be expressed as

$$n_p(t) \alpha 1 - \exp\left(-\frac{t}{T} + i\Omega t\right) \qquad \text{(AIV.12)}$$

which shows a form of relaxation oscillation with a frequency

$$f_r = \frac{\Omega}{2\pi} = \frac{1}{2\pi}\sqrt{\frac{I/I_{th} - 1}{\tau_p \tau_s}} \qquad \text{(AIV.13)}$$

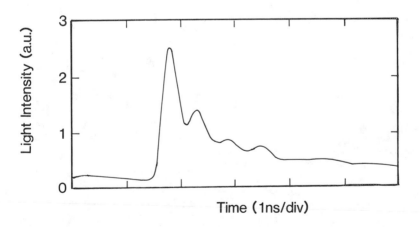

Figure AIV.2 An example of the measured waveform of an AlGaAs laser output, for which the $i(t)$ is a stepwise function (by courtesy of K. Iga and F. Koyama, Tokyo Institute of Technology, 1979).

This characteristic frequency is called the *relaxation oscillation frequency*, which limits the direct modulation bandwidths of IM and FM of a semiconductor laser. The value of f_r ranges from 1 GHz to several tens GHz. Figure AIV.2 shows the measured temporal variation of an AlGaAs laser output, where $i(t)$ is given by a step function. The envelope of this waveform decays exponentially, and its time constant is given by T of (AIV.10). The frequency of the sinusoidal variation in this waveform corresponds to f_r of (AIV.13).

Appendix V
THEORETICAL ANALYSES OF OPTICAL
PHASE-LOCKED LOOPS

It is important to provide a basis for the design of heterodyne and homodyne optical phase-locked loops through theory and simulation or experiment. To realize a precise *optical phase-locked loop* (OPLL) that satisfies the requirements of several advanced optical systems, the characteristics of phase error and the role of each building block of the OPLL should be made clear. To this end, theoretical analyses have been carried out to clarify effects of various noises and loop parameters on performances of various OPLLs [1–18]. Most of these analyses employed the linearized techniques. In [7, 11, 17], the Fokker-Planck's approach [19] was used for the analyses. From these analyses, the principal problem in loop performance is probably the large magnitude of the laser phase noise, calling for a very fast OPLL, and the main contributions to phase error variance were this noise and the shot noise generated during optical phase detection process by photodetectors.

Because FM noises in semiconductor lasers are much larger than those of microwave signals and other lasers, such as gas lasers and solid-state lasers, a digital phase comparator is preferable in the heterodyne OPLLs [20, 21]. Furthermore, in the heterodyne OPLL, digital frequency dividers have been used to extend the maximum offset frequency [21–23]. However, all these analyses assume that the phase detector is an ideal analog multiplier. In this connection, this appendix describes the linearized analysis for phase-error performance of a heterodyne OPLL with digital building blocks in the loop [1]. In addition, those of heterodyne OPLL and homodyne OPLL with an analog phase comparator also are generally discussed so that the result of this analysis can be applied to all types of OPLLs. Some simulation experiments by electronic circuits and noise generators are described as well to investigate the effect of the laser linewidths and the division rate of the frequency divider to the performances of the heterodyne OPLL.

AV.1 OPERATING PRINCIPLES OF OPTICAL PHASE-LOCKED LOOPS

Under the unlocked condition, the electric fields E_M and E_S from the master and slave lasers can be expressed as

---

$$E_M(t) = \sqrt{2P_M} \cos(\omega_M t + \theta_M) \tag{AV.1}$$

$$E_S(t) = \sqrt{2P_S} \cos(\omega_S t + \theta_S) \tag{AV.2}$$

respectively, where ω_M and ω_S are the angular frequencies, $\sqrt{2P_M}$ and $\sqrt{2P_S}$ are the amplitudes, P_M and P_S are the detected average powers, and θ_M and θ_S are the phase constants of the master and slave lasers, respectively. If the phase detector characteristics are sinusoidal, the error signal u_e detected by this phase detector is expressed as

$$u_e(t) = K_D \cos[(\omega_M - \omega_S)t + \theta_M - \theta_S] \tag{AV.3}$$

where K_D is the gain of the phase detector.

If the frequency difference $(\omega_M - \omega_S)/2\pi$ is smaller than the locking range of the OPLL, E_S can synchronize with E_M, and is expressed as

$$E_S(t) = \sqrt{2P_S} \sin(\omega_M t + \theta_S) \tag{AV.4}$$

Then, the error signal shows a dc value given by

$$u_e = K_D \sin(\theta_M - \theta_S) \tag{AV.5}$$

The control signal u_c is given by

$$u_c(t) = u_e(t) * f(t) \tag{AV.6}$$

where $*$ denotes the convolution and $f(t)$ is the impulse response of the loop filter. The $u_c(t)$ is equal to $u_e(t)$ if $f(t) = \delta(t)$, where $\delta(t)$ is the delta function. The instantaneous angular frequency ω_{SI} of the VCO (the slave laser) under phase-locked condition is given by

$$\omega_{SI} = \frac{d(\omega_S t + \theta_S)}{dt} = \omega_S + K_0 u_c \tag{AV.7}$$

where K_0 is the gain of the VCO representing the modulation sensitivity. Combining eqs. (AV.5)–(AV.7), the general time-domain loop equation is obtained, expressed as

$$\frac{d\theta_S(t)}{dt} = K_D K_0 \{\sin[\theta_M(t) - \theta_S(t)] * f(t)\} \tag{AV.8}$$

where the constant $K_D K_0$ corresponds to the open loop gain of the PLL.

When $(\theta_M - \theta_S)$ is sufficiently small, the following approximation is valid:

$$u_e \cong K_D(\theta_M - \theta_S) \tag{AV.9}$$

A general linearized equation in the time domain is then expressed as

$$\frac{d\theta_S(t)}{dt} = K_D K_0 [\theta_M(t) - \theta_S(t)] * f(t) \tag{AV.10}$$

By the Laplace transform of this equation, the transfer function $H(s)$ of the PLL is obtained, given by

$$H(s) = \frac{\Phi_S(s)}{\Phi_M(s)} = \frac{K_D K_0 F(s)}{s + K_D K_0 F(s)} \tag{AV.11}$$

where s is the Laplace variable. On the other hand, the error function of the loop is given by

$$1 - H(s) = \frac{\Phi_M(s) - \Phi_S(s)}{\Phi_M(s)} = \frac{s}{s + K_D K_0 F(s)} \tag{AV.12}$$

As we can see by these equations, the transfer and the error functions depend strongly on the type of the loop filter. In Figure AV.1, three kinds of loop filters frequently used in the second-order PLLs are shown with their transfer functions.

Considering various noise sources in the OPLL and the basic principles of the PLL given earlier, the loop equations for the heterodyne OPLL operated in the linear range of the phase detector can readily be expressed as

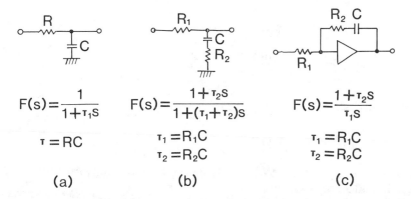

$$F(s) = \frac{1}{1 + \tau_1 s}$$

$$\tau = RC$$

(a)

$$F(s) = \frac{1 + \tau_2 s}{1 + (\tau_1 + \tau_2)s}$$

$$\tau_1 = R_1 C$$
$$\tau_2 = R_2 C$$

(b)

$$F(s) = \frac{1 + \tau_2 s}{\tau_1 s}$$

$$\tau_1 = R_1 C$$
$$\tau_2 = R_2 C$$

(c)

Figure AV.1 Loop filters with their transfer functions: (a) the one-pole low-pass filter; (b) the one-pole low-pass filter with a phase-lead compensation network; (c) the integrator with a phase-lead compensation network.

$$\frac{d\phi_D(t)}{dt} = \frac{dn_R(t)}{dt} - \frac{K_DK_0}{M}[\phi_D(t) + n_{GN}(t)] * f(t)$$

$$-\frac{d}{dt}\left[\frac{n_M(t) - n_S(t)}{M}\right] \tag{AV.13}$$

$$\frac{d\theta_B(t)}{dt} = \frac{K_DK_0}{M}[-\theta_B(t) + Mn_{GN}(t) + Mn_R(t)] * f(t)$$

$$-\frac{d}{dt}[n_M(t) - n_S(t)] \tag{AV.14}$$

The symbols used in these equations are defined as

ϕ_D = phase-error signal from the phase detector,
n_R = phase fluctuations of the microwave reference signal,
M = division rate of the frequency divider,
n_{GN} = phase-translated shot noise (i.e., phase fluctuations induced by the shot noise) in the heterodyne OPLL,
n_M = phase fluctuations of the master laser,
n_S = phase fluctuations of the slave laser,
θ_B = phase of the heterodyne signal between the master and slave lasers, detected by the photodetector, which acts as a frequency down-converter in the heterodyne OPLL.

Equations (AV.13) and (AV.14) are used to describe the performances of the OPLL between the two lasers and determine the steady-state response of the system to the modulated reference signals, respectively. The Laplace transforms of (AV.13) and (AV.14) are

$$\Phi_D(s) = N_R(s) - \frac{K_DK_0F(s)}{Ms}[\Phi_D(s) + N_{GN}(s)]$$

$$-\frac{N_M(s) - N_S(s)}{M} \tag{AV.15}$$

$$\Theta_B(s) = \frac{K_DK_0F(s)}{Ms}[-\Theta_B(s) + MN_{GN}(s) + MN_R(s)]$$

$$- [N_M(s) - N_S(s)] \tag{AV.16}$$

where Φ_D, N_R, $F(s)$, N_{GN}, N_M, N_S, and Θ_B are the Laplace transforms of ϕ_D, n_R, $f(t)$, n_{GN}, n_M, n_S, and θ_B, respectively.

The signal flow of the heterodyne OPLL is shown by Figure AV.2, where that of the homodyne OPLL is also depicted. By solving (AV.15) and (AV.16) for $\Phi_D(s)$ and $\Theta_B(s)$, the following equations are derived:

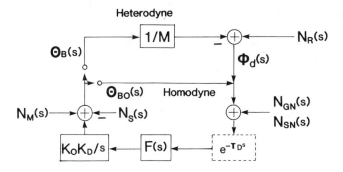

Figure AV.2 Linearized model of the optical phase-locked loop (from [1]).

$$\Phi_D(s) = [1 - H(s)]\left[N_R(s) - \frac{N_M(s) - N_S(s)}{M}\right] - H(s)N_{GN}(s) \qquad (\text{AV}.17)$$

$$\Theta_B(s) = [1 - H(s)][N_M(s) - N_S(s)] - MH(s)[N_{GN}(s) + N_R] \qquad (\text{AV}.18)$$

The transfer function $H(s)$ in these equations is given by

$$H(s) = \frac{K_D K_0 F(s)}{Ms + K_D K_0 F(s)} \qquad (\text{AV}.19)$$

In the case of the homodyne OPLL, $\Theta_{B0}(s)$ (the Laplace transform of the phase error θ_{B0} between the two lasers) can be easily obtained by referring to Figure AV.2; it is expressed as

$$\Theta_{B0}(s) = [1 - H(s)][N_M(s) - N_S(s)] - H(s)N_{SN}(s) \qquad (\text{AV}.20)$$

where $N_{SN}(s)$ is the Laplace transform of $n_{SN}(t)$, which represents the magnitude of the phase-translated shot noise in the homodyne OPLL. $H(s)$ is given by

$$H(s) = \frac{K_{OPD}K_0 F(s)}{s + K_{OPD}K_0 F(s)} \qquad (\text{AV}.21)$$

where K_{OPD} is the gain of the optical phase detector; that is, a photodetector or balanced receiver consisting of two photodetectors. It corresponds to K_D in the heterodyne OPLL.

If a first-order active loop filter with the transfer function

$$F(s) = \frac{1 + \tau_2 s}{\tau_1 s} \qquad (\text{AV}.22)$$

is used (see Figure AV.1(c)) the $H(s)$ of (AV.19) is transformed to

$$H(s) = \frac{(K/M\tau_1)(1 + \tau_2 s)}{s^2 + (K_D K_0 \tau_2/M\tau_1)s + (K_D K_0/M\tau_1)} \tag{AV.23}$$

From this equation, the natural angular frequency ω_N and the damping factor ζ of the heterodyne OPLL are found to be, respectively,

$$\omega_N = \sqrt{\frac{K_D K_0}{M\tau_1}} \quad \text{rad/s} \tag{AV.24}$$

$$\zeta = \frac{\omega_N \tau_2}{2} \tag{AV.25}$$

Time constants τ_1 and τ_2 must be appropriately adjusted when the value of M is changed because both ω_N and ζ depend on M. In the homodyne OPLL, ω_N is also found from (AV.21) to be

$$\omega_N = \sqrt{\frac{K_{OPD} K_0}{\tau_1}} \quad \text{rad/s} \tag{AV.26}$$

The damping factor ζ is derived by substituting this equation into (AV.25).
The noise bandwidth B_N of the OPLL is given by

$$B_N = \int_0^\infty |H(i2\pi f)|^2 \, df = \frac{\omega_N}{2}\left(\zeta + \frac{1}{4\zeta}\right) \quad \text{Hz} \tag{AV.27}$$

Although 3 dB bandwidth B_{3dB} is considered neither an important parameter to characterize the loop nor a measure for noise performance of a PLL, it is an understandable parameter to those familiar with the general control concept. The B_{3dB} is obtained by setting $|H(s)| = 1/\sqrt{2}$ and expressed as

$$B_{3dB} = \frac{\omega_N}{2\pi}\sqrt{2\zeta^2 + 1 + \sqrt{(2\zeta^2 + 1)^2 + 1}} \quad \text{Hz} \tag{AV.28}$$

AV.2 NOISE IN THE OPLL

Several noise sources affect the performance of the OPLL. For heterodyne OPLLs they include

1. Phase fluctuations of the input microwave reference signal,
2. Phase fluctuations of the heterodyne signal between the master laser and the free-running slave lasers,
3. Additive noises like shot noise, intensity noise of the lasers, and noises generated in other OPLL building blocks, such as the phase detector, frequency mixers if used, frequency dividers, and dc or wideband amplifiers.

For homodyne OPLLs they include

1. Phase fluctuations of the master laser and the free-running slave laser,
2. Additive noises like shot noise, intensity noise of the lasers, and noises generated in other OPLL building blocks, such as the phase detector and dc amplifiers.

Among these noises, phase noise from the lasers and shot noise are the principal limitations to the performance of OPLLs. Their characteristics will be briefly reviewed here.

AV.2.1 Phase Noise of Semiconductor Lasers

In the OPLL system, phase noises of the lasers are a most important factor governing phase error performance. Because the phase noise of lasers is large, a wide control bandwidth is required for OPLLs.

Although the FM-noise characteristics of the laser were reviewed in the section 2.4.2, they again are briefly summarized here. The one-sided power spectral density $S_{PH}(f)$ of the phase noise of a semiconductor laser usually consists of three components:

$$S_{PH}(f) = \frac{S_{FM}(f)}{f^2} = S_{FN}(f) + S_{WN}(f) + S_{RF}(f) \qquad \text{(AV.29)}$$

where

$S_{FM}(f)$ = the power spectral density of FM noise of the laser,
$S_{FN}(f)$ = the flicker FM noise that can be observed at $f <$ several hundred kHz (curve D in Figure 2.17).
$S_{WN}(f)$ = the white FM noise (flat part of curve B in Figure 2.17) that is the origin of the Lorentzian field spectral profile whose linewidth is expressed by the modified Schawlow-Townes's formula (eq. (2.58)),
$S_{RF}(f)$ = the FM noise with a peak around the relaxation oscillation resonance frequency (peak of curve B in Figure 2.17).

The power spectral density of the phase noise due to the frequency flicker noise is [24]

$$S_{FN}(f) = \frac{\xi}{f^3} \quad \text{rad}^2/\text{Hz} \tag{AV.30}$$

where $\xi \, \text{Hz}^2$ is the measure of the magnitude of the flicker noise. It has been pointed out that the linewidth of the laser field spectral profile is increased considerably by this noise [25]. The measured spectral profile therefore is deformed and approximated not by the Lorentzian but by the Gaussian when this type noise exists at around the Fourier frequency corresponding to the linewidth of the spectral profile.

The power spectral density of the phase noise due to the Gaussian white FM noise of the laser, caused by the random spontaneous emission process in laser action, is given by [3, 7, 8, 26]

$$S_{WN}(f) = \frac{\Delta \nu_L}{\pi} \frac{1}{f^2} \quad \text{rad}^2/\text{Hz} \tag{AV.31}$$

where $\Delta \nu_L$ is the spectral linewidth (full-width at half maximum) of the laser with a Lorentzian lineshape.

The power spectral density $S_{FM}(f)$ of FM noise including resonance component can be expressed by the approximated equation given by [27–29]

$$S_{FM}(f) = \frac{\xi}{f} + \frac{\Delta \nu_{ST}}{\pi} \left[1 + \frac{\alpha^2 \nu_{RF}^4}{(\nu_{RF}^2 - f^2)^2 + (\gamma_e/2\pi)^2 f^2} \right] \quad \text{Hz}^2/\text{Hz} \tag{AV.32}$$

where ν_{RF}, α, γ_e, and $\Delta \nu_{ST}$ are the resonance frequency, the linewidth enhancement factor [30], the damping constant of the laser, and the linewidth of the laser given by the Schawlow-Townes's formula, respectively.

If the OPLL is used in a system with a bandwidth wider than the resonance frequency, the phase noise due to the resonance characteristics of the laser device itself has to be taken into account for designing OPLL systems [11]. For a narrow and medium bandwidth system, (AV.31) can be used to design the OPLL.

AV.2.2 Shot Noise in OPLL Systems

In the linearized model of Figure AV.2, $N_{SN}(s)$ and $N_{GN}(s)$ are the additive noises caused by and associated with the shot noise, respectively. They originate from the optical detection process and the quantum nature of light in heterodyne and homodyne OPLLs, respectively.

In the homodyne OPLL, the signals from the master and slave lasers given by (AV.1) and (AV.2) are combined by the phase detector; that is, a photodetector. An output of the photodetector after rejecting the dc power term is expressed as

$$u_e(t) = 2\sqrt{P_M P_S}\, Rr \sin(\theta_M - \theta_S) + n_{\text{SN}}(t) \tag{AV.33}$$

where r is the load resistance of the photodetector. The responsivity of the photodiode R is defined by

$$R = \frac{e\eta}{h\nu} \quad \text{A/W} \tag{AV.34}$$

where e is the electron charge, η is the quantum efficiency of the photodetector, h is Planck's constant, and ν is the detected optical frequency. Thus, the gain of the optical phase detector is

$$K_{\text{OPD}} = 2\sqrt{P_M P_S}\, Rr \quad \text{V/rad} \tag{AV.35}$$

The power spectral density $S_{\text{SN}\nu}(t)$ of the shot noise $n_{\text{SN}}(t)$ is represented by

$$S_{\text{SN}\nu}(f) = 2eR(P_M + P_S)r^2 \quad \text{V}^2/\text{Hz} \tag{AV.36}$$

Using (AV.35) and (AV.36), the power spectral density $S_{\text{SN}}(f)$ of the phase-translated shot noise can be expressed as

$$S_{\text{SN}}(f) = \frac{S_{\text{SN}\nu}(f)}{K_{\text{OPD}}^2} = \frac{e(P_M + P_S)}{2RP_M P_S} \quad \text{rad}^2/\text{Hz} \tag{AV.37}$$

By this equation, the minimum detectable rms phase error $\theta_{\min}$, limited by the shot noise in the homodyne OPLL, can be found for $P_S \gg P_M$ to be

$$\theta_{\min} = \sqrt{\frac{eB}{2RP_M}} \quad \text{rad} \tag{AV.38}$$

where B is the detection bandwidth. To achieve this value, intensity noise of the slave laser has to be canceled by using a balanced detector, and P_S has to be sufficiently high to overcome thermal noise.

The photodetector in the heterodyne OPLL generates the shot noise as the same value as the optical phase detector given by (AV.36). However, the contribution of the shot noise is doubled because the phase locking is carried out with a heterodyne signal. In the heterodyne OPLL, using only an analog phase comparator, the power spectral density of the noise voltage induced by the shot noise is given by

$$S_{\text{GN}\nu}(f) = 4eR(P_M + P_S)r^2 \quad \text{V}^2/\text{Hz} \tag{AV.39}$$

and the power spectral density of the phase-translated shot noise is given by

$$S_{GN}(f) = \frac{e(P_M + P_S)}{RP_M P_S} \quad \text{rad}^2/\text{Hz} \tag{AV.40}$$

In the analog-to-digital signal conversion process using digital frequency dividers or a digital phase comparator in the heterodyne OPLL, the noise voltages of shot noise act as a noise switching threshold to drive the heterodyne signal between the two lasers. The sampling effect of a *zero-crossing detector* (ZCD) causes noise around each harmonic of the switching frequency, which affects the output transition time and produces a narrowband demodulated output [31]. The noise output then is the sum of all the harmonic noise sideband powers. Its power spectral density $S_{GN'}$, therefore, is given by

$$S_{GN'}(f) = N_H S_{GN}(f) \quad \text{rad}^2/\text{Hz} \tag{AV.41}$$

where an integer N_H represents the order of the maximum significant harmonic, determined by the input circuit bandwidth to the ZCD [31].

When a digital frequency divider with a division rate M is used, the power spectral density of the phase noise of the heterodyne signal is divided by M^2. However, the power of the input voltage noise is divided by M because a wideband input voltage noise to the divider mixes with M multiples of the divider output by the sampling process [31]. Then, the power spectral density $S_{GNM}(f)$ of the output voltage noise of a digital frequency divider is given by

$$S_{GNM}(f) = \frac{S_{GN'}(f)}{M} \quad \text{rad}^2/\text{Hz} \tag{AV.42}$$

This equation means that the additive voltage noises are reduced to $1/\sqrt{M}$, whereas the phase noise of the heterodyne signal is reduced to $1/M$.

Finally, the power spectral density of the phase-translated shot noise $S_{SN}(f)$ for homodyne and heterodyne OPLLs is generally expressed as

$$S_{SN}(f) = F_{SN} \frac{e(P_M + P_S)}{2RP_M P_S} \quad \text{rad}^2/\text{Hz} \tag{AV.43}$$

where F_{SN} is given as follows:

$$
\begin{aligned}
F_{SN} &= 1 \text{ (for a homodyne OPLL)}\\
&= 2 \text{ (for a heterodyne OPLL with an analog phase comparator)}\\
&= 2N_H \text{ (for a heterodyne OPLL with a digital phase comparator)}\\
&= 2N_H/M \text{ (for a heterodyne OPLL with digital frequency dividers)}
\end{aligned}
\tag{AV.44}
$$

AV.3   PHASE ERROR VARIANCE IN OPLL

Phase error variances in homodyne and heterodyne OPLLs are influenced mainly by the phase noise of two lasers and the phase noise-translated shot noise. FM noise has flicker, white, and resonant components. Among the three components of the FM noise of the laser, flicker noise is readily tracked with an OPLL as the common OPLL usually is fast enough to track such slow frequency fluctuations. Therefore, the contribution of the flicker components of laser FM noise to the phase error variance is negligible [7]. The resonance component of the laser FM noise cannot be neglected when the system bandwidth approaches or is wider than the resonance frequency. However, because the bandwidth of the general lightwave system is far narrower than the resonance frequency [7, 8], it is sufficient to consider only the white component of the laser FM noise in evaluating the phase error variance contributed by phase noise.

From eq. (AV.20), the phase error variance σ_ϕ^2 of the homodyne OPLL is given by

$$\sigma_\phi^2 = \int_0^\infty \{|H(i2\pi f)|^2 S_{SN}(f) + |1 - H(i2\pi f)|^2 [S_{PH,M}(f) + S_{PH,S}(f)]\} \, df \quad \text{rad}^2 \tag{AV.45}$$

where $S_{PH,M}(f)$ and $S_{PH,S}(f)$ are the power spectral densities of phase noises of the master and slave lasers, respectively. By rearranging this equation and using (AV.31), we get

$$\sigma_\phi^2 = S_{SN} \int_0^\infty |H(i2\pi f)|^2 \, df + \frac{\Delta\nu_M + \Delta\nu_S}{\pi} \int_0^\infty \left|\frac{1 - H(i2\pi f)}{f}\right|^2 \, df \quad \text{rad}^2 \tag{AV.46}$$

In this equation, the integrals to be carried out are

$$I_{SN} = \int_0^\infty |H(i2\pi f)|^2 \, df \tag{AV.47}$$

which corresponds to the loop-noise bandwidth given by (AV.27) and

$$I_{PN} = \int_0^\infty \left|\frac{1 - H(i2\pi f)}{f}\right|^2 \, df \tag{AV.48}$$

The results are obtained by using (AV.21), expressed as [3, 24]

$$I_{SN} = \frac{\omega_N}{2}\left(\zeta + \frac{1}{4\zeta}\right) \tag{AV.49}$$

$$I_{PN} = \frac{\pi^2}{2\zeta\omega_N} \tag{AV.50}$$

Substituting (AV.37), (AV.49), and (AV.50) into (AV.46), the phase error variance of the homodyne OPLL is given by

$$\sigma_\phi^2 = \frac{e(P_M + P_S)(4\zeta^2 + 1)\omega_N}{16\zeta RP_M P_S} + \frac{\pi}{2\zeta\omega_N}(\Delta\nu_M + \Delta\nu_S) \qquad \text{rad}^2 \tag{AV.51}$$

where the optimal value of ζ falls generally within the range of between 0.5 and 1. The minimum attainable phase error variance σ_ϕ^2 is found from this equation, given by

$$\sigma_{\phi,\min}^2 = \sqrt{\frac{\pi e(\Delta\nu_M + \Delta\nu_S)(P_M + P_S)(4\zeta^2 + 1)}{8RP_M P_S \zeta^2}} \qquad \text{rad}^2 \tag{AV.52}$$

when the ω_N is fixed to the following optimum value:

$$\omega_{N,\text{opt}} = \sqrt{\frac{8\pi(\Delta\nu_M + \Delta\nu_S)RP_M P_S}{e(P_M + P_S)(4\zeta^2 + 1)}} \qquad \text{rad/s} \tag{AV.53}$$

In the case of the heterodyne OPLL, two kinds of phase errors are to be considered. One is the phase error between the microwave reference signal and the heterodyne signals between the master and slave lasers. The other is the phase error between the master and slave lasers, which is matter of primary interest because the purpose of the heterodyne OPLL is the phase locking two lasers. Their phase error variances are given by

$$\sigma_{\phi,D}^2 = \int_0^\infty \{|H(i2\pi f)|^2 S_{SN}(f) + |1 - H(i2\pi f)|^2 [S_{PH,M}(f) \tag{AV.54}$$
$$+ S_{PH,S}(f) + S_R(f)]\}\, df \qquad \text{rad}^2$$

$$\sigma_{\phi,B}^2 = \int_0^\infty \{|H(i2\pi f)|^2 [S_{SN}(f) + S_R(f)] + |1 \tag{AV.55}$$
$$- H(i2\pi f)|^2 [S_{PH,M}(f) + S_{PH,S}(f)]\}\, df \qquad \text{rad}^2$$

respectively, where $S_R(f)$ is the power spectral density of the phase fluctuations n_R of the microwave reference signal.

In the phase error given by (AV.54), $S_R(f)$ can be neglected because the phase noise of the stable microwave reference signal is much smaller than those of the lasers. On the other hand, in (AV.55), $S_R(f)$ cannot be neglected because the phase noise of the microwave reference signal appears directly in the phase-error spectrum within the OPLL bandwidth. In other words, the limiting phase error spectrum is a replica of the phase noise spectrum of the reference signal. However, it can also be neglected if the bandwidth of a system, that employed a heterodyne OPLL as a building block, is wide enough so that the flicker phase noise of the reference signal can be negligible.

Neglecting the $S_R(f)$ for simplicity in the present discussion, (AV.55) can be reduced to

$$\sigma_{\phi,B}^2 = \frac{eF_{SN}M^2(P_M + P_S)(4\zeta^2 + 1)\omega_N}{16\zeta RP_M P_S}$$

$$+ \frac{\pi}{2\zeta\omega_N}(\Delta\nu_M + \Delta\nu_S) \qquad \text{rad}^2 \tag{AV.56}$$

Then, $\omega_{N,opt}$ and $\sigma_{\phi,min}^2$ are given by

$$\omega_{N,opt} = \sqrt{\frac{8\pi(\Delta\nu_M + \Delta\nu_S)RP_M P_S}{eF_{SN}M^2(P_M + P_S)(4\zeta^2 + 1)}} \qquad \text{rad/s} \tag{AV.57}$$

$$\sigma_{\phi,min}^2 = \sqrt{\frac{\pi eF_{SN}M^2(\Delta\nu_M + \Delta\nu_S)(P_M + P_S)(4\zeta^2 + 1)}{8RP_M P_S \zeta^2}} \qquad \text{rad}^2 \tag{AV.58}$$

respectively. Furthermore, because $P_S \gg P_M$ for most of the lightwave systems, (AV.56)–(AV.58), respectively, are then reduced to

$$\sigma_{\phi,B}^2 = \frac{eF_{SN}M^2(4\zeta^2 + 1)\omega_N}{16\zeta RP_M} + \frac{\pi}{2\zeta\omega_N}(\Delta\nu_M + \Delta\nu_S) \qquad \text{rad}^2 \tag{AV.59}$$

$$\omega_{N,opt} = \sqrt{\frac{8\pi(\Delta\nu_M + \Delta\nu_S)RP_M}{eF_{SN}M^2(4\zeta^2 + 1)}} \qquad \text{rad/s} \tag{AV.60}$$

$$\sigma_{\phi,min}^2 = \sqrt{\frac{\pi eF_{SN}M^2(\Delta\nu_M + \Delta\nu_S)(4\zeta^2 + 1)}{8RP_M \zeta^2}} \qquad \text{rad}^2 \tag{AV.61}$$

Because the loop has nonzero signal propagation time, the effect of the time delay should be taken into account for accurate analysis. The Laplace transform of the loop time delay is $e^{-\tau_D s}$, which is shown in Figure AV.2. The loop-transfer function then is given by

$$H(s) = \frac{K_D K_0 F(s) e^{-\tau_D s}}{Ms + K_D K_0 F(s) e^{-\tau_D s}} \tag{AV.62}$$

In the homodyne OPLL, K_D must be replaced by K_{OPD}. Then, I_{SN} and I_{PN}, respectively, are given by

$$I_{DSN} = 2f_N \int_0^\infty \frac{4\zeta^2 x^2 + 1}{x^4 - (4\zeta \sin\delta x)x^3 + (4\zeta^2 - 2\cos\delta x)x^2 + 1} \, dx \tag{AV.63}$$

$$I_{DPN} = \frac{2}{f_N} \int_0^\infty \frac{x^2}{x^4 - (4\zeta \sin\delta x)x^3 + (4\zeta^2 - 2\cos\delta x)x^2 + 1} \, dx \tag{AV.64}$$

Here, the normalized Fourier frequency

$$x = \frac{f}{f_N} \tag{AV.65}$$

and the normalized loop delay time

$$\delta = \omega_N \tau_D = 2\pi f_N \tau_D \tag{AV.66}$$

were used, where $f_N = \omega_N/2\pi$. As shown by Figure AV.3 [32], calculated values of these integrals which are normalized to I_{SN} and I_{PN}, respectively, are increased by

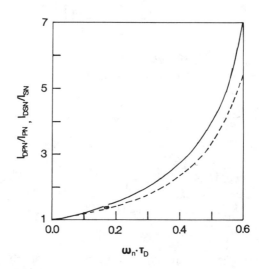

Figure AV.3 Relations between the normalized loop delay time $\omega_N \tau_D$, I_{DPN}/I_{PN} (solid line), and I_{DSN}/I_{SN} (dashed line) (from [32]).

increasing $\omega_N \tau_D$; that is, by increasing the loop delay time. The similar calculation has been carried out in a theoretical analysis for a Costas loop by Grant, Michie, and Fletcher [15]. They found that the loop was stable if

$$\omega_N \tau_D < 0.736 \tag{AV.67}$$

where the relation of $\zeta = 1/\sqrt{2}$ was assumed. If $\omega_N \tau_D < 0.04$, then inaccuracy of the analyses given here is less than 9%, even if the effect of the loop delay time is neglected.

Phase error variances for various OPLLs were calculated by using (AV.59). The calculated results are shown in Figure AV.4. In this calculation, R, ζ, and M were fixed at 0.7, $1/\sqrt{2}$, and 1, respectively. Each curve of this figure exhibits a V-shape. The left and right wings of this V-shape represent the effect of phase noises of lasers and the shot noise, respectively. Figure AV.5 shows the optimum natural frequency $f_{N,\text{opt}}$ to achieve the minimum of σ_ϕ^2 as a function of the sum of linewidths of the master and slave lasers. In actual loops, the loop delay time cannot be neglected. Considering the stability limit given by (AV.67), f_N must be less than $0.12/\tau_D$. If the loop

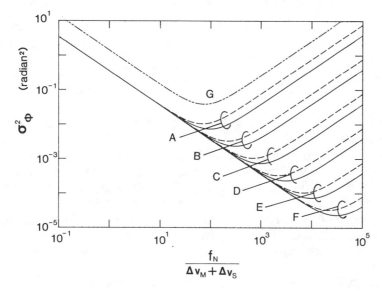

Figure AV.4 Relation between the normalized natural frequency $f_N/(\Delta\nu_M + \Delta\nu_S)$ and phase-error variances σ_ϕ^2 rad^2 calculated by using the normalized power $P_M/(\Delta\nu_M + \Delta\nu_S)$ of the master laser as a parameter (from [1]). The solid and dashed lines are for the homodyne OPLL and heterodyne OPLL, respectively: values of $P_M/(\Delta\nu_M + \Delta\nu_S)$ are (A) 1×10^{-14} W/Hz; (B) 1×10^{-13} W/Hz, (C) 1×10^{-12} W/Hz; (D) 1×10^{-11} W/Hz; (E) 1×10^{-10} W/Hz, and (F) 1×10^{-9} W/Hz; curve G is the result for $\omega_N \tau_D = 0.5$, corresponding to curve A. However, it does not include the loop time-delay effect.

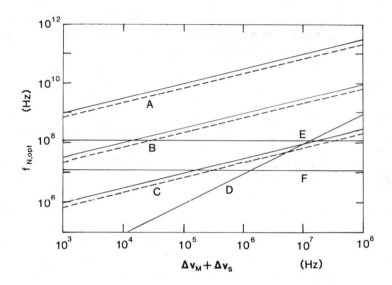

Figure AV.5 Relation between the sum of the linewidths of the master and slave lasers and the optimum natural frequency $f_{N,opt}$ ($= \omega_{N,opt}/2\pi$) calculated by using the power P_M of the master laser as the parameter (from [1]). The solid and dashed lines are for the homodyne OPLL and heterodyne OPLL, respectively. Values of P_M are (A) 1×10^{-3} W; (B) 1×10^{-6} W; and (C) 1×10^{-9} W, respectively; solid line D is the minimum required natural frequency to achieve the phase-error variance of 0.04 rad^2; solid lines E and F indicate the maximum allowable natural frequency limited by the loop time delays of 1 ns and 10 ns, respectively.

time delay is 1 ns, the maximum allowable f_N is 120 MHz, which is shown by the line E in Figure AV.5.

The coherent communication system, as an example of an OPLL application system, requires that the phase error variance be less than 0.04 rad^2. By considering only phase noises of the lasers in the range $P_M/(\Delta\omega_M + \Delta\nu_S) > 3 \times 10^{-16}$ W/Hz, a homodyne OPLL can be designed to achieve this phase error variance by widening the loop bandwidth, as can be seen in Figure AV.4, which is proportional to the natural frequency. However, further increase in the natural frequency over the optimum value causes an increase in phase error variance due to shot noise, as shown by Figure AV.4.

From (AV.59), the required natural frequency for $\sigma_\phi^2 = 0.04$ rad^2 is given by

$$f_N = 8.84(\Delta\nu_M + \Delta\nu_S) \qquad \text{Hz} \qquad (AV.68)$$

where ζ is $1/\sqrt{2}$. This is the lower limit of the natural frequency, given by line D of Figure AV.5. If the loop time delay with an upper limit of f_N is 10 ns (line F of Figure AV.5), the sum of the linewidths of the master and slave lasers must be less than about 2 MHz.

AV.4   SIMULATION EXPERIMENTS FOR THE HETERODYNE OPLL

The lasers and photodetector are replaced by electronic circuits for simulation experiments. Lasers in a heterodyne OPLL are replaced by *voltage-controlled oscillators* (VCO). Noise generators are connected to the VCOs to generate the FM noise from the VCOs whose magnitude is as large as those of semiconductor lasers. A *double-balanced mixer* (DBM) and a *low-pass filter* (LPF) are employed as a photodetector. So that the full spectral characteristics of the master laser can be transferred to the slave laser, a sufficiently wide loop bandwidth is required. To confirm this requirement quantitatively, the spectral line shapes of the slave laser were measured under the phase-locked condition with various loop bandwidths B_w, as shown by Figure AV.6. By increasing $B_w/(\Delta \nu_M + \Delta \nu_S)$, noise powers are reduced as shown in Figures

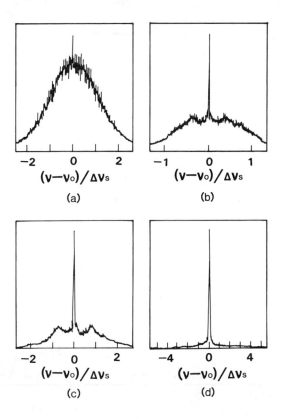

Figure AV.6 Spectral profiles of the slave laser locked to that of the master laser, obtained by simulation (from [17]). Normalized bandwidths $B_w/\Delta \nu_S$ of the slave laser are (*a*) 0.31; (*b*) 0.45; (*c*) 0.83; and (*d*) 16.7, respectively, where $\Delta \nu_S$ and B_w are the linewidth of the free-running slave laser and the bandwidth of the loop filter, respectively. Abscissas represent normalized detuning from the center frequency of the heterodyne signal ν_0; that is, $(\nu - \nu_0)/\Delta \nu_S$.

AV.6(a)–(c). Finally, the phase-locked spectral line shape of the slave laser becomes the very image of the stable master laser shown in Figure AV.6(d), where $B_w = 16.7\Delta\nu_S$.

By increasing the division rate, the phase error between two lasers is increased. As can be seen by (AV.56), phase error variance due to shot noise is increased with a factor of M because $F_{SN}M^2 \propto M$. On the other hand, phase error variance due to the phase noise of the lasers is independent of M, when values of ω_N and ζ are fixed. However, as ω_N and ζ in (AV.56) contain $1/\sqrt{M}$, respectively, as given by (AV.24) and (AV.25), the phase error variance is proportional to M when time constants of the loop filter are fixed. Figure AV.7 confirms this fact. Time constants of the loop filter must be adjusted to keep the loop operation stable when the value of M is changed because the values of ω_N and ζ depend on M. It is also desirable to adjust M so that a divided beat frequency will be higher than the bandwidth of the loop; otherwise, an increase in phase ripples may be induced by residual frequency components of the heterodyne signal within the loop bandwidth.

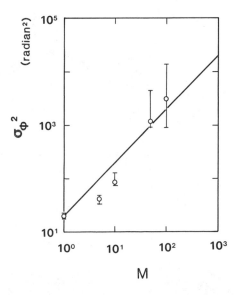

Figure AV.7 Simulation of the dependence of the phase-error variance σ_ϕ^2 on the division rate M (from [17]).

Figure AV.8 shows the results of a simulation that shows that phase error variance depends on the sum of linewidths of the master and the slave lasers. This result is approximated as

$$\sigma_\phi^2 = \frac{2(\Delta\nu_M + \Delta\nu_S)}{B_w} \qquad\qquad (AV.69)$$

This equation shows a good agreement with the theoretical result given in the second terms of the right-hand side of (AV.56); that is, the phase error variance by the phase noises of the lasers is inversely proportional to the loop noise bandwidth.

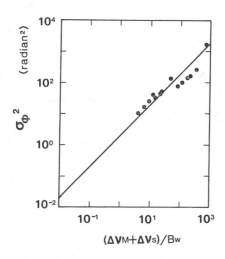

Figure AV.8 Simulation of the relation between $(\Delta\nu_M + \Delta\nu_S)/B_w$ and the phase-error variance σ_ϕ^2 (from [17]). The solid line is the least square fitted to the results of the simulation.

REFERENCES

[1] Shin, C.-H., "Optical Phase-Locking of Semiconductor Lasers," Ph.D. thesis, Tokyo Institute of Technology, January 1991.

[2] Kazovsky, L.G., "Balanced Phase-Locked Loops for Optical Homodyne Receivers: Performance Analysis, Design Considerations, and Laser Linewidth Requirements," *IEEE J. Lightwave Technology,* Vol. LT-4, No. 2, February 1986, pp. 182–195.

[3] Hodgkinson, T.J., "Phase-Locked-Loop Analysis for Pilot Carrier Coherent Optical Receivers," *Electronics Letters,* Vol. 21, Nos. 25–26, December 1985, pp. 1202–1203.

[4] Kazovsky, L.G., "Decision-Driven Phase-Locked Loop for Optical Homodyne Receivers: Performance Analysis and Laser Linewidth Requirements," *IEEE J. Lightwave Technology,* Vol. LT-3, No. 6, December 1985, pp. 1238–1247.

[5] Hodgkinson, T.G., "Costas Loop Analysis for Coherent Optical Receivers," *Electronics Letters,* Vol. 22, No. 7, March 1985, pp. 394–396.

[6] Wang, Y., and W.R. Leeb, "Sensitivity Analysis and Performance Optimization of an Optical Costas Phase-Locked Loop," *J. Optics Communication,* Vol. 8, No. 1, January 1987, pp. 29–31.

[7] Salz, J., "Coherent Lightwave Communications," *AT&T Tech. J.,* Vol. 64, No. 10, October 1985, pp. 2153–2209.

[8] Kazovsky, L.G., "Performance Analysis and Laser Linewidth Requirements for Optical PSK Heterodyne Communications Systems," *IEEE J. Lightwave Technology,* Vol. LT-4, No. 4, April 1986, pp. 415–425.

[9] Steele, R.C., J.M. Creaner, G.R. Walker, and N.G. Walker, "Optical PSK Transmission Experiment at 565 Mbit/s Incorporating an Endless Polarization Control System," *Proc. of the Int. Society of Optical Engineering* (SPIE), Vol. 988, 1988, pp. 302–309.

[10] Hodgkinson, T.G., "Receiver Analysis for Synchronous Coherent Optical Fiber Transmission Systems," *IEEE J. Lightwave Technology,* Vol. LT-5, No. 4, April 1987, pp. 573–586.

[11] Betti, S., G. De Marchis, E. Iannone, and Martellucci, "Effect of the Non-Lorentzian Lineshape of Semiconductor Laser on a PSK Coherent Heterodyne Optical Receiver," *Electronics Letters,* Vol. 23, No. 25, December 1987, pp. 1366–1367.

[12] Ramos, R.T., and A.J. Seeds, "Delay, Linewidth and Bandwidth Limitations in Optical Phase-Locked Loop Design," *Electronics Letters,* Vol. 26, No. 6, March 1990, pp. 389–391.

[13] Armor, J.B., Jr., and S.R. Robinson, "Phase-Lock Control Considerations for Coherently Combined Lasers," *Applied Optics,* Vol. 18, No. 18, September 1979, pp. 3165–3175.

[14] Zaccarin, D., D. Angers, and T.H. Huynh, "Performance Analysis of Optical Heterodyne PSK Receivers in the Presence of Phase Noise and Adjacent Channel Interference," *IEEE J. Lightwave Technology,* Vol. 8, No. 3, March 1990, pp. 353–366.

[15] Grant, M.A., W.C. Michie, and M.J. Fletcher, "The Performance of Optical Phase-Locked Loops in the Presence of Nonnegligible Loop Propagation Delay," *IEEE J. Lightwave Technology,* Vol. LT-5, No. 4, April 1987, pp. 592–597.

[16] Wu, J., C.K. Wang, and I.F. Wu, "Coding to Relax Laser Linewidth Requirements and Improve Receiver Sensitivity for Coherent Optical BPSK Communications," *IEEE J. Lightwave Technology,* Vol. 8, No. 4, April 1990, pp. 545–553.

[17] Shin, C.-H., K. Kuboki, and M. Ohtsu, "Simulation for the Heterodyne Type Optical Phase-Locked Loop by Semiconductor Lasers," *TIEE Japan,* Vol. 108-C, No. 9, September 1988, pp. 678–684 [in Japanese].

[18] Kikuchi, K., T. Okoshi, M. Nagamatsu, and N. Henmi, "Degradation of Bit-Error Rate in Coherent Optical Communciations Due to Spectral Spread of the Transmitter and Local Oscillator," *IEEE J. Lightwave Technology,* Vol. LT-2, No. 6, June 1984, pp. 1024–1033.

[19] Viterbi, A.J., "Phase-Locked Loop Dyanmics in the Presence of Noise by Fokker-Planck Techniques," *Proc. IEEE,* Vol. 51, No. 12, December 1963, pp. 1737–1753.

[20] Hall, J.L., L.S. Ma, and G. Kramer, "Principles of Optical Phase-Locking: Application to Internal Mirror He-Ne Lasers Phase-Locked via Fast Control of the Discharge Current," *IEEE J. Quantum Electronics,* Vol. QE-23, No. 4, April 1987, pp. 427–437.

[21] Kuboki, K., and M. Ohtsu, "Frequency Offset Locking of AlGaAs Semiconductor Lasers," *IEEE J. Quantum Electronics,* Vol. QE-23, No. 4, April 1987, pp. 388–394.

[22] Kuboki, K., C.-H. Shin, T. Kato, and M. Ohtsu, "Performance and Its Evaluation of Optical Tracking Generator/Optical Frequency Synthesizer by Semiconductor Lasers," *Digest 1988 Conf. on Precision Electromagnetic Measurement* (CPEM), ed. Y. Suematsu, Tsukuba, Japan, June 7–10, 1988, pp. 24–25.

[23] Kuboki, K., and M. Ohtsu, "A Synthesized Method to Improve Coherence in Semiconductor Lasers by Electrical Feedback," *IEEE J. Quantum Electronics,* Vol. 25, No. 10, October 1989, pp. 2084–2090.

[24] Blanchard, A., *Phase-Locked Loops: Application to Coherent Receiver Design,* John Wiley & Sons, New York, 1976.

[25] Ohtsu, M., and S. Kotajima, "Derivation of Spectral Width of a 0.8 μm AlGaAs Laser Considering $1/f$ Noise," *Japan J. Applied Physics,* Vol. 23, No. 6, December 1984, pp. 760–764.

[26]   Tamburrini, M., P. Spano, and S. Piazzolla, "Influence of Semiconductor-Laser Phase Noise on Coherent Optical Communication Systems," *Optics Letters,* Vol. 8, No. 3, March 1983, pp. 174–176.

[27]   Vahala, K., and A. Yariv, "Semiclassical Theory of Noise in Semiconductor Lasers—Part II," *IEEE J. Quantum Electronics,* Vol. QE-19, No. 6, June 1983, pp. 1102–1109.

[28]   Spano, P., S. Piazzolla, and M. Tamburrini, "Phase Noise in Semiconductor Lasers: A Theoretical Approach," *IEEE J. Quantum Electronics,* Vol. QE-19, No. 7, July 1983, pp. 1195–1199.

[29]   Kikuchi, K., and T. Okoshi, "Measurement of FM Noise, AM Noise, and Field Spectra of 1.3 μm InGaAsP DFB Lasers and Determination of the Linewidth Enhancement Factor," *IEEE J. Quantum Electronics,* Vol. QE-21, No. 11, November 1985, pp. 1814–1818.

[30]   Henry, C.H., "Theory of the Linewidth of Semiconductor Lasers," *IEEE J. Quantum Electronics,* Vol. QE-18, No. 2, February 1982, pp. 259–264.

[31]   Phillips, D.E., "Random Noise in Digital Gates and Dividers," Proc. 41st Annual Symp. on Frequency Control, May 27–29, 1987, Philadelphia, pp. 507–511.

[32]   Shin, C.-H., M. Teshima, and M. Ohtsu, "Heterodyne Optical Phase-Locked Loop by Semiconductor Lasers," Tech. Rep. No. OCS88-64, Institute of Electronics, Information, and Communication Engineers of Japan, February 1989 [in Japanese].

INDEX